Mathcad

User's Guide
Mathcad 6.0
Mathcad PLUS 6.0

MathSoft Inc.
101 Main Street
Cambridge
Massachusetts
02142 USA

M a t h S o f t
$\Sigma + \sqrt{} - = \times \int \div \delta$

D1157871

Warning: MATHSOFT, INC. IS WILLING TO LICENSE THE ENCLOSED SOFTWARE TO YOU ONLY UPON THE CONDITION THAT YOU ACCEPT ALL OF THE TERMS CONTAINED IN THIS LICENSE AGREEMENT. PLEASE READ THE TERMS CAREFULLY BEFORE OPENING THE PACKAGE WITH THE DISKETTES, AS OPENING THE PACKAGE WILL INDICATE YOUR ASSENT TO THEM. IF YOU DO NOT AGREE TO THESE TERMS, THEN MATHSOFT IS UNWILLING TO LICENSE THE SOFTWARE TO YOU, IN WHICH EVENT YOU SHOULD RETURN THIS COMPLETE PACKAGE WITH ALL ORIGINAL MATERIALS AND THE UNOPENED PACKAGE WITH THE DISKETTES AND YOUR MONEY WILL BE REFUNDED.

MATHSOFT, INC. LICENSE AGREEMENT

Both the Software and the documentation are protected under applicable copyright laws, international treaty provisions, and trade secret statutes of the various states. This Agreement grants you a limited, non-exclusive, non-transferable license to use the Software and the documentation. This is not an agreement for the sale of the Software or the documentation or any copy of the Software or the documentation and you have not acquired title or ownership in the Software or the documentation or any copies or part thereof. Your right to use the Software and the documentation is limited to the terms and conditions described herein.

You may use the Software and the documentation solely for your own personal or internal purposes, for non-remunerated demonstrations (but not for delivery or sale) in connection with your personal or internal purposes:

(a) if you have a single license, on only one computer at a time or by only one user at a time;

(b) if you have acquired multiple licenses, the Software may be used on either stand alone computers, or on computer networks, by a number of simultaneous users equal to or less than the number of licenses that you have acquired; and,

(c) if you maintain the confidentiality of the Software and documentation at all times.

You may make copies of the Software solely for archival purposes, provided you reproduce and include the copyright notice on any backup copy.

MathSoft, Inc. reserves all rights not expressly granted to you by this License Agreement. The license granted herein is limited solely to the uses specified above and, without limiting the generality of the foregoing, you are NOT licensed to use or to copy all or any part of the Software or the documentation in connection with the sale, resale, license, or other for-profit personal or commercial reproduction or commercial distribution of computer programs or other materials without the prior written consent of MathSoft, Inc. In particular, the DLL interface specifications, the HBK file format and other confidential information and copyrighted materials may not be used for creating computer programs or other materials for sale, resale, license, or for remunerated personal or commercial reproduction or commercial distribution without the prior written consent of MathSoft, Inc.

You must have a reasonable mechanism or process to ensure that the number of users at any one time does not exceed the number of licenses you have paid for and to prevent access to the Software to any person not authorized under the above license to use the Software. Any copy which you make of the Software, in whole or in part, is the property of MathSoft. You agree to reproduce and include MathSoft's copyright, trademark, and other proprietary rights notices on any copy you make of the Software.

Your license to use the Software and documentation will automatically terminate if you fail to comply with the terms of the Agreement. If this license is terminated, you agree to destroy all copies of the Software and documentation in your possession.

MATHSOFT, INC. LIMITED WARRANTY

Table of Contents

Computational Features

Graphics Features

Index

What is Mathcad?

Mathcad is a unique new way to work with formulas, numbers, text, and graphs. Mathcad is as versatile as the most powerful spreadsheets and programming languages, yet it's easy to learn and a pleasure to use.

Mathcad lets you type equations as you're used to seeing them, expanded fully on your screen. In a programming language, equations look something like this:

```
x=(-B+SQRT(B**2-4*A*C))/(2*A)
```

In a spreadsheet, equations go into cells looking something like this:

```
+(B1+SQRT(B1*B1-4*A1*C1))/(2*A1)
```

And that's assuming you can see them. Usually all you see is a number.

In Mathcad, the same equation looks the way you might see it on a blackboard or in a reference book:

$$x := \frac{-b + \sqrt{b^2 - 4 \cdot a \cdot c}}{2 \cdot a}$$

But Mathcad equations do much more than look good. You can use them to solve just about any math problem you can think of, symbolically or numerically. You can place text anywhere around them to document your work. You can show how they look with Mathcad's two and three dimensional plots. You can even illustrate your work with graphics taken from another Windows application.

Mathcad comes with its own on-line reference system as well. Mathcad's Electronic Books make many useful formulas, data values and diagrams available in your worksheet at the click of a button.

By combining text, graphics and equations in a single worksheet, Mathcad makes it easy to keep track of the most complex calculations. By printing the worksheet exactly as it appears on the screen, Mathcad lets you make a permanent and accurate record of your work.

Mathcad features

Here is a short list of Mathcad's features:

Interface features

- Free-form, scratchpad-type interface.

- Mix text, mathematics, and graphs anywhere on screen.

- On-screen graphical equation editing.

- Error checking: error messages flag individual equations.

- Cut and paste for equations, text, plots and graphs.

- Typing aids for Greek letters, operators, units and functions.

- Full Windows compatibility: Resize and move windows, open multiple windows, mouse support.

- Context sensitive on-line Help.

- Electronic Books with hundreds of standard formulas, constants, diagrams and more.

Computational features

- Precision: 15 decimal digits of accuracy for computed results; exact answers for symbolic results.

- Built-in units of measurement and dimension checking.

- Built-in solver for simultaneous equations and inequalities.

- Complex numbers, variables, and functions.

- Derivatives and integrals.

- Summations, products, and iteration.

- Octal, decimal, and hexadecimal numbers.

- Trigonometric, hyperbolic, exponential and Bessel functions.

- Statistical functions including linear regression, gamma function, erf, cumulative normal distribution.

- Cubic spline curve-fitting.

- Fast Fourier transforms, both one and two dimensional.

- User-definable functions.

- Vectors and matrices, including operations for matrix multiplication, matrix inverse, transpose, determinant, dot and cross product.

Symbolic features

- Symbolic integration and differentiation.

- Inverse, transpose and determinant of a matrix.

- Factoring and simplifying expressions.

- Solving equations.

Plotting features

- One keystroke to generate a plot, then fill in the blanks.

- A variety of plot types: rectangular (x-y) plots, polar plots, surface plots, contour plots, vector field plots, three dimensional bar charts, scatter plots.

- Graph axes can be linear or logarithmic, with or without grid lines.

- Multiple line types, colors and line weights on graphs.

- One or more traces per plot, identified by legends.

- Three-dimensional surface plots, with variable perspective and scaling.

- Import graphics via the clipboard.

- Animation of plots, or anything else in your worksheet.

Text and worksheet features

- Automatic word wrap.

- Place text anywhere in the worksheet.

- Spell checking with user-customizable dictionary.

- Mix font, size, and style in each text region.

- Paragraph formatting, alignment.

- Printout reflects on-screen appearance — what you see is what you get.

Programming features (Mathcad PLUS)

- Conditional branching

- Looping constructs

- Recursive definitions

Communication features

- Compatible with Microsoft Mail and cc:Mail.

- Open worksheets located anywhere on the Internet.

- Store and retrieve worksheets from Lotus® Notes™ databases.

- Establish hypertext links to other worksheets located anywhere in the world.

How to use this manual

This *User's Guide* covers both Mathcad and Mathcad PLUS. Features unique to Mathcad PLUS are marked wherever they occur. The manual is organized into the following parts:

Getting Started

This section contains information on how to install Mathcad under Windows as well as a quick introduction to Mathcad's features.

Editing and Worksheet Features

This section describes how to edit equations and worksheets. It leads you through the basic features of the Mathcad document-style interface. This section covers editing and formatting equations and text, opening, saving, and printing Mathcad worksheets, and using Mathcad with the Notes, with a mail system, and with the Internet.

Computational Features

This section describes how Mathcad interprets equations and explains Mathcad's computational features: units of measurement, complex numbers, matrices, built-in functions, equation-solving, programming and so on. This section also describes how to do symbolic calculations.

Graphics Features

This section describes how to create and format Mathcad a variety of two and three dimensional plots. It also describes how to import graphics into Mathcad and how to create an animation clip of anything in your worksheet.

The *User's Guide* ends with some useful reference appendices and a comprehensive index.

As far as possible, the topics in this manual are described independently of each other. This means that once you are familiar with the basic workings of the program, you can just select a topic of interest and read about it.

If you're trying to learn by reproducing screenshots from this *User's Guide*, keep in mind that some of them may be difficult to recreate because they contain equations other than those displayed, because default plot formats and numerical formats are not always used, because they involve random number generation or because they use data files not available to you.

Getting Started

Chapter 0
Setting up Mathcad for Windows

This chapter describes how to set up Mathcad to run under Windows, including hardware and software requirements. It describes what files Mathcad needs, and how to install them.

The following sections make up this chapter:

System requirements

Hardware and software requirements for Mathcad.

Installation

Instructions for using the installation program to copy files to the appropriate directories on your hard disk.

New Features

A summary of differences between Mathcad 6.0 and Mathcad 5.0.

System requirements

Mathcad requires the following hardware and software:

Hardware

- An 80386, 80486, or Pentium based IBM or compatible computer. A math co-processor is not required, but its presence will significantly improve performance.

- At least 8 megabytes of memory.

- A hard disk with at least 20 megabytes of free space for Mathcad files.

- An additional 3 megabytes on the hard disk on which Windows is installed.

- At least 8 megabytes of virtual memory For Mathcad PLUS you'll need 12 megabytes of virtual memory. See the Windows user manual for how to specify Virtual Memory.

- A monitor and graphics card compatible with Windows.

- A mouse supported by Windows.

- Any printer supported by Windows.

Software

- MS-DOS or PC-DOS version 3.3 or later.

- Microsoft® Windows™ version 3.1 or later, Windows NT 3.5 or later, or Windows 95.

Installation

All files on the Mathcad disks are compressed and should not be copied directly. Mathcad comes with an installation script which creates a directory on your hard disk, and expands the necessary files into this directory. By default, Mathcad creates a `c:\winmcad` directory. You can, however, choose the name of this directory during installation.

Before you install Mathcad, make sure you backup your installation disks. To install Mathcad:

- Place the disk marked "Disk 1" in the floppy disk drive.

- In Program Manager, choose **Run** from the **File** menu and type `a:\setup.exe` or `b:\setup.exe` depending on where you've inserted your disk.

- Follow the on-screen installation instructions.

- A MathSoft Apps group is created and the Mathcad program, two Electronic Books and a tutorial will be placed in it.

- To start Mathcad, double-click on the Mathcad icon.

- Choose **About Mathcad** from the **Help** menu and write down your serial number in a safe place. There's a space in the inside front cover of the *User's Guide* where you can write it down. You'll need this number to get technical support.

Please send your registration card directly to MathSoft. This will allow us to keep you informed of upgrades and new products.

If you have any problems installing Mathcad check the release notes distributed with this version of Mathcad. You can read them by opening the file `rel-notes.txt` with the Notepad.

If after having checked the release notes you are still having trouble, contact MathSoft Technical Support. See the Getting Started leaflet enclosed with your product for details.

New features

If you've used Mathcad 5.0, you'll notice many new features as well as many new ways of doing things.

Enhancements to Cartesian and polar plots
Crossed axes in polar and Cartesian plots to show all four quadrants at once. Individually select axes for labeling and formatting, plot tracing, adjusting line weights on plots.

More types of 3D plots
Scatter plots, three-dimensional bar charts, vector field plots, plotting trajectories in three dimensions.

Enhancements to 3D Plots
Improved control over axes, colored backplanes and edges, bounding boxes.

Math in text
Embed live equations in text and edit them just as if they were separate math regions.

Improved document layout
Controlling indentation and alignment of text.

Dozens of new statistical functions
Functions for generating random numbers, cumulative and inverse cumulative distributions and probability densities for a variety of commonly used probability distributions.

Programmability (Mathcad PLUS)
Programming constructs such as loops and conditional branching, local assignment, recursive function definitions.

QuickSheets™

A collection of templates for performing common procedures, all compiled into a convenient, ready to use Electronic Book™.

Notes access

Check Mathcad worksheets in and out of a Lotus® Notes™ database for version control and security.

Locked regions

Set aside a tamper-proof area of your worksheet for depositing anything you don't want anyone to accidentally change.

Advanced data smoothing functions

Smoothing with kernels and running medians, adaptive smoothing algorithms.

Advanced regression functions

Multidimensional regression, adaptive regression methods.

Mail

Connect directly to cc:Mail or Microsoft Mail compatible systems.

Internet access

Open Mathcad worksheets located on any Internet server anywhere in the world.

Animation (Mathcad PLUS)

View dynamic processes by animating plots or calculations.

Hypertext links to other Mathcad worksheets

Create "hot-spots" for jumping to other Mathcad worksheets, either on your own file system, in a Notes database, or anywhere in the world via the Internet.

Dragging across worksheets

Drag regions directly from one worksheet to another, bypassing the clipboard altogether.

Operator extensibility

Define your own custom operators as easily as you'd define a function.

Chapter 1
The Basics

This chapter describes everything you need to get started with Mathcad. The following sections make up this chapter:

First principles

Mathcad's design and interface.

What you can do with Mathcad

Starting Mathcad.

A simple calculation

Calculating with Mathcad.

Definitions and variables

Creating simple Mathcad equations.

Entering text

Adding notes and labels to a worksheet.

Regions and menus

How equations, text, and plots make up a worksheet; Mathcad's menu commands.

Iterative calculations

Using range variables to repeat an equation for several values.

Graphs

Building a simple two dimensional plot.

Saving, printing, and quitting

The **Save** and **Print** commands from the **File** menu.

Help

Mathcad's on-line help system, its context sensitive help, and the use of QuickSheets™ for live examples.

Electronic Books

Using Mathcad's Electronic Books to paste common formulas and diagrams into your worksheet.

Mathcad looks simple, and it is. It was created according to basic design principles to make it powerful, flexible, and easy to use. In Mathcad:

- **Everything appears in familiar math notation.** If there's a standard mathematical way to show an equation, operation, or graph, Mathcad uses it.

- **What you see is what you get.** There is no hidden information; everything appears on the screen. When you print, the output looks just like the screen display.

- **To create simple expressions, just type them.** Mathcad uses the standard keys for standard mathematical operations.

- **Typing aids make equations easier to enter.** There are palettes for many of the less common operators. Click on formulas or pictures in Mathcad's Electronic Books to insert them into your worksheet.

- **Fill in the blanks.** Mathcad guides you through the creation of plots, integrals, and other mathematical expressions by laying down the framework and letting you fill in the blanks.

- **Calculation features are modular.** If you don't want to use a feature — like complex numbers, units, or matrices — you can just pretend it isn't there.

- **The numerical algorithms are robust, standard, and predictable**. Mathcad's numerical algorithms for things like integrals, matrix inversion, and equation solving are reliable standard methods.

- **On-line help.** Pressing [**F1**] brings up an extensive on-line help system. Click on error messages, operators and functions and press [**F1**] to display the relevant help screen. There's no need to search for the topic you're interested in. The manual includes more detail on all the features, with step-by-step instructions and illustrative examples. At the back of the manual is a complete cross-referenced index.

- **QuickSheets.** A collection of commonly used Mathcad procedures in a live document interface. If you have a particular task in mind, you can look in QuickSheets for a prefab working template and drag it right into your own worksheet.

- **Electronic Books.** A variety of useful formulas, constants and graphic images are compiled in the Desktop Reference Book shipped with Mathcad. You can insert many of them directly into your worksheet by clicking with the mouse.

This chapter provides a quick introduction to Mathcad and demonstrates a few more advanced features like iterative calculation and plotting. After you read this chapter, you'll have enough information to begin to solve your own problems in Mathcad. The rest of this manual describes all the features in detail, so you can learn more about any selected topic.

Notations and conventions

This manual uses the following notations and conventions:

Italics represent scalar variable names, function names, and error messages.

`Bold Courier` represents keys you should type.

■ Filled squares indicate steps you should follow.

Bold represents a menu command. It is also used to denote vector and matrix valued variables.

An arrow such as that in "**Change Defaults⇒Font**" indicates a pull-right menu command.

Function keys and other special keys are enclosed in brackets. For example, [↑], [↓], [←], and [→] are the arrow keys on the keyboard. [**F1**], [**F2**], etc., are function keys; [**Esc**] is the Escape key; [**Del**] is the Delete key; [**BkSp**] is the Backspace key; and [**Tab**] is the Tab key.

[**Ctrl**], [**Shift**], and [**Alt**] are the Control, Shift, and Alt keys. When two keys are shown together, for example, [**Ctrl**]**V**, press and hold down the first key, and then press the second key.

The symbol [↵] and [**Enter**] refer to the same key.

All mouse clicks refer to the left mouse button unless indicated otherwise.

When this manual shows spaces in an equation, you need not type the spaces. Mathcad automatically spaces the equation correctly.

A Mathcad window takes on a variety of appearances depending on how you've configured the various palettes. To maximize available space, nearly all screenshots in this manual are taken with all palettes, tool bars and font bars hidden.

If you're not using Mathcad PLUS, certain features described in this manual will not be available to you. This is indicated in a variety of ways:

■ By the word PLUS at the footer on every page in a chapter when *all* features described in that chapter are unique to Mathcad PLUS.

■ By the symbol shown on the left at the beginning of every section which describes *some* features unique to Mathcad PLUS.

⊕ ■ By the symbol shown on the left at the beginning of every function or operator description unique to Mathcad PLUS.

Mathcad combines the live document interface of a spreadsheet with the WYSI-WYG interface of a word processor. With Mathcad, you can typeset equations on the screen exactly the way you see them in a book. But Mathcad equations do more than look good on the screen. You can use them to actually do math.

Like a spreadsheet, as soon as you make a change anywhere in your worksheet, Mathcad goes straight to work, updating results and redrawing graphs. With Mathcad, you can easily read data from a file and do mathematical chores ranging from adding up a column of numbers to evaluating integrals and derivatives, inverting matrices and more. In fact, just about anything you can think of doing with math, you can do with Mathcad.

Like a word processor, Mathcad comes with a WYSIWYG interface, multiple fonts, and the ability to print what you see on the screen on any Windows supported printer. This, combined with Mathcad's live document interface, makes it easy to produce up-to-date, publication quality engineering reports.

Starting Mathcad

For instructions on how to install Mathcad on your computer, see the previous chapter, "Setting up Mathcad for Windows."

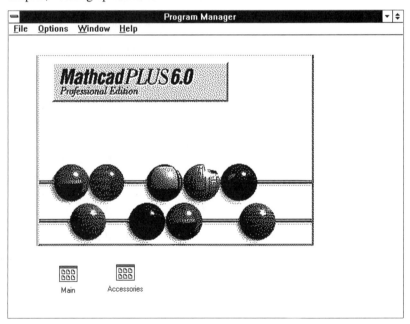

Figure 1: Mathcad's splash screen.

When you double-click on the Mathcad icon, you'll see the splash screen shown in Figure 1. This opens an application window as shown in Figure 2. If you've installed Mathcad PLUS, you'll see the window shown in Figure 3.

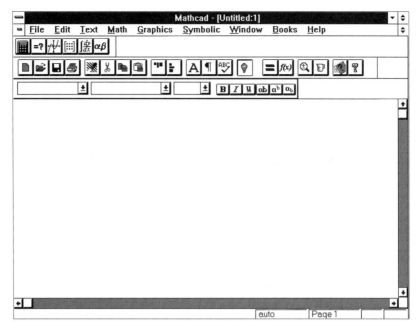

Figure 2: Click the button on the upper right corner to fully expand the Mathcad window.

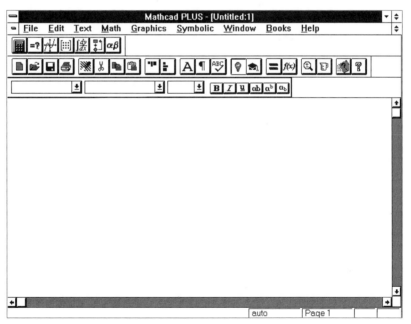

Figure 3: A Mathcad PLUS window.

You can place equations anywhere in the Mathcad worksheet. To get to places not visible in the window, use the scroll bars as you would in any Windows application. See Chapter 3 for a brief review of how to work with Windows.

Like other Windows applications, Mathcad contains a menu bar. To pull down a menu, you can either click on it with the mouse, or press the [Alt] key together with the underlined letter. For example, to pull down the **File** menu, press [Alt]F.

Each button in the strip of buttons just below the menus opens a symbol palette. You can insert many operators, Greek letters, and plot regions by clicking on the buttons found on these palettes. From left to right, these palettes are:

Button	Opens palette...
	Common arithmetic operators.
	Equal signs for evaluation and definition. Boolean expressions.
	Various two and three dimensional plot types.
	Matrix and vector operators.
	Derivatives, integrals, limits and iterated sums and products.
	Programming constructs. (Mathcad PLUS only).
	Greek letters.

Below this strip of buttons is the tool bar. Many menu commands can be accessed more quickly by clicking a button on the tool bar. To learn what a button does, click on the button and read the message line. If you don't want to activate the button, move the pointer away without releasing the mouse button. If you just want to know what the button does, let the pointer rest on the button momentarily. You'll see some text beside the pointer telling you what that button does.

The font bar is immediately under the tool bar. This contains scrolling lists and buttons used to specify font characteristics in equations and text.

To conserve screen space, you can show or hide each of these features individually by choosing the appropriate command from the **Window** menu. Throughout the figures in this manual, the symbol palette, the tool bar and the font bar have all been hidden to allow more space for examples.

You can also detach each of these window elements and drag them around your window. To do so, place the mouse pointer anywhere other than on a button or a text box. Then press and hold down the mouse button and drag. You'll find that the tool bar and the symbol palette will rearrange themselves appropriately depending on where you drag them. The font bar, on the other hand, will retain its shape no matter where you drag it.

A simple calculation

Although Mathcad can perform sophisticated mathematics, you can just as easily use it as a simple calculator. To try your first calculation, follow these steps:

- Click anywhere in the worksheet. You see a small crosshair. Anything you type appears at the crosshair.

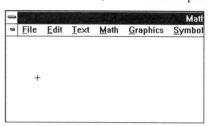

- Type 15-8/104.5= . When you press the equals sign, Mathcad computes and shows the result.

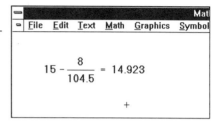

This calculation demonstrates the way Mathcad works:

- Mathcad shows equations as you might see them in a book or on a blackboard, expanded fully in two dimensions. Mathcad sizes fraction bars, brackets, and other symbols to display equations the same way you would write them on paper.

- Mathcad understands which operation to perform first. In this example, Mathcad knew to perform the division before the subtraction and displayed the equation accordingly.

- As soon as you type the equals sign, Mathcad returns the result. Unless you specify otherwise, Mathcad processes each equation as you enter it. See the section "Controlling calculation" in Chapter 6 to learn how to change this.

- As you type each operator (in this case, − and /), Mathcad shows a small rectangle called a *placeholder*. Placeholders hold spaces open for numbers or expressions not yet typed. As soon as you type a number, it replaces the placeholder in the equation. The placeholder that appears at the end of the equation is used for unit conversions. Its use is discussed in the section "Displaying units of results" in Chapter 8.

Once an equation is on the screen, you can edit it by clicking in the appropriate spot and typing new letters, digits, or operators. You can type many operators and Greek letters by clicking in the symbol palette located just below the menu bar. Chapter 2, "Editing Equations," explains in detail how to edit Mathcad equations.

Definitions and variables

Mathcad's power and versatility quickly become apparent once you begin to use *variables* and *functions*. By defining variables and functions, you can link equations together and use intermediate results in further calculations.

The following examples show how to define and use several variables.

Defining variables

To clear the previous equation and define a variable *t*, follow these steps:

■ Click in the equation you just typed and press the [↑] key until the selection box encloses the entire expression. Then choose **Cut** from the **Edit** menu.

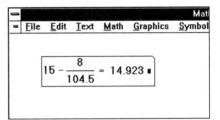

■ Now begin defining *t*. Type `t:` (the letter *t*, followed by a colon). Mathcad shows the colon as the definition symbol `:=`.

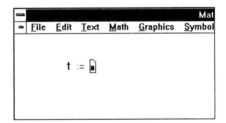

■ Type `10` in the empty placeholder to complete the definition for *t*.

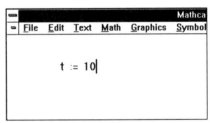

If you make a mistake, click on the equation and press the [↑] key until the selection box encloses the entire equation, just as you did earlier. Then delete it by choosing **Cut** from the **Edit** menu.

These steps show the form for typing any definition:

■ Type the variable name to be defined.

■ Type the colon key to insert the definition symbol.

■ Type the value to be assigned to the variable. The value can be a single number, as in the example shown here, or a more complicated combination of numbers and previously defined variables.

Mathcad worksheets read from top to bottom and left to right. Once you have defined a variable like *t*, you can compute with it anywhere *below and to the right* of the equation that defines it.

Now enter another definition.

- Press [↵]. This moves the crosshair below the first equation.

- To define *acc* as –9.8, type: `acc:-9.8`. Then press [↵] again.

Figure 4 shows the two definitions you just entered.

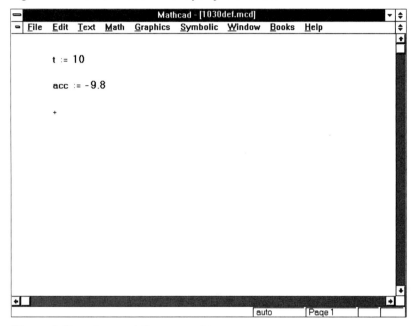

Figure 4: Equations to define acc and t.

Calculating results

Now that the variables *acc* and *t* are defined, you can use them in other expressions.

- Click the mouse a few lines below the two definitions (see Figure 4).

- Type `acc/2[Space]*t^2`. The caret symbol (^) represents raising to a power, the asterisk (*) is multiplication, and the slash (/) represents division.

- Press the equals sign "=."

This equation calculates the distance traveled by a falling body in time *t* with acceleration *acc*. When you enter the equation, Mathcad returns the result as shown in Figure 5. The window now contains two *definitions*, which define variables, and one *evaluation*, which computes a result.

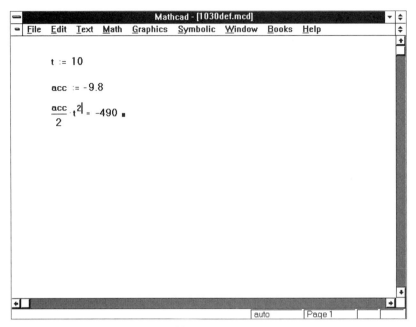

Figure 5: Calculating with variables.

Mathcad updates results as soon as you make changes. For example, If you click on the 10 on your screen and change it to some other number, Mathcad changes the result as soon as you press [↵] or click outside of the equation.

Entering text

Mathcad handles text as easily as it does equations, so you can make notes about the calculations you are doing. To begin typing text, click in an empty space and choose **Create Text Region** from the **Text** menu, press the double-quote key (") or click on the text region button on the tool bar.

Here's how to enter some text:

- Click in the blank space to the right of the equations you entered. You'll see a small crosshair.

- Press **"** to tell Mathcad that you're about to enter some text. Mathcad changes the crosshair into a vertical line called the insertion point. Characters you type appear behind this line. A box surrounds the insertion point, indicating you are now in a text region. This box is called a text box. It will grow as you enter text.

- Type `Equations of motion`

Mathcad shows the text in the worksheet, next to the equations (Figure 6).

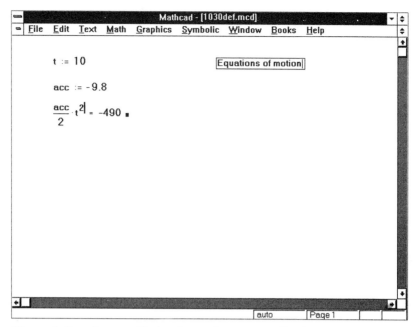

Figure 6: Entering text. Notice the text box surrounding it.

To enter a second line of text, just press [↵] and continue typing:

- Press [↵].

- Then type **for falling body under gravity.**

- Click in a different spot in the worksheet or press [**Shift**][↵] to move out of the text region. The text box will disappear once you have done this. Don't use the [↵] key. If you press [↵], Mathcad will insert a line break in the text instead of leaving the text region.

Figure 7 shows the worksheet with two lines of text and the cursor outside the text region. Since you are outside the text region, the cursor appears as a small cross, and the text box is no longer visible.

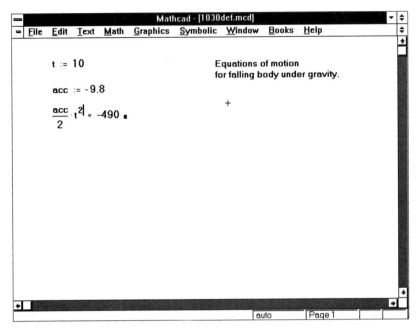

Figure 7: After clicking outside of a text region.

You can set the width of a text region and change the font, size, and style of the text in it. For more information on how to do these things, see Chapter 4, "Text."

Regions and menus

Mathcad lets you enter equations and text anywhere in the worksheet. Each equation or piece of text is a *region*. Mathcad creates an invisible rectangle to hold each region. A Mathcad worksheet is a collection of such regions. To see these regions, choose **Regions⇒View Regions** from the **Edit** menu. Mathcad will display blank space in gray and leave any regions in the default color. To turn the blank space back into the default color, choose **Regions⇒View Regions** from the **Edit** menu again.

To start a new region, you must first click in blank space. This leaves a small crosshair wherever you clicked the mouse. Then either type an equation or choose **Create Text Region** from the **Text** menu. When you're in a text region, a text box surrounds it, and the crosshair turns into an insertion point. When you're in an equation, the crosshair turns into either an insertion point or a selection box.

In addition to equations and text, Mathcad supports a variety of plot regions. Plots are described later in this chapter.

Chapter 1 The Basics

Mathcad can do repeated or iterative calculations as easily as individual calculations. Mathcad uses a special variable called a *range variable* to perform iteration.

Range variables take on a range of values, such as all the integers from 0 to 10. Whenever a range variable appears in a Mathcad equation, Mathcad calculates the equation not just once, but once for each value of the range variable.

This section describes how to use range variables to do iterative calculations.

Creating a range variable

To compute equations for a range of values, first create a range variable. In the problem shown in Figure 7, for example, you can compute results for a range of values of t from 10 to 20 in steps of 1. To do so, follow these steps:

- First, change t into a range variable by editing its definition. Click on the `10` in the equation `t := 10`. The insertion point should be next to the 10 as shown on the right.

$$t := 10|$$

- Type `,11`. This tells Mathcad that the next number in the range will be 11.

$$t := 10, 11|$$

- Type `;20`. This tells Mathcad that the last number in the range will be 20. Mathcad shows the semicolon as a pair of dots.

$$t := 10, 11 .. 20|$$

- Now click outside the equation for t. Mathcad begins to compute with t defined as a range variable. Since t now takes on eleven different values, there must also be eleven different answers. These are displayed in the table shown in Figure 8. You may have to resize your window or scroll down to see the whole table.

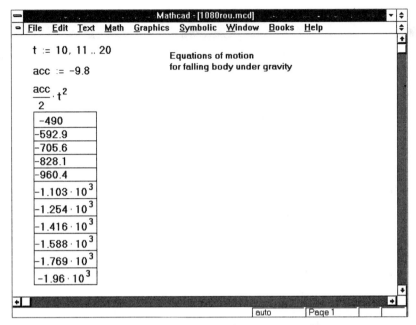

Figure 8: Generating a table of answers with a range variable.

Defining a function

You can gain additional flexibility by defining functions. Here's how to add a function definition to your worksheet:

- First delete the table. To do so, click anywhere in the table and use the [↑] key to enclose everything in a selection box. Then press [Ctrl]X or choose **Cut** from the **Edit** menu.

$$\frac{acc}{2} \cdot t^2$$

-490
-592.9
-705.6

- Now define the function $d(t)$ by typing d(t):

$$d(t) := \blacksquare$$

- Complete the definition by typing this expression:
  1600+acc/2[Space]*t^2[↵]

$$d(t) := 1600 + \frac{acc}{2} \cdot t^2$$

The definition you just typed defines a function. The function name is *d*, and the argument of the function is *t*. You can use this function to evaluate the above expression for different values of *t*. To do so, simply replace *t* with an appropriate number. For example:

- To evaluate the function at the value 12.5, type d(12.5)=. Mathcad returns the correct value as shown on the right.

  $$d(12.5) = 834.375$$

- To evaluate the function once for each value of *t* you defined earlier, click below the other equations and type d(t)=.

Mathcad shows a table of values (Figure 9). The first two values, $1.11 \cdot 10^3$ and $1.007 \cdot 10^3$, are in exponential (powers of 10) notation.

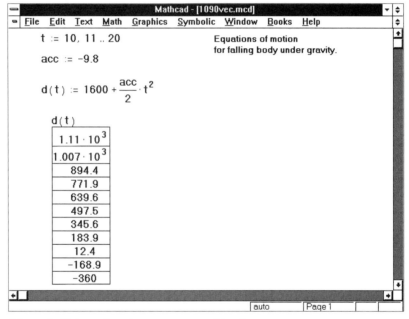

Figure 9: Using a function to return a table of answers.

Formatting a result

You can set the display format for any number Mathcad calculates and displays. This means changing the number of decimal places shown, changing exponential notation to ordinary decimal notation, and so on.

For example, here's how to change the table in Figure 9 so that none of the numbers in it are displayed in exponential notation:

- Click on the table with the mouse. This places a selection box as shown on the right.

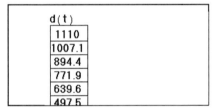

d(t)
$1.11 \cdot 10^3$
$1.007 \cdot 10^3$
894.4
771.9
639.6

- Choose **Numerical Format** from the **Math** menu. You see the Numerical Format dialog box. This box contains settings that affect how results are displayed, including the number of decimal places, the use of exponential notation, and whether the number is shown in decimal, octal, or hexadecimal. The option button beside "Local" should be filled in. This indicates that whatever you do in this dialog box affects only the result you've selected.

- The default setting for Exponential Threshold is 3. This means that only numbers greater than or equal to 10^3 are displayed in exponential notation. Click to the right of the 3, press [**BkSp**] and type **6**.

- Click the "OK" button. The equation changes to reflect the new result format — 1110 is no longer shown in exponential notation.

d(t)
1110
1007.1
894.4
771.9
639.6
497.5

When you format a result, only the display of the result is affected. Mathcad maintains full precision internally.

Mathcad can show both two-dimensional Cartesian and polar graphs, contour plots, surface plots as well as a variety of other three-dimensional plots. These are all examples of *plot regions*.

This section describes how to create a simple two-dimensional graph showing the points calculated in the previous section.

Creating a graph

To create a graph in Mathcad, click in blank space where you want the graph to appear and choose **Create X-Y Plot** from the **Graphics** menu. An empty graph appears with placeholders for the expressions to be graphed. Graphs are driven by range variables: Mathcad will graph one point for each value of the range variable used in the graph.

For example, here's how to create a graph of $d(t)$ versus t, with one point for each value of t:

- Click below the equation for $d(t)$ and choose **Create X-Y Plot** from the **Graphics** menu. Mathcad creates an empty graph.

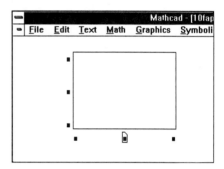

- The selection box should now be at the center of the bottom axis, on the x-axis placeholder. Type the variable name **t**. This tells Mathcad to graph t on this axis.

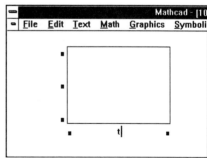

- Now click on the placeholder half-way up the left axis (the *y*-axis placeholder). Type **d(t)** here, to tell Mathcad to graph *d(t)* on this axis. The remaining placeholders are for *axis limits* — the high and low values for the axis. If you leave these blank, Mathcad automatically fills them when it creates the graph.

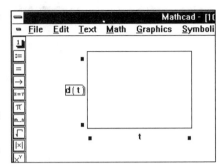

- Click anywhere outside the graph. Mathcad calculates and graphs the points as shown in Figure 10. A sample line appears under the "*d(t)*." This helps you identify the different curves when you plot more than one function. Unless you specify otherwise, Mathcad draws straight lines between the points and fills in the missing axis limits.

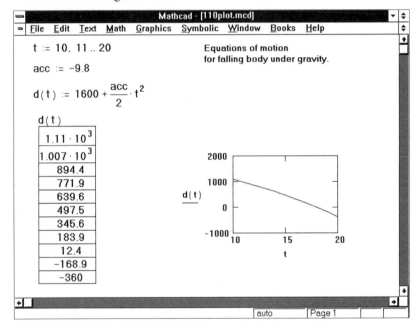

Figure 10: Graph of d(t) versus t.

For detailed information on creating and formatting graphs, see Chapter 19, "Graphs."

Resizing a graph

The graph shown in Figure 10 is the default size. It's easy to make a graph in Mathcad any size you want: just select the graph and stretch it to the desired size.

To resize a graph, follow these steps:

■ Click the mouse just outside the graphics region. This anchors one corner of the selection rectangle.

■ Press and hold down the left mouse button. With the button still held, drag the mouse toward the plot region. A selection rectangle emerges from the anchor point.

■ When the selection rectangle just encloses the graphics region, let go of the left mouse button.

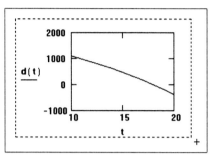

■ Move the mouse pointer to the right or bottom edge of the selection rectangle. It will change to a double headed arrow.

■ Press and hold down the mouse button. With the mouse button still pressed, move the mouse. The graphics region will be stretched in the direction of motion.

■ Once the graphics region is the right size, let go of the mouse button.

■ Click outside the graph to deselect it.

Figure 11 shows the result: a larger graph.

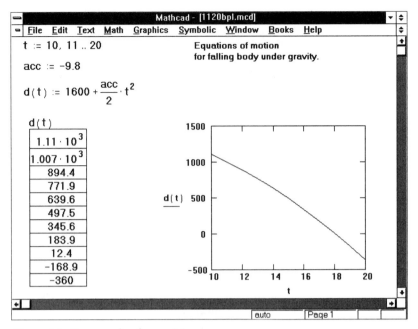

Figure 11: New graph, after resizing.

Formatting a graph

The graph in Figure 11 still has the default characteristics: numbered linear axes, no grid lines, and points connected with solid lines. You can change these characteristics by *formatting* the graph, just as you earlier formatted a number.

To format the graph, follow these steps:

- Double-click on the graph to bring up the appropriate dialog box. This box contains settings for all available plot format options. To learn more about these settings, see Chapter 19, "Graphs."

- Click on the Traces tab in the dialog box to see the correct page.

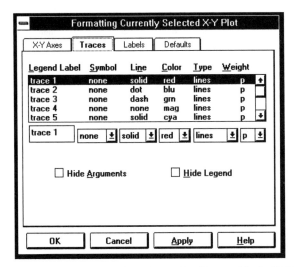

- Click on "trace 1" in the scrolling list under "Legend Label." Mathcad places the current settings for trace 1 in the boxes under the corresponding columns of the scrolling list.

- Click on the arrow under the Type column to see a drop-down list of trace types.

- Choose "bar" from this drop-down list by clicking on it.

- Click on the "OK" button to show the result of changing the setting. Mathcad shows the graph as a bar chart instead of connecting the points with lines (Figure 12). Note that the sample line under the $d(t)$ now has a bar on top of it.

- Click outside the graph to deselect it.

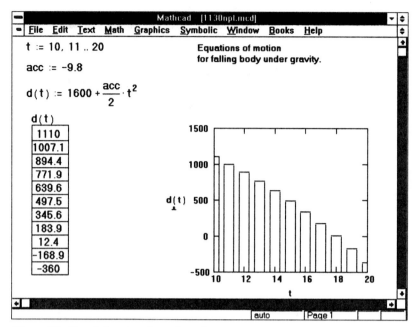

Figure 12: Graph formatted as a bar chart.

Saving, printing, and quitting

Once you've created a worksheet, you will probably want to save or print it. This section explains how to save and print in Mathcad.

Saving a worksheet

To save the file,

- Choose **Save** from the **File** menu or click on the disk icon in the tool bar. If the file has never been saved before, the Save As dialog box appears. Otherwise, Mathcad saves the file with no further prompting.

- Type the name of the file in the text box provided. By default, Mathcad saves the file either in the directory in which Mathcad is installed or in the directory from which you most recently opened a worksheet during the current session. To save to another directory, type the pathname in the text box.

For more information on saving and opening files, see Chapter 3, "Documents and Windows."

Printing

To print, choose **Print** from the **File** menu or click on the printer icon in the tool bar. Mathcad uses whatever printer is your default Windows printer.

For more information on printing, see Chapter 3, "Documents and Windows."

Exiting Mathcad

When you're done using Mathcad, choose **Exit** from the **File** menu, or press [Alt][F4]. Mathcad closes down all its windows and returns you to the Program Manager. If you've made any changes in your worksheets since the last time you saved, a dialog box appears asking if you want to discard or save your changes.

Help

Mathcad provides several ways to get help without having to consult this *User's Guide*.

- Pressing [F1] opens a Windows Help file similar to those in other Windows applications.

- Choosing **QuickSheets** from the **Help** menu opens a collection of examples in a live document interface similar to Mathcad's. You can drag these right into your worksheet and use them as templates for your own work.

- Pressing [Shift][F1] while on an operator, function, menu command, or error message opens context sensitive help on that message.

- Choosing **Technical Support** from the **Help** menu opens help on commonly asked questions and on hardware related issues.

- Holding the mouse pointer momentarily over various buttons and other window elements displays a message describing whatever is under the mouse pointer.

- Various operations like editing result in informative tips on the message line at the bottom of the Mathcad window.

The following sections describe the first three help systems in some detail. The remaining two need no further discussion.

On-line help

To see Mathcad's on-line Help at any time, choose **Index** from the **Help** menu, or press [**F1**]. Mathcad shows the Help window (Figure 13).

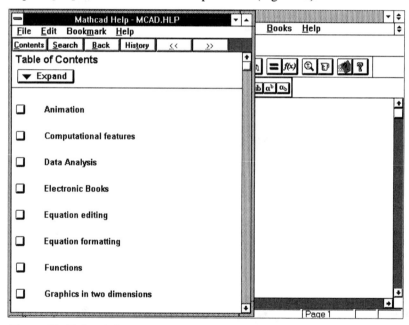

Figure 13: Help window.

To get help on a particular topic, click on the underlined word that suggests that topic. The "Search" button on the help window is good for finding help on something that may appear under several topics.

QuickSheets

If you learn best from examples, choose **QuickSheets** from the **Help** menu. When you do, Mathcad will open a small window containing a list of commonly used techniques you might need as you do your work.

Double-click on underlined text or on indicated buttons to jump to an example illustrating that technique. You can use the navigational buttons at the top of the QuickSheet window to browse through the QuickSheets. These buttons are described in the "Electronic Books" section later in this chapter.

Once you've found an example illustrating the particular technique you're looking for, you'll be able to experiment with variations on that procedure right in the QuickSheet. QuickSheets will update results just as if you were in a Mathcad worksheet.

Mathcad's QuickSheets also work as prefab building blocks for more complicated problems. For example, if occassionally you want to apply a cubic spline interpolation to some data, you may not remember all the details involved in using the *cspline* function. Rather than taking the time to refresh your memory, you may prefer to have a sort of "black box" that you can just plug into your worksheet.

QuickSheets are designed as self-contained units so you can easily drag them into your worksheet and get them working with just a few minor changes. To do so:

- Open a QuickSheet on the appropriate topic.

- Enclose the regions you want to copy in a selection rectangle by dragging the mouse around them.

- Drag the mouse pointer from the QuickSheet window to wherever you want to place the example in your worksheet. You'll see outlines of the selected regions following the pointer into the the worksheet.

- Release the mouse to drop your selection in the correct spot.

- Replace any data or any parameters used in the QuickSheet with your own data as required.

- To print the QuickSheet window, close all other open windows and choose **Print** from the **File** menu.

Figure 14 shows an example of a QuickSheet. Most QuickSheets also have a button you can use to copy whatever is currently on the QuickSheet to a clipboard. When you double-click this button, the pointer changes to indicate that it is "carrying" information. To "drop" this information into your worksheet, move the pointer wherever you want to drop the information and double-click on the mouse.

Figure 15 shows a Mathcad worksheet into which a QuickSheet example has been dragged. You'll find that by assembling pre-built and tested modules for routine tasks like those found in QuickSheets, you'll be able to put together solutions to problems in a fraction of the time.

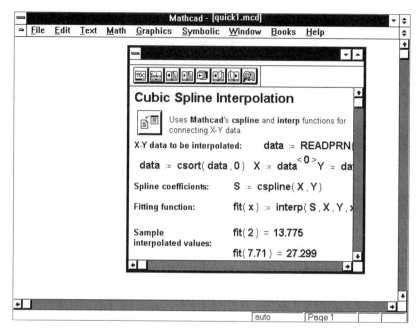

Figure 14: A QuickSheet window.

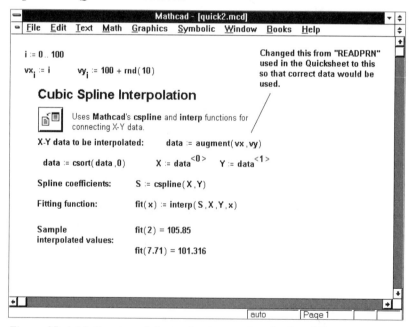

Figure 15: A Mathcad worksheet after integrating the QuickSheet example into the surrounding material.

The QuickSheets book also contains special pages on which you can save anything you want quick access to. Look for "Personal QuickSheets" or "Math Symbols" in the table of contents. Anything you enter in these sheets will be saved when you close QuickSheets. Changes made to any other QuickSheets will be discarded when you close QuickSheets.

Context sensitive help

You can get context sensitive help while using Mathcad. For menu commands you can simply click on the command and read the message line at the bottom of your window. For toolbar or palette buttons, hold the pointer over the button momentarily to see a tool tip.

You can also get more detailed help on menu commands or on many operators and error messages. To do so:

- Click on an error message, a built-in function or variable, or an operator.

- Press [**F1**] to bring up the relevant Help screen.

To get help on menu commands or on any of the palette buttons:

- Press [**Shift**][**F1**]. Mathcad changes the pointer into a question mark.

- Choose a command from the menu. Mathcad shows the relevant Help screen.

- Click on any palette button. Mathcad displays the operator's name and a keyboard shortcut on the message line.

To resume editing, press [**Esc**]. Mathcad changes the mouse pointer back into an arrow.

Electronic Books

Each Mathcad Electronic Book is a collection of up to several hundred Mathcad worksheets containing text, pictures, formulas, and data. A Mathcad Electronic Book is like any book, but it has some features that make it especially useful when you're working with Mathcad:

- Every page of an Electronic Book is a live Mathcad worksheet: You can change values, calculate results, and experiment right on the electronic "page" in front of you.

- If you have a second Mathcad worksheet open, you can paste data and formulas from the Electronic Book into your worksheet simply by double-clicking on them, then going to the worksheet in which you want to paste them and double-clicking again.

- Each Electronic Book has a table of contents and an extensive Index. Double-clicking on a section title, index entry, or cross reference automatically opens the appropriate section.

■ A palette of Electronic Book controls lets you browse through the Electronic Book page by page or section by section, or jump directly to the table of contents or Index.

Mathcad comes with an Electronic Book called the *Desktop Reference*. This contains useful mathematical and engineering formulas, physical constants, properties of various materials and other useful information you would ordinarily look up in any reference book. Several other Electronic Books on various mathematical and engineering topics are also available. Once you install additional Electronic Books, you can operate them just as you would the Desktop Reference.

To open the Desktop Reference, choose **Desktop Reference** from the **Books** menu. Mathcad opens a window showing the front cover of the book.

Click on the button labeled "TOC" to see the table of contents for the Desktop Reference. You can browse through this window by using the scroll bars, just as you would any Mathcad window. You can also use the palette buttons to move around the book. The function of each button is given in the following table.

Button	Function
[TOC]	Jumps to book's table of contents.
[Index]	Jumps to book's index.
[◀]	Goes backward one book section.
[▶]	Advances one book section forward.
[←]	Backtracks to whatever book section was last viewed.
[ ]	Goes to previous page of current section.
[▶]	Goes to next page of current section.
[ ]	Search book for a particular word.

The key combinations [**Shift**][**PgDn**] and [**Shift**][**PgUp**] have the same effect as the *Next Page* and *Previous Page* buttons. To move one screen to the right or left, click to the right or left of the scroll box in the horizontal scroll bar.

Mathcad keeps a record of where you've been in the Electronic Book. When you click on the *Backtrack* button, Mathcad goes back to the last section you opened and the page you were on when you left it. Backtracking is especially useful when you have double-clicked to look at a cross reference and you want to go back to the section you just came from. When you go to the table of contents, Mathcad starts its record over. This means you cannot backtrack beyond the last time you viewed the table of contents.

If you don't want to go back one section at a time or if you want to go back further than the backtrack button will take you, you can choose **History** from the **Books** menu. This opens a window listing all the sections you've viewed since you first opened the Electronic Book.

Finding information in an Electronic Book

An Electronic Book, like a paper one, comes with a table of contents and an index. To see these, click on either the "TOC" button or the "Index" button on the palette. When you double-click on an entry in either the index or the table of contents, Mathcad jumps to the appropriate page.

In addition to the table of contents and the index, you can search for all occurrences of a particular word. To do so:

- Choose **Search Book** from the **Books** menu to open the Search Book dialog box.

- Type a word in the text box. As you type, the scrolling list displays words that closely match the letters you type.

- Select a word and click on the Search Book button to see a list of topics containing that word and the number of times it occurs in each topic.

- Choose one of these topics and click on Go to Section. Mathcad opens an Electronic Book section containing the word you want to search for.

Click on Next Occurrence or Prev. Occurrence to bring the next or previous occurrence of the word into the window. If Next Occurrence is grayed out, the last occurrence of that word is currently visible. If Prev. Occurrence is grayed out, the first occurrence of that word is currently visible.

Note that this feature will not locate any annotations you may have saved using the **Annotate Book** command described on page 42.

Copying information from an Electronic Book

There are three ways to copy information from an Electronic Book into your Mathcad worksheet:

- You can use the Windows clipboard by selecting text or equations in the Electronic Book, using **Copy** from the **Edit** menu, clicking on the appropriate spot and choosing **Paste**,

- You can drag regions from the Book window into your worksheet, or

- You can double-click on whatever you want to paste to "pick it up," move the mouse pointer to your Mathcad worksheet and double-click again to "put it down."

Double-clicking with the left mouse button on most formulas, numbers, and pictures allows you to paste them directly from the book into your worksheet, bypassing the Windows clipboard in the process. If your book's author has designed a region to do something other than this, you'll see a message on the status line when you click on that region.

To paste something from the book into your worksheet:

- In the book window, double-click on whatever you want to paste. The pointer changes to indicate that it is "carrying" information from the book. Figure 16 shows how the pointer looks when it is carrying information.

- Move the pointer to the worksheet and double-click where you want to paste.

Mathcad pastes the image, formula, or number directly into the worksheet. The pointer's original appearance is restored to indicate that it has "discharged" the information it was carrying. Note that some Electronic Books have buttons which, when double-clicked on, will paste several equations or graphs. Click once to see on the status line what double-clicking was designed to do.

Figure 16 shows the pointer after having just "picked up" a circuit diagram of an oscillator from an Electronic Book. It is usually more convenient to tile the windows as shown in Figure 16 whenever you use the books. To do so:

- Make sure only one document window is open.

- Choose **Tile Vertical** from Mathcad's **Window** menu.

Figure 17 shows the result of double-clicking again. The pointer drops what it was carrying and recovers its original appearance.

To switch to another book, pull down the **Books** menu. Mathcad shows all available books in the default directory. Select the book you want to open. Mathcad opens a new book window showing the title screen of the new book.

If you've installed an Electronic Book in a directory other than the default directory, choose **Open Book** from the **Books** menu and use the Open Book dialog box to locate and open the book.

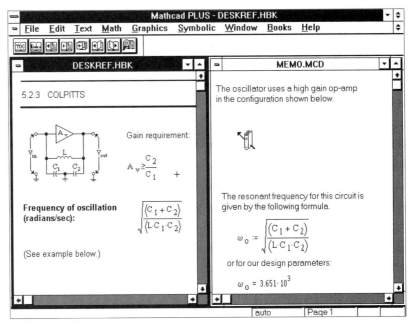

Figure 16: The pointer becomes a book pierced by an arrow to indicate that it is carrying information from the Electronic Book.

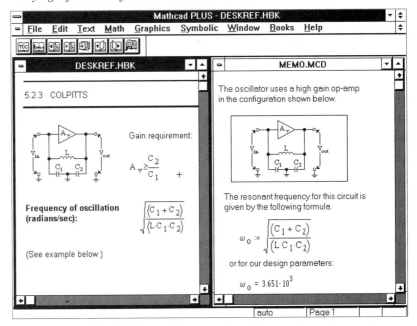

Figure 17: Double-clicking again causes the pointer to drop whatever it was carrying wherever you double-clicked.

Annotating an Electronic Book

By default, when you make changes in an Electronic Book, Mathcad remembers those changes as long as the book is open. When you close the book, whatever changes you make are lost. The next time you open that Electronic Book, it will appear as if it had never been changed at all.

If you want to save a copy of your Electronic Book, choose **Annotate Book** from the **Books** menu before making any changes. This places a checkmark beside the menu command to indicate that you can now save an annotated copy of your Electronic Book. The original copy of your Electronic Book will, of course, remain untouched.

As you make changes and type in your Electronic Book, you may want to mark the regions you change. To do so, choose **Annotate Options⇒Highlight Edits** from the **Books** menu. After you've done so, Mathcad displays any changed regions in a different color. You can set this color by choosing **Change Color⇒Annotation Color** from the **Windows** menu. To stop highlighting regions, choose **Annotate Options⇒Highlight Edits** from the **Books** menu again. This removes the checkmark from beside the menu command and disables this feature.

Once you've made changes in your Electronic Book, choose **Annotate Options** from the **Books** menu. You will have the option of:

- Choosing **Save Edited Section** to save only the changes you've made in the section you're working on, or ...

- Choosing **Save All Edits** to save all changes since you last opened the book.

Once Mathcad saves an annotated copy of the Electronic Book, you'll see an asterisk beside the title whenever you turn to an annotated section. The next time you open that Electronic Book, Mathcad will open the annotated rather than the original copy.

If you've made changes to an Electronic Book and you *haven't* chosen one of the above options, you'll see the dialog box below once you close the book:

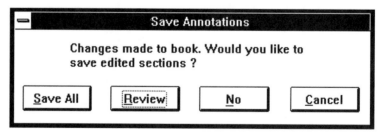

If you click on the Save All button in this dialog box, Mathcad will save all changes you've made since you last opened the Electronic Book. If you click the Review button, Mathcad will show you the titles of all changed sections, one at a time, and prompt you to either save or discard the changes you've made to each section.

Deleting your annotations

Once you've saved an edited copy of an Electronic Book, Mathcad will open up that copy rather than the original unedited copy. Whenever you turn to a section that's been annotated and saved, you'll see a "*" in the title bar beside that section's title.

The original section, as it appeared in the original copy of the Electronic Book before you made any changes, is still available. To see it, choose **View Original Section** from the **Annotate Options** pull-right off the **Books** menu. If you want to go back to the corresponding section in the annotated copy of the Electronic Book, choose **View Edited Section** from the same menu.

You can permanently delete the annotations in a particular section by choosing **Restore Original Section** from the **Annotate Options** pull-right off the **Books** menu. To delete your annotated copy of the Electronic Book altogether, choose **Restore Original Book** instead. This will delete all the annotations you've made to that Electronic Book.

Editing Features

Chapter 2
Editing Equations

This chapter describes the mechanics of creating mathematical expressions and making changes in existing mathematical expressions.

The following sections make up this chapter:

Building expressions

How to create mathematical expressions in a straightforward way by just typing a stream of characters. How to create expressions by exploiting their structure.

Editing tools

Describes the crosshair, insertion point, and selection box.

Editing an existing expression

Inserting and deleting operators, changing the names of variables, using Cut, Clear, Paste and Copy to streamline your editing. How to add a line break to a lengthy expression.

Rearranging your worksheet

How to move one or more expressions to another part of your worksheet.

Building expressions

You can create many mathematical expressions by simply typing in a stream of characters. Certain characters, like letters and digits, make up parts of names and numbers. Other characters, like * and + represent operators. For example, if you type the characters

    3/4+5^2=

you get the result shown below:

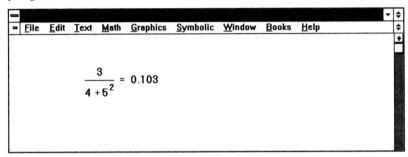

Figure 1: An expression and its computed value.

You can type many of these operators by clicking on the appropriate button in the various operator palettes. Each button on the strip of buttons just under the menus calls up one of these palettes. Most of the operators used in this chapter are on the *arithmetic palette* which you can open by clicking on the left-most button (the one with a calculator on it). For example, instead of typing 5^2, type 5, click on the button labelled x^y on the arithmetic palette, and type 2 in the placeholder.

On the surface, Mathcad's equation editor seems very much like a simple text editor, but there's more to it than this. Mathematical expressions have a well-defined structure and Mathcad's equation editor is designed specifically to work within it. In Mathcad, mathematical expressions are not so much typed in as they are built.

Mathcad automatically assembles the various parts that make up an expression using the rules of precedence and some additional rules that simplify entering denominators, exponents, and expressions in radicals. For example, when you type / to create a fraction, Mathcad stays in the denominator until you explicitly tell it to leave by clicking outside, typing [Space], or using the arrow keys. This means that the characters 3/4+5^2 generate what you see in Figure 1 rather than

$$\frac{3}{4} + 5^2$$

The following section, "An annotated example," introduces Mathcad's equation editor through a step-by-step example.

An annotated example

The key to editing expressions in Mathcad is to enclose the correct part of the equation in the selection box. A good rule of thumb is the following:

- *Whatever you enclose inside the selection box becomes an operand of the very next operator you type.*

When it comes to editing equations, knowing how to use of the selection box assumes an importance similar to knowing where to put the flashing vertical bar you see in most word processors. A word processor can get away with a vertical bar because text is one-dimensional, like a line. New letters go either to the left or to the right of old ones. But equations are really *two-dimensional*, more like trees than like a line of text. So Mathcad uses a two-dimensional version of that same vertical bar: namely the selection box.

Suppose, for example, that you want to type the slightly more complicated expression

$$\frac{x - 3 \cdot a^2}{-4 + \sqrt{y + 1}}$$

Watch what happens to the selection box in the following steps:

- Type **x-3*a^2**. So far, the rules of precedence allow us to just type the characters in. This is as far as we can go like this. Since the insertion point is on the 2, only the 2 becomes the numerator when you press **/**. Since we want the whole expression, $x - 3 \cdot a^2$, to be the numerator, we must expand the selection box.

$$x - 3 \cdot a^2$$

- To enclose $x - 3 \cdot a^2$ in a selection box, press the [↑]. The insertion point turns into a selection box. Press [↑] three more times and the selection box becomes progressively larger until it encloses the entire expression.

$$x - 3 \cdot a^2$$

You may wish to experiment with other arrow keys to see how they affect the size of the box and what's enclosed within it. You can also click the mouse on the operators of the expression to select different parts of it with this box. Be sure the entire expression is enclosed before you proceed to the next step.

- Press **/** to create a division bar.

- Now type `-4+` and click on the button labelled "√" on the arithmetic palette. Then type `y+1` under the radical to complete the denominator.

$$\frac{x - 3 \cdot a^2}{-4 + \sqrt{y + 1|}}$$

- To add something *outside* the radical sign, press [Space] twice to leave the radical. For example, to add the number π to the denominator, press [Space] twice to place the selection box around the radical sign. You can also click on the radical itself.

$$\frac{x - 3 \cdot a^2}{-4 + \boxed{\sqrt{y + 1}}}$$

- Press `+`. The selection box surrounds an empty placeholder. Note how the rule of thumb applies. Since the radical was inside the selection box, it became the first operand when you pressed `+`.

$$\frac{x - 3 \cdot a^2}{-4 + \sqrt{y + 1} + \blacksquare}$$

- Click on the button labeled "π" on the arithmetic palette. This is one of Mathcad's built-in variables.

$$\frac{x - 3 \cdot a^2}{-4 + \sqrt{y + 1} + \pi|}$$

Sticky operators

The division, power, and radical are "sticky" in Mathcad. This means that after you type one of these operators, everything you type next will be part of the denominator, exponent, or radical until you explicitly move the cursor by pressing [Space], the [↑] key, or by clicking the mouse. The following example illustrates how to build the expression:

$$x^3 + \frac{1}{a+b} \cdot x^{c+d} - \sqrt{x+1} + 1$$

- Type `x^3[Space]`. Note that the selection box now encloses the *x* and the 3.

$$\boxed{x^3}$$

- Now type
`+1/a+b[Space][Space]`
`*x^c+d[Space][Space]`

- Type `-\x+1[Space][Space]`

■ Type **+1** to complete the expression.

$$x^3 + \dfrac{1}{a+b} \cdot x^{c+d} - \sqrt{x+1} + 1\,|$$

Selecting an expression

In the last section, you saw that pressing the [↑] or the [**Space**] key makes the selection box larger. This section describes two additional ways to manipulate the selection box:

■ You can use the arrow keys on the right side of your keyboard.

■ You can move the mouse to an appropriate spot and click the left mouse button.

Notice that the selection box encloses an operator and all the operands associated with it. This operator is the *outermost operator* enclosed by the box. The outermost operator of an expression is that operator which applies to everything in the expression. For example, in the expression

$$(3+2) \cdot (5-8)$$

the outermost operator is the multiplication. You cannot change anything in the above expression without changing the outcome of the multiplication itself.

The plus sign is *not* the outermost operator in this expression. You can change the 5, 8, the "−" and the "·" without changing the outcome of 3 + 2. However, the plus sign *is* the outermost operator for the expression 3 + 2.

The idea of an outermost operator in a mathematical expression is very important in understanding Mathcad's equation editor. In the examples throughout this chapter, pay special attention to how the selection box is used to enclose different parts of an expression.

By pressing the arrow keys or clicking in different parts of an expression, you can move and change the size of the selection box within an expression. The table on the next page summarizes the actions of the various arrow keys when you are in an equation. When outside the equation, these keys simply move the crosshair in the indicated direction.

To leave the expression altogether, you can either:

■ Press [**Shift**] together with one of the arrow keys,

■ Click outside the equation with the mouse, or

■ Press [↵].

The selection box cannot select anything smaller than a name or number. To change the individual characters that make up a name or number, you must use the insertion point. If the selection box encloses the name or number you want to change, you can turn it into an insertion point by pressing the [↓] key. Use the [→] and [←] arrow keys to move the insertion point right or left respectively. Alternatively, you can just click the mouse wherever you want to position the insertion point.

Key	Action
[↑]	Makes the selection box bigger. Turns an insertion point into a selection box.
[↓]	Makes the selection box smaller. If the selection box encloses a name or number, turns it into an insertion point.
[→]	Moves the insertion point to the right. If an expression is selected, encloses the right hand subexpression (if any) in a selection box.
[←]	Moves the insertion point to the left. If an expression is selected, encloses the left hand subexpression (if any) in a selection box.
[Shift][↑]	Places the crosshair outside and just above the expression.
[Shift][↓]	Places the crosshair outside and just below the expression.
[Shift][→]	Places the crosshair outside and just to the right of the expression.
[Shift][←]	Places the crosshair outside and just to the left of the expression.
[Space]	Encloses operand of a sticky operator in selection box. Equivalent to one or more [↑]'s. Once topmost expression is enclosed, moves out of the equation altogether.

You can also use the mouse to enclose different parts of the expression. Just click on the appropriate operator. For example, clicking the left mouse button with the pointer resting on the minus sign in the numerator selects the numerator in the expression shown on page 50. This is because the two operands of the minus sign are x and $3 \cdot a^2$, the same two terms that make up the numerator.

Mathcad provides three tools for editing equations. One of these tools is always selected. You can tell which tool you've selected by the way it looks in the worksheet. The three tools are as follows:

- **Crosshair:** Use this to position a new equation, plot, or text region. The crosshair can be selected only in the empty space between other regions. Additional uses are discussed in the section "Rearranging your worksheet" later in this chapter.

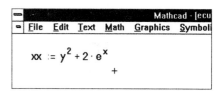

- **Insertion point:** In equations, use this for inserting and deleting parentheses, operators, and the individual characters making up names and numbers. In text, use it for inserting and deleting characters. This tool can be selected in a math, text, or graphics region.

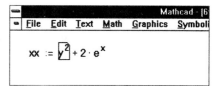

- **Selection box:** Use for inserting and deleting operators, numbers, and variable names. This tool can only be selected in a math or graphics region.

Understanding the distinction between these tools is the key to editing equations. The following sections discuss these tools in more depth.

Crosshair

The small cross that you first see when you start Mathcad is called the *crosshair*. The crosshair's most common function is to determine where in the worksheet the next region you create will appear. This tool is the only one that can be selected in an empty worksheet, or in the empty space between regions in a worksheet.

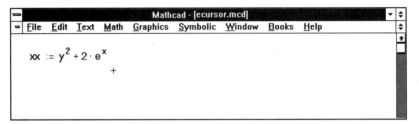

You can select the crosshair tool in three ways:

- By clicking in the blank space between equations, text regions, and graphics regions. This places the crosshair wherever the mouse pointer was when you clicked it.

- By pressing [↵] in a math region. This works when there's no region directly under the region you're in. If you're in text, Mathcad inserts a linebreak instead of exiting the region.

- By holding down the [**Shift**] key and pressing any of the four arrow keys. This places the crosshair adjacent to whatever equation or graph you were in.

There are several ways to move the crosshair tool to different parts of the worksheet. The easiest is to click the mouse in some empty space between regions. This leaves the crosshair wherever you clicked the mouse. You can also use the four arrow keys, the [**PgUp**] and [**PgDn**] keys, and several other keystroke combinations. These are summarized in Appendix A in the section "Arrow and movement keys."

Note that you can scroll the crosshair through equation, text, and graphics regions as if they weren't there. You can "enter" one of these regions by scrolling the crosshair into it, then pressing [↵]. As soon as you enter the region this way, the crosshair tool is replaced by either an insertion point or a selection box as appropriate.

Insertion point

This tool looks and functions very much like the insertion point in a typical word processor. It appears blue and thick in math regions and red and thin in text regions. Use it to insert and delete individual characters, parentheses, and operators.

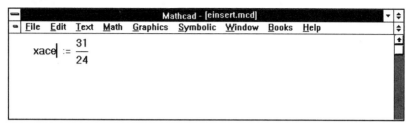

When this tool is selected in a text region, any character you type appears to the left of the insertion point. Pressing [**BkSp**] deletes the character to the left of the insertion point. This is the only tool that can be selected in text. Its behavior in text is discussed more fully in Chapter 4, " Text."

When this tool is selected in a math region, it works very much as it does in text. Use it to insert and delete characters of a number or variable name. You can also use this tool to insert and delete most operators and parentheses. However, the insertion point does not insert a space in math as it does in text. Instead, Mathcad formats the equation as you type, inserting spaces whenever necessary.

There are two ways to move the insertion point:

- You can click the mouse in another variable name or a number. Do not click on an operator since this changes the insertion point into a selection box.

- You can press the [←] or [→] arrow keys.

There are two ways to select the insertion point tool:

- The simplest way is to click the mouse with the pointer over a variable name, function name, or number.

- You can also press the [↓] key one or more times to make the selection box smaller and smaller until it turns into the insertion point.

Selection box

This tool appears as a box with a notched corner, usually on the upper right. The box itself can vary in size. For example, it can enclose just a single variable name, the numerator of a fraction, or an entire graphics region.

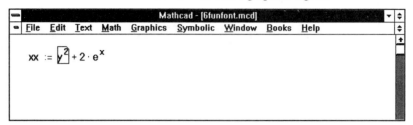

The selection box is used in two ways: cutting and pasting parts of an equation, and inserting and deleting operators.

The following two rules apply to cutting and pasting:

- Whatever is enclosed in the selection box gets cut or copied to the clipboard the next time you choose **Cut** or **Copy** from the **Edit** menu.

- If you enclose a placeholder in a selection box, whatever is on the clipboard gets pasted there the next time you choose **Paste** from the **Edit** menu.

The following two rules apply to inserting and deleting operators:

- Whatever is enclosed in the selection box becomes the first operand of the next operator you type.

- If you enclose an expression in a selection box and press [Del], you delete the outermost operator in the expression.

There are several ways to enclose parts of an expression in a selection box:

- Use the [↑] to turn an insertion point into a selection box that surrounds whatever expression the insertion point was in.

- Use the arrow keys to move the selection box to different parts of an expression. The table on page 52 describes these arrow keys in more detail.

- Click on the outermost operator of whatever part of the expression you want to enclose. In the example above, you could enclose the "$2 \cdot e^x$" by clicking the mouse on the multiplication dot.

- Double-click on a single name or a constant to enclose it.

Editing an existing expression

This section describes how to make changes to an existing expression.

The simplest changes you can make are discussed in "Changing a name or number." Here, the equation editor behaves very much like a text editor.

Most difficulties in editing equations arise from working with operators. The key here is to position the selection box correctly. The next section, "Replacing an operator," describes how to delete an operator and insert another operator in its place.

The equation editor normally inserts operators from left to right. If you want to insert an operator *before* an existing expression, or if you want to apply a function to an existing expression, see the sections "Inserting an operator" and "Applying a function to an expression."

Mathcad inserts parentheses wherever they are required to prevent ambiguity. If you want to add parentheses to clarify an expression, you can use the technique described in "Inserting and deleting parentheses."

When you want to move or delete complicated parts of an expression, it is often easier to exploit the structure of mathematical expressions. The sections "Moving parts of an expression" and "Deleting parts of an expression" describe how to use **Cut**, **Copy**, and **Paste** to do so.

Changing a name or number:

To edit a name or number:

- Click on it with the mouse. This places the insertion point wherever you clicked the mouse.

- Move the insertion point if necessary by pressing the [→] and [←] arrow keys. Alternatively, put the mouse pointer wherever you want the insertion point to go, and click the mouse.

- If you type a character, it will appear just to the left of the insertion point. Pressing [**BkSp**] removes the character to the left of the insertion point.

If you need to change several occurrences of the same name or number, you may find Mathcad's find and replace features useful. To search for a string of characters, choose **Find** from the **Edit** menu. To search for a string of characters and replace it, choose **Replace** from the **Edit** menu. These features are discussed further in Chapter 4, "Text."

Replacing an operator

The key to replacing an operator is to position the selection box so that the operator you want to replace becomes the outermost operator. For example, to change the minus sign in the numerator of

$$\frac{x^2 - 3 \cdot a}{-4 + \sqrt{y + 1}}$$

to a plus sign:

- Position the selection box as shown to the right. You can click on the minus sign or use the arrow keys. The outermost operator is now the minus sign.

- Now press the [**Del**] key. The outermost operator gets deleted. It is replaced by an empty operator placeholder. Note that pressing the [**Del**] key again would delete the entire numerator.

- Now press the **+** key. Mathcad inserts a plus sign into the operator placeholder.

Inserting an operator

The easiest place to insert an operator is between two characters in a name or constant. For example, here is how to insert a division sign between two characters:

- Place the insertion point where you want the operator to be.

- Press the **/** key.

It is also easy to insert operators that require only one operand. Examples are the square root, absolute value, and the complex conjugate operators. To insert one of these, select the entire expression you want to apply the operator to and press the appropriate keystroke. Many of these operators are available on the arithmetic palette as well. For example, to turn $x+y$ into $\sqrt{x+y}$ you would:

- Enclose the entire expression, $x+y$, in a selection box as shown on the right.

- Click on the button labelled "$\sqrt{\ }$" on the arithmetic palette.

In the section entitled "An annotated example," you learned that by enclosing an expression in a selection box and typing an operator, you could make that expression the first operand of that operator. For example, to turn x^2 into $x^2 + 1$, you would enclose the x^2 in a selection box and type **+1**. As a rule, if you use the arrow keys or the mouse to select an expression, that selected expression will become the first operand of the next operator you type.

Suppose however, that you want whatever is in the selection box to be the *second* operand instead of the first. For example, suppose you want to turn

$$x^2$$

into

$$1 + x^2$$

The following annotated pictures show how to do this:

- Begin by typing **x^2** as you did before. The insertion point is now beside the 2. However, since it is x^2 and not just 2 you want as the second operand of the addition operator you must enclose it in a selection box. To do so, press the [↑] key twice or press [**Space**]. The selection box now encloses the x^2 and the notched corner of this box is on the upper right.

- Press the [**Ins**] key. Note that the selection box turns red and that the notched corner is now the upper left. This means that whatever is enclosed by the selection box becomes the *second*, rather than the first, operand of the next operator you type.

- Now type the **+**. Note that Mathcad now inserts a placeholder for the first rather than the second operand. You can now type **1** in the placeholder to complete the expression.

Deleting an operator

Mathcad allows you to delete an operator connecting two variable names or constants, or operators that require only one operand. When an operator connects two expressions, for example:

$$(a - b) + (a - c)$$

you probably want to replace, rather than delete it. See the section on page 58 for information on replacing an operator.

To delete an operator connecting two variable names or constants:

- Place the insertion point after the operator.

$$\frac{a}{b} + c$$

- Press the [**BkSp**] key.

$$ab + c$$

You may also delete an operator by placing the insertion point before it and pressing the [**Del**] key.

To delete an operator that has only one operand, such as the $\sqrt{x}$, |x| or x!:

- Position the selection box so that the operator is enclosed, as shown on the right.

$$\sqrt{x + y}$$

- Press the [**Del**] or [**BkSp**] key. This deletes the operator you had enclosed with the selection box.

$$x + y$$

Inserting a minus sign

The minus sign that means "opposite of" behaves differently from the one that means "subtract" because it only has one operand. Here's how to insert a minus sign in front of an expression like sin(a).

- Enclose the sin(a) in a selection box. Click on the sin(a) and use the [↑] key if necessary.

$$\sin(a)$$

- Press [**Ins**]. The notched corner of the selection box is now on the left side.

$$\sin(a)$$

- Type "–" to insert a minus sign before the selected expression.

$$-\sin(a)$$

If you want to make an expression the second operand of a minus sign, for example to turn sin(*a*) into 1 − sin(*a*), insert another operator as described in the previous section "Inserting an operator." Then replace the operator with a minus sign as described in "Replacing an operator."

Applying a function to an expression

To turn an expression into the argument of a function, follow these steps:

- Enclose the entire expression, *w·t* − *k·z*, in a selection box as shown on the right.

$$\boxed{w \cdot t - k \cdot z}$$

- Type the single-quote key (the same as the double-quote key, but unshifted). The selected expression is enclosed by parentheses.

$$(\boxed{w \cdot t - k \cdot z})$$

- Press the [**Space**]. The selection box now encloses the parentheses as well.

$$\boxed{(w \cdot t - k \cdot z)}$$

- Press the [**Ins**] key. The notch on the selection box switches sides.

$$\boxed{(w \cdot t - k \cdot z)}$$

- Now type the name of the function. If the function you wish to use is a built-in function, use the **Choose Function** command from the **Math** menu and double-click on the name of the function.

$$\cos|(w \cdot t - k \cdot z)$$

Inserting parentheses

Mathcad places parentheses automatically as needed to maintain the precedence of operations. There may be instances however, when you want to place parentheses to clarify an expression or to change the overall structure of the expression. You can insert one pair at a time or individually.

To enclose an expression with a pair of parentheses:

- Select the expression you want to enclose. The expression should be surrounded by the selection box as shown in the figure on the right.

- Type the single-quote key. The selected expression is enclosed by parentheses and the entire expression is in a selection box. Press [↑] to enclose the parentheses inside the selection box as well.

$$\left(\frac{a+b}{a-b}\right)\cdot c$$

It is sometimes necessary to insert parentheses one at a time using the "(" and ")" keys. For example, to change $a - b + c$ to $a - (b + c)$ do the following:

- Move the insertion point just to the left of the *b*. Either click there or use the [→] or [←] keys.

$$a - b + c$$

- Type "(". Now click to the right of the *c*.

$$a - (b + c)$$

- Type ")"

$$a - \boxed{b + c}$$

Deleting parentheses

Parentheses can be deleted as a pair or individually. One way to delete a pair of parentheses:

- Select the expression surrounded by parentheses. The selection box should completely enclose the expression as shown on the right.

$$\boxed{\left(\frac{a+b}{a-b}\right)}\cdot c$$

- Press [**Del**] or [**BkSp**].

$$\frac{a+b}{a-b}\cdot c$$

Another way to delete a pair of parentheses:

- Move the insertion point to the right of the left parenthesis.

- Press the [**BkSp**] key. Both parentheses will be deleted. Note that you could also begin with the insertion point to the left of the right parenthesis and press the [**Del**] key.

Individual parentheses can be deleted by placing the insertion point to the left or right and pressing the [**Del**] or [**BkSp**] key. To delete parentheses used when defining a function of more than one variable, delete the argument and then the parentheses.

Chapter 2 Editing Equations

Be careful in deleting parentheses since you can easily bring about radical changes in the structure of an expression by doing so. If you accidentally delete a parentheses pair, choose **Undo Last Edit** from the **Edit** menu or press the eraser button on the tool bar.

Moving parts of an expression

The menu commands **Cut**, **Copy**, and **Paste** from the **Edit** menu are useful for editing complicated expressions. They function as follows:

- **Cut** deletes whatever is inside the selection box and copies it to the clipboard.

- **Copy** takes whatever is inside the selection box and copies it to the clipboard.

- **Paste** takes whatever is on the clipboard and places it in a selected place-holder.

As a shortcut, you can use the keys [**Ctrl**]X, [**Ctrl**]C, and [**Ctrl**]V instead of choosing **Cut**, **Copy**, and **Paste** from the **Edit** menu.

The following example shows how to use **Copy** and **Paste** to eliminate retyping. Suppose you want to build the expression

$$\cos(\omega t + \phi) + \sin(\omega t - \phi)$$

The argument to the sine function is nearly identical to that of the cosine function. You can take advantage of the similarity between the arguments of these two functions by doing the following:

- Build the first term, then leave an empty placeholder where the argument to the sine should go. Type `sin()` to do this.

  $\cos(\omega \cdot t + \phi) + \sin(\blacksquare)$

- Select the argument to the cosine function. The expression looks like that shown on the right.

  $\cos(\boxed{\omega \cdot t + \phi}) + \sin(\blacksquare)$

- Choose **Copy** from the **Edit** menu.

- Click on the empty placeholder in-side the sine function.

  $\cos(\omega \cdot t + \phi) + \sin(\blacksquare)$

- Choose **Paste** from the **Edit** menu. The expression now looks like that shown on the right.

  $\cos(\omega \cdot t + \phi) + \sin(\boxed{\omega \cdot t + \phi})$

Now replace the "**+**" with a "**−**" as described in the section "Replacing an operator." Press [**Del**] to delete the plus sign, and press "**−**" to insert the minus sign.

The **Copy** and **Paste** commands described above use the Windows clipboard to move expressions from one place to another. There may, however, be times when you don't want to disturb the Windows clipboard. You can bypass the clipboard by using Mathcad's drag and drop feature.

Suppose, as in the previous example, that you want to copy the expression $\omega{\cdot}t + \phi$ and place it in the empty placeholder inside the sine function.

- Select the argument to the cosine function. The expression looks like that shown on the right.

$$\cos(\boxed{\omega \cdot t + \phi}) + \sin(\blacksquare)$$

- Press and hold down the [**Ctrl**] key and the left mouse button. Make sure the *entire* expression you want to copy and drag is selected before proceeding. The pointer changes as shown on the right to indicate that it carries with it the expression enclosed by the selection box. It continues to carry this expression for as long as you continue to press the left mouse button.

$$\cos(\boxed{\omega \cdot t + \phi}) + \sin(\blacksquare)$$

- With the mouse button still held down, drag the small box at the arrow's tip over the empty placeholder.

$$\cos(\boxed{\omega \cdot t + \phi}) + \sin(\blacksquare)$$

- Release the mouse button. The expression is dropped into the empty placeholder. The pointer recovers its original shape to indicate that its contents have been discharged.

$$\cos(\omega \cdot t + \phi) + \sin(\boxed{\omega \cdot t + \phi})$$

You can drag and drop expressions into empty placeholders in other expressions or into any blank space in your worksheet. Just be sure you don't let go of the mouse button before you've dragged the pointer wherever you want to drop the expression. If you're trying to drop the expression into a placeholder, be sure to position the center of the cross carefully over the placeholder.

If you don't want to leave behind a copy of the expression as shown in the above example, follow the same procedure using the [**Shift**] key instead of the [**Ctrl**] key.

Deleting parts of an expression

You can avoid having to repeatedly press the [Del] key by choosing **Cut** from the **Edit** menu. This will delete whatever is inside the selection box and place it on the clipboard. You can also press [Ctrl]X to cut an expression.

The following example shows how you can use the cut command to delete a significant part of an expression.

Suppose you want to change the expression

$$\cos\left(\frac{\omega t + \phi}{2}\right)$$

into

$$\cos\left(\frac{\phi}{2}\right)$$

Rather than repeatedly pressing the [Del] key, you can do the following:

- Select the numerator as shown on the right.

- Choose **Cut** from the **Edit** menu. The numerator disappears, leaving behind a placeholder.

- Type f[Ctrl]G in the placeholder to create the Greek letter φ. You can also use the Greek letter palette. To see this palette, click on the right-most button on the strip of buttons directly below the menus (the one labelled αβ). On the Greek letter palette, click on the button labelled "φ".

Rearranging your worksheet

This section describes how to rearrange expressions, graphics and text in your worksheets. The techniques described here work equally well for everything in your worksheet: equations, plots, sketches and text. Before you use the methods in this section, click in the empty space between regions to select the crosshair tool.

You can get an overall view of how your worksheet looks by choosing **Zoom** from the **Window** menu and choosing a magnification from the Zoom dialog box. Set the magnification:

- Less than 100% to zoom out for an overall view.

- Greater than 100% to zoom in for a close-up view.

Selecting, cutting, pasting and aligning regions work the same way regardless of the magnification you choose.

Selecting regions

Before you can move or copy one or more regions, you must select them. To do so:

- Press and hold down the left mouse button to anchor one corner of the selection rectangle.

- Without letting go of the left mouse button, move the mouse so as to enclose everything you want to select inside the selection rectangle.

- Once the selection rectangle encloses everything you want to select, release the mouse button. Mathcad encloses those regions you have selected in rectangles.

Figure 2 shows how the worksheet might look just before you release the mouse button.

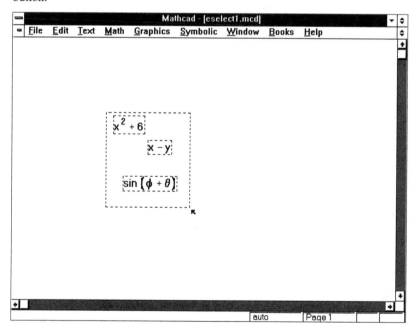

Figure 2: Several regions enclosed in a selection rectangle.

Copying regions

Once the regions are selected, you can copy them:

- by using **Copy** and **Paste**, or
- if the regions start out in either an Electronic Book or in a locked area, by dragging them with the mouse

To use the **Copy** and **Paste** commands:

- Select the regions as described in the previous section.
- Choose **Copy** from the **Edit** menu. This copies the selected regions into the clipboard.
- Click the mouse wherever you want to place a copy of the regions. You can click either someplace else in your worksheet or in a different worksheet altogether. Make sure you've clicked in an empty space. You should see the crosshair tool.
- Choose **Paste** from the **Edit** menu.

If the regions you want to copy are coming from a locked area or from an Electronic Book, you can also copy them by dragging them with the mouse. To do so:

- Select the regions as described in the previous section.
- Place the crosshair in any selected region.
- Hold down the left mouse button.
- Without letting go of the button, move the mouse. You'll see the rectangular outlines of the selected regions move as you move the mouse.

At this point, you can either copy the selected regions to another spot in the worksheet, or you can copy them into another worksheet.

To copy the selected regions to another spot in the worksheet, move the rectangular outlines to wherever you want to place the regions and let go of the mouse button. If you want to copy the region to a spot beyond what you can see in the window, just drag the regions in the appropriate direction. Mathcad will automatically scroll in that direction.

To copy the selected regions into another worksheet, press the left mouse button and drag the rectangular outlines toward the destination worksheet. Do not linger near the window's frame; drag the regions decisively across the frame and into the destination worksheet. Mathcad responds to hesitation near the window's frame by autoscrolling the document in the indicated direction.

Moving regions

Once the regions are selected, you can move them by:

- dragging with the mouse or,
- using **Cut** and **Paste**.

To drag regions with the mouse:

- Select the regions as described in the previous section.
- Place the crosshair in any selected region.
- Press and hold down the left mouse button.
- Without letting go of the button, move the mouse. You'll see the rectangular outlines of the selected regions move as you move the mouse.

At this point, you can either drag the selected regions to another spot in the worksheet, or you can drag them to another worksheet.

To move the selected regions to another spot in the worksheet, move the rectangular outlines to wherever you want to place the regions and let go of the mouse button. If you want to move the region to a spot beyond what you can see in the window, just drag the regions in the appropriate direction. Mathcad will automatically scroll in that direction.

You can also move the selected regions by using **Cut** and **Paste**. To do so:

- Select the regions as described in the previous section.
- Choose **Cut** from the **Edit** menu. This deletes the selected regions and puts them on the clipboard.
- Click the mouse wherever you want the regions moved to. Make sure you've clicked in an empty space. You can click either someplace else in your worksheet or in a different worksheet altogether. You should see the crosshair tool.
- Choose **Paste** from the **Edit** menu.

Aligning Regions

Once regions are selected, you can align them either horizontally or vertically by choosing **Align Regions** from the **Edit** menu. This is a pull-right menu. Drag the mouse to the right to display two additional choices: **Horizontal** and **Vertical**. You can also choose these commands by clicking on the appropriate button on the tool bar.

When you choose **Align Regions**⇒**Vertical** from the pull-right menu, Mathcad does the following:

- Mathcad draws an invisible vertical line halfway between the right edge of the right-most selected region and the left edge of the left-most selected region.

- All selected regions to the right of this line are moved left until their left edges are aligned with this line.

- All selected regions to the left of this line are moved right until their left edges are aligned with this line.

Choosing **Align Regions⇒Horizontal** works in much the same way. Mathcad draws an invisible horizontal line halfway between the top edge of the upper-most region and the bottom edge of the lowest region. Selected regions below and above this line are moved up and down respectively until the midpoints of their left edges are on this line.

Note that this means it is possible to inadvertently make regions overlap. If, for example, the regions you select are almost horizontally aligned, choosing **Align Regions⇒Vertical** may result in overlapping regions.

Deleting regions

To delete one or more regions:

- Select the regions by dragging.

- Choose **Cut** from the **Edit** menu.

Choosing **Cut** removes the selected regions from your worksheet and puts them on the clipboard. If you don't want to disturb the contents of your clipboard or if you don't want to save the selected regions, choose **Clear** from the **Edit** menu instead.

Alternative ways to select regions

There are actually three different ways to select regions. Which one you choose depends on the arrangement of the regions you want to select.

The most common, selection by dragging the mouse, was discussed in a previous section. This is useful when the regions you want to select are not too far apart, and can be enclosed in a rectangle.

The two additional methods are:

- Shift-clicking on the regions you want to select.

- Marking the two endpoints of a selection by clicking on them with the [Ctrl] key held down.

Shift-clicking is useful when you want to select or deselect a region without affecting any other regions. For example, you should shift-click when:

- You can't easily enclose the regions you want to select inside a rectangle. For example, if one region is near the top of a worksheet and the other is near the bottom, you cannot enclose them both in a rectangle without also enclosing many other regions in between.

- You want to add several more regions to a collection of regions you may have selected some other way.

- Several regions are selected and you want to deselect one of them.

To select regions by shift-clicking, do the following:

- Move the mouse pointer to the first region you want to select,

- Press and hold down the [**Shift**] key and click the left mouse button.

Mathcad surrounds the selected region in a selection rectangle. To select additional regions, repeat these steps with the mouse on the region you want to select. Make sure you hold down the [**Shift**] key while clicking. If you don't, Mathcad will select whatever you shift-click on, but deselect all other selected regions.

When there are a lot of regions to select, the selection rectangle may become unwieldy. In such cases, you can fill in your selection by control-clicking as follows:

- Select one or more regions either by shift-clicking, or by using the selection rectangle.

- With the [**Ctrl**] key held down, click on the last region in your selection.

Mathcad selects all regions between the first selected region and whatever region you control-clicked on. This may include regions beyond the right or left edges of your window. You can think of control-clicking as a quick way to shift-click every region between the first and last regions selected.

The last region selected need not be the one you control-click on. If you control-click on a region between two selected regions, Mathcad selects all regions between the two selected regions.

Inserting or deleting blank lines

You can easily insert one or more blank lines into your worksheet. The procedure is as follows:

- Click on the blank line below which you want to insert one or more blank lines.

- Choose **Ins/Del Blank Lines** from the **Edit** menu. The Insert/Delete Blank Lines dialog box shown below opens.

- Type the number of blank lines you want to insert into the text box and click "Insert."

To delete one or more blank lines from your worksheet:

- Click above the blank lines you want to delete.

- Choose **Ins/Del Blank Lines** from the **Edit** menu. The Insert/Delete Blank Lines dialog box shown above opens.

- Type the number of blank lines you want to delete into the text box and click "Delete." If the number exceeds the number of blank lines to the next region below the cursor, Mathcad displays the number of blank lines that can be deleted.

You can also bypass the dialog box when you want to insert or delete a single blank line at a time. To insert a single blank line press [`Ctrl`][`F9`]. To delete a single blank line press [`Ctrl`][`F10`].

Separating regions

As you move and edit the regions in a Mathcad worksheet, they may end up overlapping one another. If you make changes that cause errors in an equation, the error messages may overlap other regions in the worksheet. Overlapping regions don't interfere with each other's calculations, but they do make worksheets hard to read.

A good way to determine whether regions overlap is to choose **Regions⇒View Regions** from the **Edit** menu. Mathcad will display blank space in gray and leave the regions in white. Figure 3 shows an example.

To separate all overlapping regions, choose **Regions⇒Separate Regions** from the **Edit** menu. Wherever regions overlap, this command will move the regions in such a way as to avoid overlaps while preserving the order of the calculations.

Warning: The **Separate Regions** menu command can have far-reaching effects, since it can move many regions in the worksheet. If you want finer control, drag regions individually, add space by choosing **Insert Blank Line** from the **Edit** menu, or cut and paste the equations so they don't overlap.

Figure 4 shows the worksheet from Figure 3 after having chosen **Regions⇒Separate Regions** from the **Edit** menu. To turn the blank space back into white, choose **Regions⇒View Regions** from the **Edit** menu.

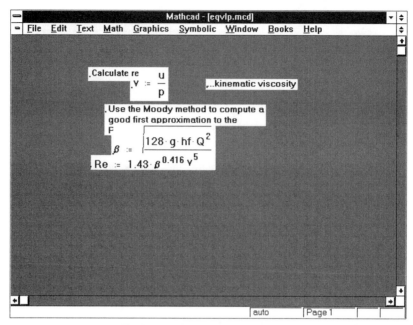

Figure 3: Worksheet with overlapping regions.

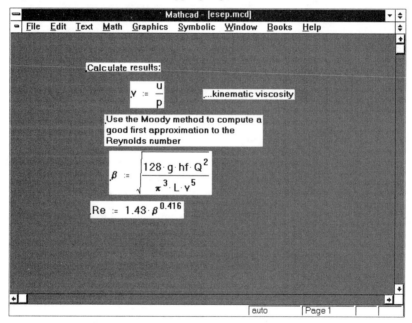

Figure 4: After separating the regions.

Chapter 3
Documents and Windows

This chapter describes how to navigate within a window, and how to save, load and print your work. The following sections make up this chapter:

Window management

How to scroll a window, how to move and resize windows, and how to open several worksheets at once.

Worksheet management

How to save your work and how to load previously saved work. Incorporating an existing worksheet. How to export your work to other applications. Mailing worksheets.

Working with a Lotus Notes database

How to store and retrieve Mathcad worksheets from a Notes database without having to leave Mathcad.

Safeguarding your calculations

How to write-protect selected areas of your worksheet.

Printing

How to print a worksheet. Includes a discussion of inserting headers and footers, numbering pages, adjusting margins, and previewing your printed output.

Configuration files

How to save values of system variables and default settings for plots and numerical display.

Window management

When you double click the Mathcad icon in the Program Manager window, it expands into an application window of its own. This window contains a *document* window named "Untitled:1" within it. This document window opens out onto a Mathcad *worksheet*. Figure 1 shows some useful terminology about Mathcad windows.

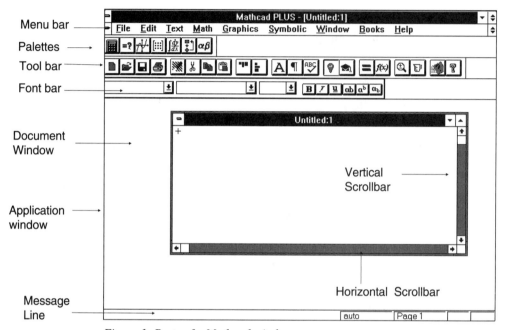

Menu bar

Palettes

Tool bar

Font bar

Document Window

Application window

Message Line

Vertical Scrollbar

Horizontal Scrollbar

Figure 1: Parts of a Mathcad window.

There are times when a Mathcad worksheet cannot be displayed in its entirety because the document window is too small. To bring unseen portions of a worksheet into view, you can:

- Use the scroll bars and arrow keys to move around the worksheet.

- Make the document window larger.

- Choose **Zoom** from the **Window** menu and choose a number smaller than 100%.

"Scrolling around a worksheet" describes how to use the scroll bars and the keypad to move beyond what you can see in a document window.

"Moving and resizing a window" describes how to drag a window to another part of the screen and how to change its size.

Mathcad windows work very much like those of most Windows applications. If you've worked with Windows applications before, much of the material in this chapter will already be familiar to you.

Chapter 3 Documents and Windows

Scrolling around a worksheet

There are several ways to move from one part of a worksheet to another:

- Move the mouse pointer and click the mouse button. The cursor jumps from wherever it was to wherever you clicked.

- Use the arrow keys [↑], [↓], [→], and [←] to move the crosshair up, down, right and left respectively. Mathcad scrolls the window whenever necessary. Note that the crosshair will pass through equations as if they weren't there. To actually edit an equation, you must first move the crosshair into it with an arrow key and press [↵]. Alternatively, you can click directly in the equation with the mouse.

- Click in the scroll bar to position the scroll box.

- With the mouse pointer on the scroll box, press and hold down the mouse button and move the mouse to drag the scroll box to another part of the scroll bar.

- Click on the arrows at the ends of the scroll bars to nudge the scroll box in the directions indicated by the arrows.

- Press [PgUp] and [PgDn] to move the cursor up and down by about one fourth the height of the window. You can also use [Ctrl][PgUp] and [Ctrl][PgDn] to move the cursor up and down by about 80% of the height of the window.

- Press [Ctrl][Home] to go to the first region of the worksheet, and [Ctrl][End] to go to the last region of a worksheet.

- Press [Shift][PgUp] and [Shift][PgDn] to position the preceding or following page break at the top of the window.

- Choose **Go to Page** from the **Edit** menu and enter the page number you want to go to in the dialog box below. When you click "OK," Mathcad places the top of the page you specify at the top edge of the window.

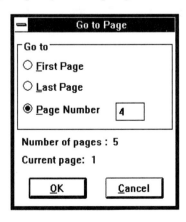

The position of the scroll box within the scroll bar serves as a rough guide to the position of the window relative to the rest of the worksheet. If the top of the window is a third of the way down from the top of the worksheet, the scroll box will be about a third of the way down the vertical scroll bar. The page number for whatever page is visible in the window is shown on the message line at the bottom of the window.

Moving and resizing a window

You can move and resize windows the same way you do in most Windows applications. The techniques described here apply to both the application window and the document windows contained within it.

To move a window, place the mouse pointer in the window's title bar (see Figure 1), press and hold down the mouse button, and drag the window to a new spot.

As is the case with all Windows applications, you cannot move a document window outside of the application window.

To resize a window:

■ Place the mouse pointer on the window border. The pointer turns into a double-headed arrow.

■ Hold down the left mouse button and move the mouse. An outline of the window will move with it.

■ When the outline reaches the desired size and shape, release the mouse button.

Another way to resize a document window is to click on the arrows at the upper-right corner of a window. These arrows perform different functions depending on whether they are on the Mathcad application window itself, or on one of the document windows contained within it. The table below summarizes their function.

Button	Name	Function
▲	Maximize	■ Enlarges the document window to fill the application window. ■ Enlarges the application window to fill the desktop.
▲▼	Restore	■ Restores the window size to whatever it was before you pressed the "Maximize" button.
▼	Minimize	■ Collapses the document window into an icon at the bottom of the application window. ■ Collapses the application window into an icon at the bottom of the desktop. To restore the window, double-click on it with the left mouse button.

Multiple windows

You can have up to eight document windows at one time. This allows you to work on several worksheets at once by simply clicking the mouse in whatever document window you want to work in. If the worksheet you want to work in is buried behind many other windows, pull down the **Window** menu and choose its name.

To open a new document window, choose **New** from the **File** menu. To open a window into a previously saved worksheet, choose **Open** from the **File** menu.

If the application window gets cluttered, refer to the section "Window Management" to learn how to move and resize windows. You can also choose either **Tile Vertical**, **Tile Horizontal** or **Cascade** from the **Window** menu. Figure 2 shows the effect of **Tile Vertical** on the window layout.

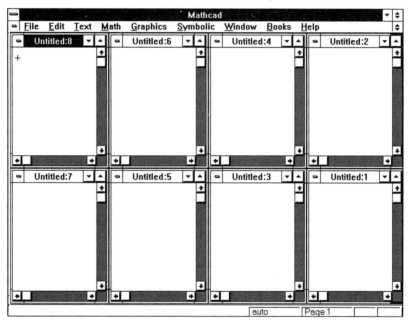

*Figure 2: Choosing **Tile Vertical** from the **Window** menu.*

Worksheet management

This section describes how to save and open worksheets, how to insert one worksheet into another, and how to export a document in RTF (Rich Text Format) so that a word processor capable of reading RTF will be able to open it.

Opening a worksheet

To work on a worksheet that you saved before, choose **Open** from the **File** menu. Mathcad prompts you for a name by displaying the dialog box shown below.

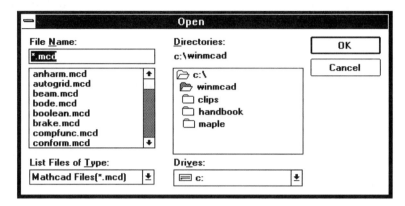

- The current directory is shown below the word "Directories." If the file you want to open is in this directory, skip to the next step. Otherwise, move the pointer to the scrolling list of directories and double-click on the directory containing the file you want to open. This box lists all subdirectories of the current directory. To switch to another drive, click on the arrow near the "Drives" box, then select the drive letter.

- Next to the Directory list is a scrolling list of all files in the current directory with the extension `mcd`. Double-click on one of these names to open it. You can also select a filename, then click "OK."

At the bottom of the **File** menu, Mathcad maintains a list of the most recently opened worksheets. You can bypass the Open dialog box by choosing from this list.

Opening a worksheet on the Internet

If the Mathcad worksheet you want to open is on the World Wide Web, you should open it by choosing **Open URL** from the **File** menu. When you do so, you'll see the following dialog box:

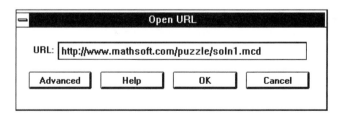

Type the worksheet's URL (Uniform Resource Locator) in the text box. This identifies the name of the computer on which the worksheet is saved together with the path to that worksheet within that computer's file system.

MathSoft maintains a collection of linked Mathcad worksheets. To access these, choose **QuickSheets** from the **Help** menu and click on "MathSoft Web Site".

Note that in order to use this feature, you must have a TCP/IP stack installed on your system. If you don't, you'll see the error message "Cannot find WIN-SOCK.DLL". If this occurs, ask your system administrator to to set up a TCP/IP stack. Not all TCP/IP stacks will be compatible. The following stacks are, however, supported: Microsoft's Wolverine™, FTP Software's ONnet™, and Net-Manage's Chameleon™.

Before using this feature, you also need to know whether you have direct access to the Internet or whether you'll be using a proxy. If you use a proxy, ask your system administrator for the proxy machine's name as well as the socket you'll be using to connect to it. Once you have this information, choose **Open URL** from the **File** menu and click on the "Advanced" button. Then enter this information in the appropriate places in the Advanced Internet Options dialog box.

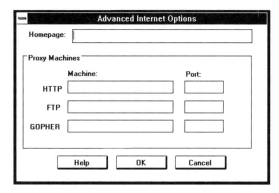

Saving your work

There are two choices in the **File** menu that have to do with saving files to your local file system: **Save** and **Save As**.

To save a worksheet that has never been saved before, you can choose either option. The **Save As** dialog box appears, prompting you for a filename.

To overwrite an original worksheet with a revised one, choose **Save**. Mathcad overwrites the original copy of the worksheet with the new copy (shown in the document window).

To make changes to an existing worksheet without modifying the original, you must choose **Save As** from the file menu. When you choose **Save As**, Mathcad brings up the following dialog box.

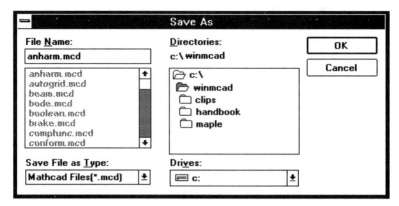

To specify the new filename, do the following:

- Specify the drive where you want the file saved in the "Drives" box. Click on the arrow to the right to see a list of drives.

- Specify the directory path either by typing it in or by double-clicking on its name in the Directories list.

- Type the name of the file in the text box. If you leave off the extension, Mathcad adds the `mcd` extension for you.

- Click on "OK" to save the worksheet.

Incorporating one worksheet inside another

There may be times when you want to use formulas and calculations from one worksheet in another. You can of course simply open both worksheets and use **Copy** and **Paste** from the **Edit** menu to move whatever you need to move. However when many regions or worksheets are involved, this method is cumbersome.

There are two other ways to make formulas from one worksheet available in another. The choice of which method to use depends on whether you want to actually *see* the regions in the second worksheet or whether you just want the second worksheet to behave *as if* you could see the formulas there. The first method is called "inserting" a worksheet; the second is called "including" a worksheet.

Whether you choose to insert or include a worksheet, the first step is the same: click the mouse wherever you want to insert the worksheet. Make sure you click in empty space and not in an existing region. The cursor should look like a crosshair.

To insert one worksheet into another:

- Choose **Insert** from the **File** menu, Mathcad displays a dialog box identical to that described in the earlier section, "Opening a worksheet."

- Use this dialog box to specify the name of the worksheet you want to insert, then click "OK."

When you click "OK", Mathcad moves any regions below your crosshair down to make room for the incoming worksheet. It then pastes all the regions from the first worksheet into the second wherever the crosshair is located.

If you want to "include" rather than insert a worksheet, you must have both worksheets open at the same time:

- Open the worksheet you want to include, either by choosing **Open** or, if the worksheet is on the Internet, by choosing **Open URL** from the **File** menu.

- Click on the window in which you want to include the worksheet and put the crosshair wherever you want to include it.

- Choose **Include** from the **Edit** menu. You'll see the following dialog box:

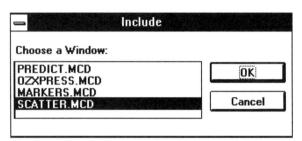

- In the list of open windows, select the window containing the worksheet you want to include. Note that this list excludes any untitled windows you may have open. A worksheet must have been saved at least once before it can be included in another worksheet.

When you click "OK", Mathcad pastes a small icon wherever you had the crosshair as shown in Figure 3. All definitions in the included worksheet will be available below or to the right of this icon. If you double-click on this icon, Mathcad displays the included file. You can move or delete this icon just as you would any other Mathcad region.

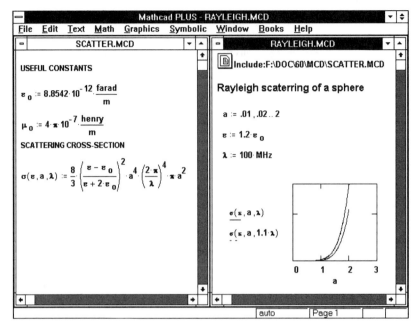

Figure 3: An icon representing an included worksheet. Definitions in the included worksheet are available below and to the right of this icon.

Once a worksheet has been included, there is no need to have the included file open. You only need to have the included worksheet open when you first include it.

This mechanism will work no matter where the included worksheet is located. The included worksheet could be on your file system, stored on a Notes database, or kept someplace on the Internet. All that's necessary is that you be able to open that worksheet. Once you've included a worksheet, Mathcad remembers where the file was when you first included it. Of course, if you move the included file *after* having included it, Mathcad will display an error message indicating that it can no longer find it.

Mailing your worksheet

If you're connected to a mail system that's compatible with either cc:Mail or Microsoft Mail, you'll be able to use that system to send both your worksheet and a short message. When you send your mail, whoever receives it will receive your worksheet as an attached file.

To send your worksheet:

- Open the worksheet you want to send.

- Choose **Mail** from the **File** menu.

Once you do so, you'll see a series of dialog boxes generated by your mail system prompting you for your password, an address and whatever else your system needs to send mail. The details of these dialog boxes will vary depending on the particular mail system you're using.

If your mail system doesn't respond, you may have to add the directory containing your mail server to your path statement. If you happen to have two mail servers using the same protocol, (*e.g.* SMI), Mathcad will use whichever is listed first in your path.

Exporting your worksheet

There are two ways to export your Mathcad worksheet into a word processor. You can cut and paste as described in the section "Importing and exporting text" on page 114, or you can save the document in RTF format as described here.

To export your entire worksheet as an RTF file readable by any word processor capable of reading an RTF file with embedded graphics:

- Scroll to the bottom of your document to update all calculated results.

- Choose **Export Worksheet** from the **File** menu.

- In the Export dialog box, type the name of the RTF file you want to create, then click "OK."

When you open this RTF file with a word processor, you'll find all the Mathcad regions lined up one above the other at the left edge of the document. You can then use your word processor to move these regions wherever you want to.

Once the Mathcad regions have been loaded into a word processor, you'll no longer be able to edit equations and graphs. You will, however, still be able to edit text.

Working with a Lotus Notes database

If you have access to Lotus Notes, you'll be able to manage your worksheets by attaching them to a Notes database. Mathcad comes with a template you can use to keep track of different versions of a Mathcad worksheet. For each version, you'll be able to see who made the changes along with whatever annotations are supplied by whoever made those changes.

The database template that ships with Mathcad is designed so that although any number of people can look at a worksheet at any time, only one person can actually "check out" a worksheet at any instant. That person is the only one who can actually update that worksheet and put it back into the Notes database. Once the worksheet is "checked in" to the Notes database, any other person can check it back out.

This mechanism is useful in keeping track of different versions of a worksheet. If two people were able to check out a worksheet at the same time, changes made by one would end up not containing changes made by the other. Keeping track of changes would then become very difficult.

This mechanism is also useful for keeping track of the history or evolution of a particular worksheet. Since every version of the worksheet is always available, it's easy to rollback to a previous version whenever you have to.

Keep in mind, however, that some Notes databases can be "replicated". When this occurs, it is possible for two people to check out the same worksheet at the same time. Under these circumstances, any attempt to store a copy of the worksheet may result in an error message indicating a "replication conflict." You can prevent this by using Notes to make the database unreplicable but this will inconvenience those who don't have access to your Notes server.

Setting up a Notes database

You'll find a file called **mathsoft.ntf** in the directory in which you installed Mathcad. This file is a template to be used for creating Mathcad databases. Since this file should go on your Notes server, and since Notes servers are generally not freely writeable, you should give **mathsoft.ntf** to your Notes administrator to put in the proper place.

Once this is done, you'll be able to create a Mathcad database. To do so:

- Choose **New Database** from the Notes **File** menu.

- Choose "Mathcad Notes Template" from the list of templates in the New Database dialog box.

- Fill in the remaining text boxes in the New Database dialog box just as you normally would. See your Notes documentation for details.

Storing a worksheet in a Notes database

Once you've created a Mathcad Notes database as described in the previous section, you're ready to start putting worksheets into it. To do so:

- Open the worksheet you intend to store in the Notes database.

- Choose **Save To Notes** from the **File** menu. You'll see the following dialog box:

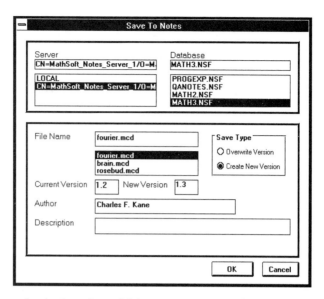

- Locate the database into which you want to store the worksheet.

- Fill in the remaining text boxes with whatever you find necessary to describe the worksheet.

Note that you can't create a Notes database by just storing a worksheet. You must actually create the database first as described in the section "Setting up a Notes database".

Retrieving a worksheet from a Notes database

When you retrieve a worksheet from a Notes database, you in effect "check it out." As long as a worksheet is checked out by you, nobody else will be able to modify the original worksheet in the Notes database. This does not prevent others from simply *viewing* the worksheet, it simply prevents others from making changes to it.

To retrieve a worksheet from a Notes database:

- Choose **Get from Notes** from the **File** menu. You'll see the dialog box below:

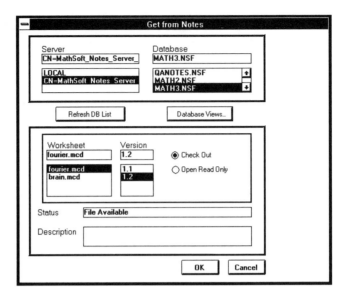

- Locate the database from which you want to retrieve the worksheet. If you don't see the database in the scrolling list, you may have to click the "Refresh DB List" button to update the list of databases.

- Locate the Mathcad worksheet you want to retrieve. If necessary, use the "Database Views" button to sort the database in different ways so you can locate the worksheet more easily.

- If you intend to make changes to the worksheet and you want those changes checked back into the database, make sure the "Check Out" button is filled. Otherwise, click the "Open Read Only" button to make sure you don't accidentally check the worksheet back into the database.

- Click the "OK" button. Mathcad opens a new document window and puts the worksheet into it.

If the worksheet has been checked out by someone else you'll see an appropriate message in the Status text box. If this is the case, you won't be able to save any changes you make back to the Notes database. You will, of course, be able to save the worksheet to your own drive by choosing **Save As** from the **File** menu.

From time to time, you may want to save the worksheet you're working on. This may occur before you're ready to check the worksheet back into the database. If this is the case, use the **Save As** from the **File** menu to save to your local drive.

Safeguarding your calculations

The ease with which you can alter a Mathcad worksheet can present a problem. It is all too easy to alter a worksheet and to change things which are not meant to be changed. For example, if you've developed and thoroughly tested a set of equations, you may want to prevent anyone from tampering with them.

To avoid this, you may want to safeguard these equations by locking them up in such a way that you'll still be able to use them even though nobody will be able to change them. To do this:

- You designate a particular area in your worksheet as a lockable area.

- You place the calculations that you want to lock up into that lockable area.

- You lock the area.

Once an equation is safely inside a locked area, nobody will be able to edit it. That equation will, however, continue to affect other equations in the document. For example, if you define a function inside a locked area, you'll still be able to use that function anywhere below and to the right of its definition. You will not, however, be able to change the function definition itself.

The remainder of this section describes how to specify the beginning and the end of the lockable area as well as how to lock and unlock that area once you've created it.

Specifying the lockable area

A lockable area is designated by two lines as shown in Figure 4. The text above and below these lines indicate that the area is now unlocked. As long as this area remains unlocked, you can edit equations and text in within it as freely as you would anywhere else in the worksheet.

To designate a lockable area:

- Choose **Lock Regions**⇒**Set Lockable Area** from the **Edit** menu. Mathcad inserts a pair of lines like those in Figure 4. These mark the boundaries of the lockable area.

- Select either of these boundary lines just as you'd select any region: by dragging the mouse across the line or by shift-clicking on the line itself.

- Once you've selected the boundary line, drag it just as you'd drag any other region.

You should position the boundaries so that there's enough space in between them for whatever equations you want to lock. You can have any number of lockable areas in your worksheet. The only restriction is that you cannot have one lockable area inside another.

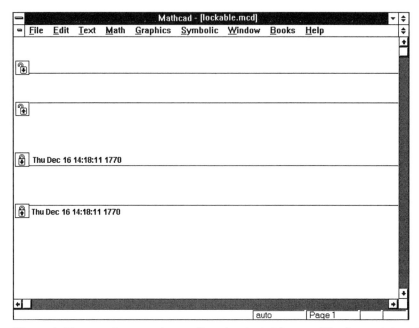

Figure 4: The area between the two lines is a lockable area. The first pair is still unlocked; the second pair was locked on the date shown.

Locking up the calculations

Once you've placed whatever equations you want to lock up inside the lockable area, you are ready to lock it up. You'll be able to lock it up either with or without a password. To do so:

- Click in the lockable area.

- Choose **Lock Regions**⇒**Lock Area** from the **Edit** menu.

- You'll see a dialog box asking you if you want to set a password. Click "Yes" if you want to require a password to unlock the area. Otherwise click "No."

- If you clicked "Yes," you'll be prompted for a password. Type any combination of letters and numbers. Keep in mind that the password is case sensitive.

Once locked, the locked area looks like the lower pair of lines in Figure 4. The date and time the area was last locked is shown above and below the boundary lines.

Locking without a password is useful when you just want to prevent yourself from absent-mindedly changing something and you don't want to worry about having to remember a password. When a region is locked without a password, anyone will be able to unlock it by simply choosing **Lock Regions**⇒**Unlock Area** from the **Edit** menu.

Locking with a password is useful when you want to prevent unauthorized changes to a worksheet. When you choose this option, make sure you remember your password. If you forget your password, you may find yourself permanently locked out of that lockable area.

Unlocking the calculations

If you want to make changes to an equation inside a locked area, you'll have to unlock it first. To do so:

- Click on one of the boundary lines of the region you want to unlock. Mathcad highlights the boundary line.

- Choose **Lock Regions⇒Unlock Area** from the **Edit** menu.

- If a password is required, you'll be prompted for the password.

Once an area is unlocked, you'll be able to make whatever changes you want to just as freely as you would anywhere else in your worksheet.

Deleting a lockable area

You can delete a lockable area just as you would any other region. To do so:

- Make sure the area is unlocked. You cannot delete a locked area.

- Select either of the two lines indicating the extent of the locked area by dragging the mouse across it.

- Choose **Cut** from the **Edit** memu.

To print all or part of a Mathcad worksheet, choose **Print** from the **File** menu. Your dialog box will depend on the particular printer you've selected. A typical dialog box is shown below.

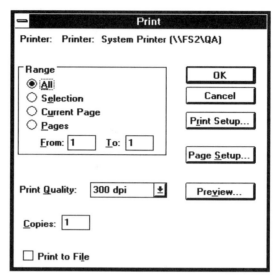

This dialog box lets you control what pages to print and what printer to print on. It also provides access to the Page Setup dialog box for controlling the location of all margins, and the presence of headers and footers. The remainder of this section discusses these options in detail.

Choosing what to print

You can choose to print the entire worksheet, selected pages, or selected regions. To control what Mathcad prints, click on one of the following buttons:

- **All:** Click this button to print all pages in the worksheet.

- **Selection:** Click this to print only the selected regions. If the button is gray, you have not selected any regions to print. To select regions for printing, use the dashed selection rectangle as described on page 66.

- **Current Page:** Click this button to print the page currently visible in your document window. If a pagebreak divides your window, Mathcad prints the page above the pagebreak. The current page number appears on the message line at the bottom of the document window.

- **Pages:** Click this button to print a range of pages. Then fill in the two text boxes to indicate your selection. If you've selected a plotter as your output device, you'll only be able to print one page; the text box beside "To:" will be greyed out.

If you find more pages than you expect coming out of the printer, keep in mind that Mathcad worksheets may be *wider* than a sheet of paper as well as longer. See "Printing wide worksheets" on page 92.

Choosing what to print on

By default, Mathcad sends its output to whatever printer you installed as a default printer under Windows. The installed printer is shown below the title bar of the Print dialog box. To redirect your output, either to a file or to another printer:

- Choose **Print** from the **File** menu.
- Click on the Print Setup button in the Print dialog box. This brings up the Windows Print Setup dialog box.
- Consult your Windows documentation for instructions on how to proceed.

Setting margins

Mathcad worksheets have four user-setable margins. To set these margins, click on the Page Setup button in the Print dialog box. Alternatively, choose **Page Setup** from the **File** menu. This brings up the Page Setup dialog box shown below:

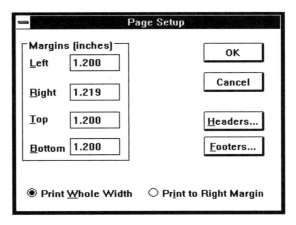

The four text boxes in this dialog box show the distances from the margin to the corresponding edge of the actual sheet of paper on which you will be printing.

- **Left Margin:** This is the distance from the left edge of the physical sheet of paper to the left edge of the print area.

- **Right Margin:** This appears as a solid vertical line in your window. You may have to scroll to the right to see it. In addition to marking the right edge of the printed area, the right margin serves as a wrap margin for all text regions.

  You can use the right margin to line up text in neat columns by temporarily moving it to the appropriate spot and typing text to its left. An easy way to do this is to click in the desired spot and choose **Right Margin⇒Set** from the **Edit** menu. Be sure to restore the right margin to its original location before printing.

  Don't confuse the solid vertical line marking the right margin with the dashed vertical line marking the right page boundary. This line marks the right-hand edge of the sheet of paper itself. Its location depends on your choice of printer. If you haven't chosen a printer, you won't see this dashed line at all.

- **Top Margin:** This is the distance from the top edge of the physical sheet of paper to the top edge of the print area. If your worksheet has a header, it appears just above this margin.

- **Bottom Margin:** This is the distance from the bottom edge of the physical sheet of paper to the bottom edge of the print area. If your worksheet has a footer, it appears just below this margin.

If you want the margin settings in the current worksheet available to other worksheets, save them in a configuration file as discussed on page 97. Executing that configuration file will load the saved configuration, including margin settings.

Printing wide worksheets

Because Mathcad worksheets can be wider than a sheet of paper, the idea of a "page" is not as clear as it would be in, for example, a word-processor. Regions separated by the dashed vertical line will print on separate sheets of paper, yet the page number at the bottom of the Mathcad window does not change as you scroll to the right.

You can think of the worksheet as being divided into vertical strips as shown in Figure 5. Mathcad begins printing at the top of the left-most strip and continues until it reaches the last region in this strip. It then goes to the top of the adjacent strip and prints every page down to the last region in that strip. This procedure is repeated until everything in the worksheet has been printed. Note that certain layouts will produce one or more blank pages. Figure 5 illustrates such a case.

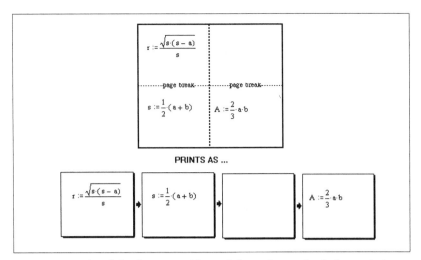

Figure 5: Mathcad divides very wide worksheets into strips before printing.

You can control whether or not Mathcad prints the entire worksheet or just the left-most strip shown in Figure 5. To do so, open the Page Setup Dialog box, either by choosing **Page Setup** from the **File** menu or by clicking the Page Setup button in the Print dialog box. Then:

- To suppress printing of anything to the right of the right margin, click on the Print to Right Margin button.

- To print all the regions in the worksheet, even those to the right of the right margin, click on the Print Whole Width button.

Pagebreaks

Mathcad provides two kinds of pagebreaks:

- **Soft pagebreaks:** Mathcad uses your default printer settings and your top and bottom margins to insert these pagebreaks automatically. These show up as dotted horizontal lines. You cannot add or remove soft pagebreaks.

- **Hard pagebreaks:** You can insert a hard pagebreak by placing the cursor on the appropriate line and choosing **Insert Pagebreak** from the **Edit** menu.

To delete a hard pagebreak, select it by shift-clicking the left mouse button on the bend at the extreme left of the horizontal line marking it. Then choose **Cut** from the **Edit** menu, or press [**Ctrl**]**X**. The crosshair over the bend in the page-break shown in Figure 6 shows where to click.

You can ask Mathcad to print a range of pages in the worksheet by typing the page range in the Print dialog box. The page numbers in the dialog box refer only to horizontal divisions. For example, if your worksheet looks like that shown in Figure 5, and you ask Mathcad to print page 2, you will see two sheets of paper corresponding to the lower-left and lower-right quadrants in Figure 5.

To print only the lower-left-hand page shown in Figure 5:

- Choose **Print** from the **File** menu.

- Type "2" in the boxes next to the words "From" and "To." This suppresses printing of the upper-left and upper-right quadrants.

- Click on the button next to "Print to Right Margin only." This suppresses printing of the lower-right quadrant.

- Click on "OK."

Note that this makes it impossible to print the upper or lower right quadrants by themselves.

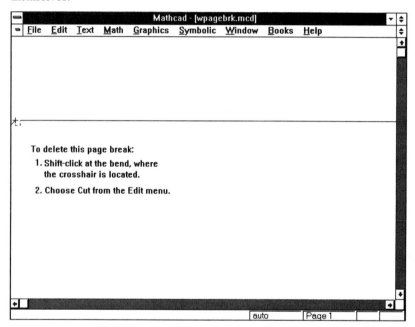

Figure 6: To select a hard pagebreak, click where the pagebreak bends.

Headers and Footers

To add a header or a footer to every printed page, choose **Headers/Footers** from the **Edit** menu. This opens the Header/Footer dialog box shown below:

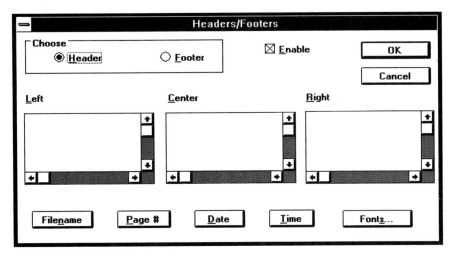

To add a header:

- Click on the Header button.

- Type the header into one or more of the text boxes on the left side of the dialog box. Whatever you type into the Left, Center and Right text boxes will appear left-justified, centered, and right-justified respectively.

- To automatically insert the page number, current date, time or filename wherever the insertion point is, click on the appropriate button below the text boxes. Mathcad inserts a special code into the text box. This will be replaced by the correct page number, date, time or filename when you print the worksheet. Note that Mathcad always begins numbering at page 1.

- Make sure the Enable check box is checked. When this is unchecked, Mathcad suppresses the display of headers and footers.

To add a footer:

- Click on the Footer button.

- Follow the rest of the instructions for inserting headers.

Print preview

To check your worksheet's layout before printing, choose **Print Preview** from the **File** menu. This brings up the following dialog box showing a bird's-eye view of how your worksheet will look when printed.

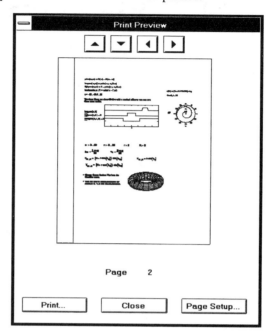

This dialog box shows the current page together with its four margins. You cannot edit the current page or change its margins in this view. To edit the page, return to the normal worksheet view by clicking the Close button. To move the margins, click on the Page Setup button and proceed as described on page 91.

The page you see in this dialog box is the same page you were viewing when you chose **Print Preview** from the **File** menu. This is indicated by the page number at the bottom of the dialog box.

To view a different page, click on the arrow buttons at the top of the dialog box. Mathcad will display the adjacent page in the direction indicated by the arrow.

Once you're satisfied with the layout, click on the Print button. Mathcad opens the Print dialog box shown on page 90.

A configuration file saves numerical and text format settings and the values for built-in variables. This lets you apply them to all new Mathcad worksheets or to transfer them easily from one worksheet to another. There are two ways to save a configuration file:

- In the default configuration file `mcad.mcc`.

- In a configuration file with a different name.

Upon opening a new worksheet:

- Mathcad searches in the directory in which it is installed for a file called `mcad.mcc`.

- If it finds this file, it uses it to set the default values for formatting and for various system variables.

This allows you to set a preferred format for all your new worksheets. For example, if you have preferred text and math font choices that are different from Mathcad's defaults, do the following to use these choices in all new worksheets:

- Choose **Save Configuration** from the **File** menu while you are in a worksheet that uses your preferred settings. You will see the dialog box below.

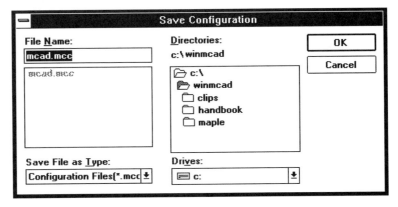

- Click "OK" to save your settings in the file `mcad.mcc`.

Now each new worksheet you open will automatically use these font settings.

Sometimes you'll want to save a configuration that will only be used for some of your worksheets. For example, you might want to set a high displayed precision and small zero tolerance for a particular group of worksheets. To do this, follow the steps below:

- Choose **Save Configuration** from the **File** menu while you are in a worksheet that uses the global numerical format in question.

- Specify the drive and directory path where you want to save the worksheet's configuration file.

- Change the suggested filename to a different name, for example, **number.mcc**. Then click "OK."

From now on, you can apply these format settings to any worksheet. To do so:

- Choose **Execute Configuration File** from the **File** menu.

- Click on **number.mcc** in the scrolling list of configuration files, and click "OK."

Your worksheet will now use the formats found in **number.mcc**. Note that these formats will be saved when you save the worksheet. This means that if you save this worksheet, you won't need to execute **number.mcc** again for this worksheet.

The format settings that are saved in a configuration file are listed below. See the appropriate chapter for more on each of these settings.

- The default character properties (Chapter 4)

- The default paragraph properties (Chapter 4)

- The definitions of all math font tags (Chapter 5)

- The margins for printing (Chapter 3)

- The numerical result formats (Chapter 5)

- Values for Mathcad's built-in variables (Chapter 7)

- The names of Mathcad's basic units (Chapter 8)

- The default calculation mode (Chapter 6)

Chapter 4
Text

Text in Mathcad worksheets comes in two varieties: *text regions* and *paragraphs*. Text regions are resizable areas of text that can appear anywhere within the worksheet. Paragraphs are areas of text that extend the full width of the page. Text regions and paragraphs function as commentary in a Mathcad worksheet, explaining and annotating the equations and plots.

Mathcad text can include any combination of fonts, sizes, and type and paragraph styles. Text automatically wraps, breaking lines according to margins that you specify. For paragraphs, you can specify the alignment and indentation.

This chapter describes Mathcad's commands for creating and editing text regions and paragraphs.

This chapter includes the following sections:

Inserting text

Creating text regions and paragraphs; resizing text regions and paragraphs.

Inserting equations into text

Embedding equations into text regions and text paragraphs.

Text editing

Manipulating text that is already in a region: cutting and pasting; changing font properties, alignment and indentation; and typing Greek letters.

Find and Replace

Finding and replacing text strings and variable names.

Spellchecking

Using the **Check Spelling** command to find and correct spelling errors in text.

Linking to other worksheets

How to make Mathcad jump to another worksheet when you double-click on a region.

This section describes how to create text regions and paragraphs. Text regions are useful for inserting comments around the equations and plots in your worksheet. Paragraphs, on the other hand, are useful for creating page-wide blocks of text. Mathcad ignores text when it performs calculations.

Creating a text region

To intersperse small amounts of text among the equations and plots in your worksheet, you can create text regions.

To create a text region, follow these steps:

- Click in blank space to position the crosshair where you want the text region to begin. Then choose **Create Text Region** from the **Text** menu (or click the "A" button on the toolbar). Mathcad begins a text region. The crosshair changes into an insertion point and a text box appears.

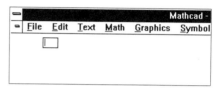

- Now begin typing some text. Mathcad displays the text and surrounds it with a text box. As you type, the insertion point moves and the text box grows.

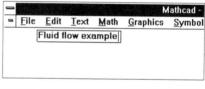

- When you've finished typing the text, click outside the text region. The text box will disappear.

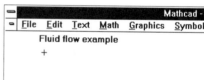

You cannot leave a text region by pressing [↵]. You must leave the text region by:

- Clicking outside the region, or

- By pressing [**Shift**][↵].

Figure 1 on the next page shows a Mathcad worksheet containing several text regions followed by equations.

To insert text into an existing text region:

- Click between two characters in a text region. A text box will surround your text. Anything you type gets inserted at the insertion point.

To delete text from an existing text region, click in the text region and:

- Press [**Bksp**] to delete the character to the left of the insertion point, or

- Press [**Del**] to delete the character to the right of the insertion point.

To overtype text:

- Place the insertion point to the left of the first character you want to overtype.

- Press the [**Ins**] key and begin typing. The vertical bar now has a break in the middle to indicate that you are in *overtype* mode. To return to the default *insert* mode, press [**Ins**] again.

To break a line or start a new line in a text region, press [↵]. Mathcad inserts a *hard line break* and moves the insertion point down to the next line. When you rewrap the text by changing the width of the text region, Mathcad will maintain a line break at this spot in the text.

To delete a hard line break, click at the beginning of the next line in the text region and press [**Bksp**].

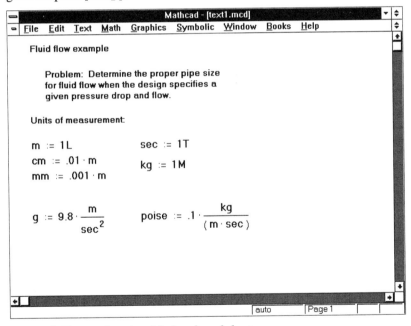

Figure 1: Text regions in a Mathcad worksheet.

Changing the width of a text region

When you start typing in a text region, the region grows as you type, wrapping only when you reach the right margin or page boundary. Press [↵] whenever you want to start a new line. Often you would like to set a width for your whole text region, and have lines wrap to stay within that width as you type. To do this:

- Type normally until the first line reaches the width you want.

- Type a space and press [**Ctrl**][⏎].

All other lines will break to stay within this width. When you add to or edit the text, Mathcad rewraps the text according to the width set by the line at the end of which you pressed [**Ctrl**][⏎].

To change the width of an existing text region do the following:

- Press and hold down the mouse button near the text region.

- With the button still pressed, drag the mouse to enclose the text region in the selection rectangle.

- Release the mouse button and move the pointer to the right edge of the text region until it changes to a double arrow. You can now change the size of the text region the same way you change the size of any window: by dragging the mouse.

Creating paragraphs

Paragraphs are designed for text that stretches from one edge of a Mathcad worksheet to the other. They differ from text regions in the following ways:

- Paragraphs start at the left edge of the worksheet and extend to the right margin. If a paragraph occupies a line on the screen, equations or plots cannot occupy the same line. Other regions must be either above the paragraph or below it. Because of this, you can't create a paragraph on a line containing any other text, math or graphics region. If you try to do so you'll see a message telling you that the paragraph would overlap other regions.

- Paragraphs push other regions out of the way as you type. In this way, paragraphs behave more like a conventional text editor. Similarly, if a paragraph shrinks as you delete text, Mathcad pulls the regions below it upward to fill the empty space.

- All the paragraphs in a worksheet resize and rewrap when you change the right margin. Text regions wrap at the right margin when you are first creating them, but they are then unaffected by changes in the right margin.

By automatically moving other regions as a paragraph grows and shrinks, Mathcad makes it easy to add and delete text.

To create a paragraph:

- Click on a blank line in the worksheet.

- Choose **Create Text Paragraph** from the **Text** menu (or click "¶" on the toolbar). Mathcad creates the first line of the paragraph. This is indicated by two horizontal lines stretching across the page. The insertion point appears at the left edge of the page.

- Begin typing text into the paragraph.

Figure 2 shows a worksheet with a paragraph. Note that the lines above and below the paragraph are visible only when the cursor is inside the paragraph.

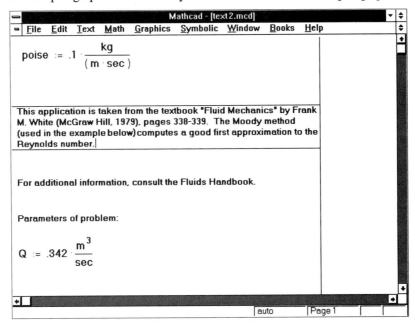

Figure 2: A worksheet with a paragraph.

When you use paragraphs, imagine that the worksheet is divided up into horizontal bands of different types. Within the paragraphs, Mathcad behaves like an ordinary text editor. Between the paragraphs are regions that contain equations, plots, and small text regions.

Once you've created a paragraph, you can type into it just as you would with a text region. The wrap margin for a paragraph is the right margin. (See "Changing the width of paragraphs," at the end of this section, if you want to change the wrap margin for paragraphs.) If you type more text than will fit on a line, the text will wrap, just as it does in a text region.

As you create more lines of text, Mathcad pushes the regions below the text downward. Paragraphs are designed to keep a constant amount of space between the last line of the paragraph and the first region below it.

As in a text region, you can insert hard line breaks in a paragraph to force the text to break at desired places.

Changing the width of paragraphs

All paragraphs in a Mathcad worksheet have the same width. While you can change the paragraph width for a worksheet, the change will affect all the paragraphs in the worksheet.

To change the width of paragraphs in your worksheet:

- Click on the worksheet where you want the right margin to be. The crosshair marks the location.

- Choose **Right Margin**⇒**Set** from the **Edit** menu.

Mathcad changes the width of all paragraphs in a worksheet, rewrapping the text as necessary. A message appears at the bottom right of the screen indicating how far the right margin is from the right edge of the paper. Note that setting the right margin will affect how your worksheet prints; see the section on printing in Chapter 3.

If you try to change the width of a single paragraph by following the instructions for changing the width of a text region, Mathcad will ask if you want to convert the paragraph into a text region. If you convert the paragraph into a text region, you will be able to resize it by dragging as described in the section "Changing the width of a text region."

Moving text regions and paragraphs

To move a text region, a paragraph, or group of regions and paragraph, follow the same steps that you would with math regions:

- Click on an empty spot, hold the left mouse button down, and drag the selection rectangle across the region or regions you want to select . When you release the mouse button, outlines show which regions are selected.

- Now move the mouse pointer inside the selected region, hold down the left mouse button, and drag it to the desired spot. If you've selected more than one region, the selected regions will move as a group.

You can also cut, paste, and copy text regions and paragraphs as you would any other regions. Select the regions and then choose **Cut**, **Paste**, or **Copy** from the **Edit** menu. You can also use the corresponding buttons on the toolbar.

Equations in text

This section describes how to insert equations into your text regions or paragraphs. Equations inserted into text have the same properties as those in the rest of your worksheet. You can edit them using the methods described in Chapter 2.

Entering an equation into text can affect the spacing between the lines of the text region or paragraph. If the equation is taller than a single line, the spacing (or leading) between all the lines in the paragraph adjusts to make room for the equation.

Inserting an equation into text

You can place an equation into text either by creating a new equation or by pasting an existing equation into a text region or a paragraph.

To add a new equation into a text region or a paragraph, follow these steps:

- Click in the text region or paragraph to place the insertion point where you want the equation to start.

- Choose **Embed Math** from the **Text** menu.

- Type in the equation just as you would in a math region.

- When you've finished typing in the equation, click on any text to return to the text region.

To paste an existing equation into either a text region or a paragraph, follow these steps:

- Select the equation you want to paste into the text.

- Choose **Copy** from the **Edit** menu.

- Click in the text region or paragraph to place the insertion point where you want the equation to start.

- Choose **Paste** from the **Edit** menu.

Editing equations in text

Once you've embedded an equation into a text region or paragraph, you can edit it in the same way you edit equations anywhere else. For detailed procedures, see Chapter 2, "Editing Equations."

Turning embedded equations on and off

When you first insert an equation into text, it behaves just like an equation in a math region; it affects calculations throughout the worksheet. If you want the equation to be purely cosmetic, you can turn it off. To do so:

- Click on the equation you want to turn off.

- Choose **Toggle Equation** from the **Math** menu.

Once you've done so, the equation will neither affect nor be affected by other equations in the worksheet. To turn it back on, do the same thing you did to turn it off. The **Toggle Equation** command works like a push-button light switch.

For a more general discussion of turning equations on and off, see "Disabling equations" in Chapter 6.

Text editing

This section describes Mathcad features for editing existing text. This includes changing the words themselves, either manually, by clicking and typing, or automatically using the Find and Replace feature and the Spellchecker. It also includes changing the way the words look by changing various font properties, and changing the way they're arranged by changing the alignment within text regions.

Moving the insertion point in text

In general, the procedures in this *User's Guide* tell you to move the insertion point around text regions and paragraphs by clicking with the mouse wherever you want to put the insertion point. However, as an alternative, you can also use the arrow keys to move the insertion point. This section briefly describes these keys.

The arrow keys move the insertion point character by character or line by line within text. Pressing [Ctrl] and an arrow key moves the insertion point word by word or paragraph by paragraph. These and other ways of moving the insertion point are summarized in the table below.

Key	Action
[→]	Move right one character.
[←]	Move left one character.
[↑]	Move up to the previous line.
[↓]	Move down to the next line.
[Ctrl][→]	Move to the beginning of the next word.
[Ctrl][←]	Move to the beginning of the current word. If the insertion point is already there, move to the beginning of the previous word.
[Ctrl][↑]	Move to the beginning of the current paragraph. If the insertion point is already there, move to the beginning of the previous paragraph.
[Ctrl][↓]	Move to the beginning of the next paragraph.
[Home]	Move to the beginning of the current line.
[End]	Move to the end of the current line.

Selecting text

The commands described in the "Inserting text" section above involve selecting the whole text region or paragraph by dragging the selection rectangle. The commands described in this section on text editing involve working with strings of text *within* a text region or paragraph. There are several ways to select a string of text:

- Click in the text region or paragraph so that the text box or top and bottom lines appear. Drag across the text holding the mouse button down. Mathcad highlights the selected text, including any full lines between the first and last characters you selected.

- Click in the text and press [**Shift**] and an arrow key. Mathcad highlights the text in the direction of the arrow key used.

- Click in the text and press [**Ctrl**][**Shift**] and an arrow key. If a left or right arrow is used, Mathcad highlights from the insertion point to the beginning of the current or next word. If an up or down arrow is used, Mathcad highlights text from the insertion point to the beginning or end of a line.

- Select just one word of text by double-clicking on it.

When text is selected, Mathcad displays the phrase "Selected Text" in the left-most window on the font bar. This phrase indicates that Mathcad will apply any character property changes to that selected text and not to the default text.

Once text is selected, you can delete it, copy it, check the spelling, or change its font, size, style, or color.

Cutting and copying text

To cut a string of characters from a text region or paragraph, follow these steps:

- Click in the text region or paragraph and select the desired string of text. The highlighted text is shown in "reverse video."

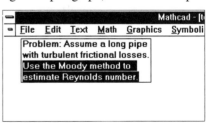

- Choose **Cut** from the **Edit** menu. Mathcad deletes the text from the text region or paragraph, copies it to the clipboard, and rewraps the remaining text.

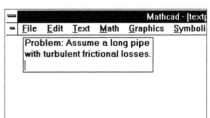

You could also copy text to the clipboard without deleting it. To do so, choose **Copy** instead of **Cut** from the **Edit** menu.

Once you've cut or copied text to the clipboard, you can paste it back into any text region, paragraph or into an empty space to create a new paragraph. To do so:

- Click in the spot where you want to paste the text. This can be anywhere in an existing text region, a paragraph, or in an empty area of your worksheet.

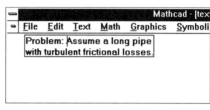

- Choose **Paste** from the **Edit** menu. Mathcad pastes the text from the clipboard into the text region or paragraph. If the cursor looks like a crosshair when you choose paste, Mathcad creates a new *paragraph* containing the pasted text.

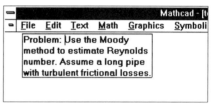

Note that if you want to insert the entire contents of a text region or paragraph into an existing region, you should select the material you want to insert as a text string by clicking in the text and dragging to highlight it. If you copy an entire region selected with the selection rectangle, you can paste this selection only into a blank area of your worksheet.

Changing text fonts

When you first enter text, its properties are determined by the worksheet defaults. To change the font, size, style, position, and color of text, you must first select it and choose **Change Font** from the **Text** menu. Any properties that you define for selected text using this process override your worksheet's default properties, even when you change those default properties.

To change the properties of selected text:

- Select some text using one of the methods described in the section "Selecting text."

- Choose **Change Font** from the **Text** menu. Mathcad displays a dialog box showing available fonts. Alternatively, use the font bar.

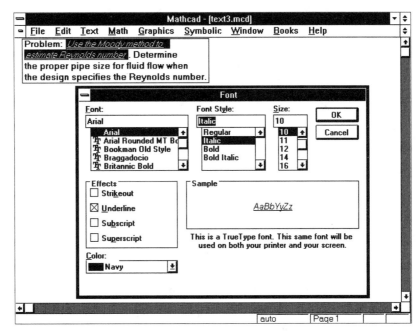

Figure 3: Change Font dialog box.

■ Change the appropriate properties in the dialog box and click "OK." You can change the following properties:

Font

To change the font of the selected text, scroll through the Font list in the dialog box and choose an available font.

Size

To change the size of the selected text, scroll through the Size list in the dialog box. Font sizes are in points. Note that some fonts are available in many sizes and others aren't. Remember that if you choose a bigger font, the text region you're in may grow and overlap nearby regions. Choose **Regions⇒Separate** from the **Edit** menu if necessary.

Style

To change the style of the selected text, scroll through the Font Style list in the dialog box.

As you scroll through the Font Style list you'll notice that some style combinations are unavailable. For example, some fonts come in bold or italic, but not in bold and italic at the same time. If you're using the font bar buttons and nothing seems to be happening, check the dialog box to see if the style you want is available for the font family you're using.

Effects

To make selected text superscripted, subscripted, or underlined, click on the appropriate Effects option in the dialog box.

Color

To change the color of the selected text, scroll through the color list in the dialog box. Note that you can't use the font bar to change color. You can only use the dialog box.

When you place the insertion point in existing text and start typing, the new text takes its character properties from the immediately preceding character.

Changing default text fonts

Your worksheet has default text properties that determine the appearance of each new character that you enter in your worksheet, unless that character is preceded by a character for which you've changed the properties. If you want to make global changes to the appearance of text in your worksheet, you can change these defaults.

To change the default text properties in your worksheet, follow these steps:

- Choose **Change Defaults⇒Font** from the **Text** menu. Mathcad brings up a dialog box showing the current default text properties.

- Follow the procedures in the previous section for changing fonts. Note that you cannot select subscript or superscript as a default.

- Click "OK".

You can redefine the default text properties at any time. Any text already in your worksheet will be converted to the new properties, unless you've explicitly selected it and set its properties as described in the preceding section, "Changing text fonts." Any new text you type will have the new default text properties.

The default text properties that you define only affect text in the *current worksheet*. You can save these defaults for use with other worksheets by either:

- using configuration files as described on page 97, or

- choosing **Change Color⇒Text Color** from the **Window** menu if you want to save just the default color and not the other font characteristics.

Changing paragraph formats

When you first create a paragraph in your worksheet, its properties are determined by your worksheet's defaults. Paragraph properties consist alignment and indentation. You can change these properties for an individual paragraph by doing the following:

- Select the paragraph by clicking on it.

- Choose **Change Paragraph Format** from the **Text** menu. Mathcad displays the following dialog box:

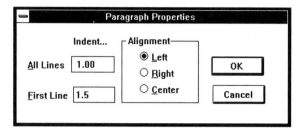

- Change the appropriate properties in the dialog box and click "OK". You can change the following properties:

Alignment

To align the text at either the left or right margin, or to center the text, use these three alignment buttons.

Indentation

To indent every line in the paragraph use the Indent All Lines text box. To indent just the *first* line of the paragraph relative to all the other lines use the Indent First Line text box. For a hanging indent, use a negative number in the Indent First Line text box. Both these text boxes expect a number in inches.

Changing default paragraph properties

Your worksheet has default paragraph properties that determine the appearance of each paragraph you create in your worksheet. If you want to make global changes to the appearance of paragraphs in your worksheet, you can change these defaults. To do so:

- Choose **Change Defaults⇒Pargraph Format** from the **Text** menu. Mathcad opens a dialog box showing current default paragraph properties.

- Change the paragraph properties as needed to describe your new default properties. Follow the procedures in the previous section, "Changing paragraph formats."

- Click "OK".

You can redefine the default paragraph properties at any time. Any paragraphs already in your worksheet will inherit these new properties, unless you've explicitly set their properties as described in the section, "Changing paragraph formats." Any new paragraphs will have the new default paragraph properties.

Greek letters in text

To type a Greek letter in a text region or paragraph:

- Type the roman equivalent from the following table and press [**Ctrl**]**G**, or

- Open the Greek letter palette by clicking on the button labeled αβ on the button strip under the menus, then click on the appropriate button on the palette.

The table on the following page lists all the Greek letters and their roman equivalents. These are the same roman equivalents used in the Windows Symbol font. To insert an uppercase Greek letter, use the uppercase roman equivalent. To insert a lowercase Greek letter, use the lowercase roman equivalent.

Name	Uppercase	Lowercase	Roman equivalent
alpha	A	α	A
beta	B	β	B
chi	X	χ	C
delta	Δ	δ	D
epsilon	E	ε	E
eta	H	η	H
gamma	Γ	γ	G
iota	I	ι	I
kappa	K	κ	K
lambda	Λ	λ	L
mu	M	μ	M
nu	N	ν	N
omega	Ω	ω	W
omicron	O	o	O
phi	Φ	φ	F
phi(alternate)		φ	J
pi	Π	π	P
psi	Ψ	ψ	Y
rho	P	ρ	R
sigma	Σ	σ	S
tau	T	τ	T
theta	Θ	θ	Q
theta(alternate)	ϑ		J
upsilon	Y	υ	U
xi	Ξ	ξ	X
zeta	Z	ζ	Z

To change existing text into its Greek equivalent, select the text and either:

■ Press [Ctrl]G, or

■ Choose **Change Fonts** from the **Text** menu and select the Symbol font.

Importing and exporting text

Mathcad's text is formatted using Microsoft's "Rich Text Format" (RTF) specification. This means you can export text from Mathcad text regions or paragraphs to word processing programs that read files in RTF format. For many word processing programs running under Windows concurrently with Mathcad, you can export directly via the clipboard. To do so:

- Click in a text region or paragraph to place the insertion point (a vertical bar).

- Drag to highlight the text you want to export.

- Choose **Copy** from the **Edit** menu.

- Click in the target application's window and paste from the clipboard.

You can also import text from most other Windows applications. To do so:

- Place the text in the clipboard.

- Click in an empty region of the Mathcad worksheet. You should see the crosshair.

- Choose **Paste** from Mathcad's **Edit** menu.

Mathcad creates a paragraph containing the text on the clipboard. If the text contains RTF formatting codes, Mathcad formats the text as directed. If you want the text to be in a text region instead of a paragraph, see the end of the section "Changing the width of paragraphs" earlier in this chapter.

For Windows applications that function as OLE servers, you can *embed* the text into your worksheet. This means that when you double-click on the embedded text, the word processor that created the text opens and a copy of the text is placed in its document window. You can then do all your editing in the word processor. To do so,

- Copy the text you want to paste from the word processor into the clipboard.

- Click in the Mathcad worksheet and choose **Paste Special** from Mathcad's **Edit** menu.

To open the word processor, double-click on the embedded icon in your Mathcad worksheet. This will start the word processor associated with that document.

You can also export the entire worksheet, including equations and plots, in RTF format using the methods described in the section "Exporting your worksheet" on page 83.

Find and Replace

Mathcad's Find and Replace commands work in both text and equations. When you search for a string of characters, Mathcad looks for that string as part of a variable or function name or as a piece of text in a text region or paragraph.

Searching for text

To find a string of characters,

- Choose **Find** from the **Edit** menu. Mathcad brings up the dialog box shown in Figure 4.

- Enter the string you want to find in the text box labeled "Find".

- Click on "Next" or "Previous" to find the occurrence of the string immediately after or before the current insertion point location.

For example, to search for all occurrences of the letters **lb** in a worksheet:

- Choose **Find** from the **Edit** menu Mathcad brings up a dialog box and prompts you for a string to find.

- Type **lb** and click on "Next".

Mathcad searches forward from the insertion point position for a region containing the letters **lb**, whether in text or in an equation. When Mathcad finds a match in a text region or paragraph, it shows it in reverse video; when it finds a match in an equation it positions the insertion point in the string. The dialog box remains up so that you can continue searching (Figure 4). When you're done with the search, close the Find dialog box by double-clicking on the button on its upper-left corner.

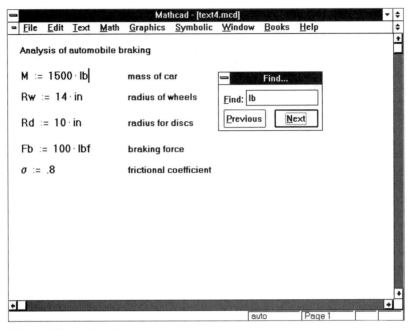

Figure 4. Searching for a text string.

Note that Mathcad's Find command is case-sensitive, but not font-sensitive. For example, if you're searching for **b**, you won't find **B**, but you will find β, since this is the same as lowercase **b** in Greek or Symbol font.

Replacing characters

To search and replace, choose **Replace** from the **Edit** menu. For example, to replace instances of the name *sec* with *s*:

- Choose **Replace** from the **Edit** menu to bring up the Replace dialog box shown in Figure 5.

- Enter the string you want to find (the target string) in the text box labeled "Find".

- Enter the string you want to replace it with in the text box labeled "Change to".

You now have four choices:

- Click on "Find Next" to find and select the next instance of your target string.

- Click on "Change" to replace the currently selected instance of the string.

- Click on "Change & Find Next" to replace this instance and find the next one.

- Click on "Change All" to replace all instances without further prompting.

Figure 6 shows the result of choosing "Change All."

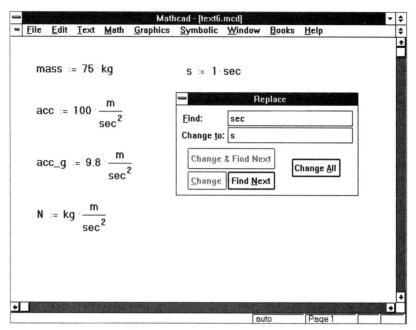

Figure 5: Before replacing all instances of sec with s.

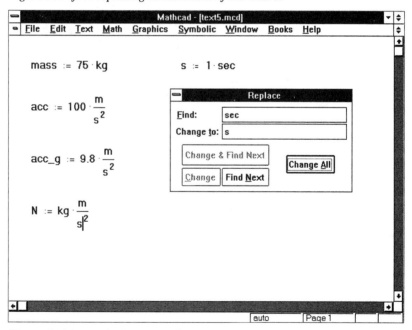

Figure 6: After replacing sec with s.

After creating text, you can have Mathcad search it for misspelled words. Mathcad will find misspelled words and suggest replacements. It will also let you add words that commonly use to your dictionary. Note that Mathcad will spellcheck only text regions and paragraphs, not math or graphics regions.

Checking text for misspelled words

To begin spellchecking, you first have to tell Mathcad what portions of the worksheet to spellcheck. There are two ways to do this:

■ Click at the beginning of wherever you want to spellcheck. Mathcad will spellcheck starting from this point and continue to the end of the worksheet. Mathcad will then let you either continue the spellcheck from the beginning of the worksheet or quit spellchecking.

■ Alternatively, select the text you want to spellcheck by dragging the mouse across the text.

Once you've defined a range over which to spellcheck:

■ Choose **Check Spelling** from the **Text** menu. When Mathcad finds a misspelled word, it opens the dialog box shown below.

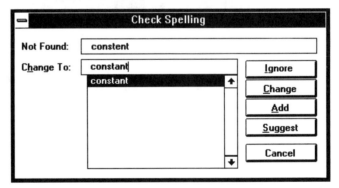

The dialog box shows the misspelled word along with a suggested replacement. It may also show a list of other suggested replacements. If Mathcad has no immediate suggestions, it will show only the misspelled word. However, if you click the "Suggest" button, Mathcad will show a list of words that are less likely but possible replacements.

After the dialog box appears, you've several options:

■ To change the word to the suggested replacement, click on "Change".

■ To change the word to one from the list of replacements, select one and click "Change".

- To see additional but less likely replacements, click "Suggest". Note that if Mathcad can offer no additional suggestions, the "Suggest" button will be grayed out.

- To change the word to one not listed, type the replacement into the "Change to" box and click "Change".

- To leave the word as is, click "Ignore" or "Add". If you click "Ignore", Mathcad will leave the word alone and continue spellchecking, ignoring all future occurrences of the word as it does so. If you click "Add", Mathcad will add the word to your dictionary. The following section explains this dictionary in more detail.

Personal dictionaries

To determine whether a word is misspelled, Mathcad compares it with the words in the following dictionaries:

- A general dictionary of common English words supplemented by mathematical terms.

- A personal dictionary.

When a word is not found in either dictionary, Mathcad will warn you that it may be misspelled.

If there are certain correctly spelled words throughout your worksheet which Mathcad nevertheless shows as being misspelled, you may want to add them to your personal dictionary. This will prevent Mathcad from considering them misspelled.

To add a word to your personal dictionary:

- When Mathcad shows the word in the Check Spelling dialog box, click "Add".

This will add the word to your dictionary. For future spellchecks, Mathcad will not show it as being misspelled.

Linking to other worksheets

You can create a link from any text region or paragraph to any Mathcad worksheet. When a reader clicks on this link, Mathcad will jump to the Mathcad worksheet designated by the link.

Mathcad can jump to any worksheet, no matter where it's stored. All that's required is that you be able to open that worksheet. The worksheet can be stored either in your own file system, in a Notes database, or anywhere on the World Wide Web.

Creating a new link

To create a link, you must specify two pieces of information:

- What to double-click on in order to jump to another worksheet. This is the "doorway".

- What worksheet to jump to. This is the "target worksheet."

To specify these two pieces of information, you must have both worksheets open at the same time. Begin by specifying the doorway:

- Click in the worksheet which is to contain the doorway.

- Select the text which you want to use to jump to the target worksheet whenever you double-click on it.

The next step is to specify the target. To do so:

- Open the target worksheet, either by choosing **Open** or **Open URL** from the **File** menu.

- Choose **Link**⇒**New** from the **Edit** menu. You'll see the following dialog box:

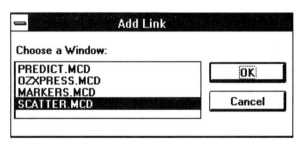

- In the list of open windows, select the target worksheet and click "OK." Note that this list excludes any untitled windows you may have open. A worksheet must have been saved at least once before it can become a target worksheet.

Once you've done this, Mathcad marks your gateway by underlining the text and making it bold. The next time you double-click on this gateway, Mathcad will open up the target worksheet. Note that you don't need to have the target worksheet already open before using the gateway. You only need to have it open when you're first creating the gateway.

This mechanism will work no matter where the target worksheet is located. All that's necessary is that you be able to open that worksheet in one of three ways:

- If the worksheet is in your own file system, choose **Open** from the **File** menu.

- If the worksheet is in a Notes database, choose **Get from Notes** from the **File** menu.

- If the worksheet is someplace on the World Wide Web, choose **Open URL** from the **File** menu.

Once you've created the link, you no longer need to know which of these commands to use or even where the file is. Mathcad remembers where the file was when you first created the link and does whatever is has to do to get there again. Of course, if you move the target file *after* having created the link, Mathcad will no longer be able to find it.

Erasing a link

To remove a link to another worksheet, simply click anywhere in the gateway and choose **Link⇒Erase** from the **Edit** menu. Mathcad will remove all traces of the link.

Links from other regions

The gateway to a target worksheet need not be a text string as described in the section "Creating a new link". Any Mathcad region will do. The procedure is identical to that described in that section except that you don't specify the gateway by selecting text. Instead, you do one of the following before choosing **Link⇒New** from the **Edit** menu:

■ To make an equation or a plot a gateway, click anywhere in the equation or plot.

■ To make an entire text region or paragraph a gateway, place the insertion point anywhere within it.

There are two significant disadvantages to using something other than selected text as a gateway:

■ When you do so, Mathcad automatically makes the font bold and underlined to indicate that a link exists there. No corresponding indication is possible when you choose something other than selected text as a gateway.

■ The link preempts the normal response to double-clicking. For example, if you choose a plot as a gateway, you will no longer be able to double-click on that plot to open a formatting dialog box.

For these reasons, we recommend that you use only selected text as a gateway to another worksheet.

Chapter 5
Equation and Result Formatting

Although Mathcad shows equations in standard math notation, you do have some control over the way they are displayed. You can determine the font, size, and style used for letters and numbers in equations. You can also determine how Mathcad displays answers, including specifying the number of decimal places, the base in which they are displayed, and the use of scientific notation.

The following sections make up this chapter:

Formatting results

Changing the display of computed values in equations.

Math fonts

Changing the font, size, and style used in equations and plots.

Highlighting equations

Making a particular equation stand out from all the other equations and regions in your worksheet.

The way that Mathcad displays numbers (the number of decimal places, whether to use *i* or *j* for imaginary numbers, and so on) is called the *result format*. You can set the result format for a whole worksheet (the *global format*) or for a single calculated result (the *local format*).

Setting global result format

To change the default display of numerical results, click on an empty space and choose **Numerical Format** from the **Math** menu. You will see the dialog box shown below. Default values for the four precision settings are shown in parentheses. The range of values allowed for each setting is shown to the right of the corresponding text box.

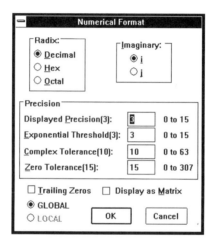

Change the desired settings and click "OK." Mathcad changes the display of all results whose formats have not been explicitly specified. You can control the display of a single result without affecting any others by setting the *local result format*. The next section discusses how to do this.

This is the meaning of each of the settings in the dialog box:

Radix

This allows you to set the radix (base) in which results are displayed. The default is decimal. If you select "Octal" or "Hex," Mathcad truncates the number to an integer and displays it as octal or hexadecimal. Hexadecimal results are indicated by the letter "h" after the number, octal results by the letter "o." (Mathcad does not reliably show hexadecimal or octal numbers of magnitude greater than 2^{31}, or about $2 \cdot 10^9$).

Imaginary

Click on the i or j button. Mathcad uses the selected letter to indicate an imaginary result. The default is i. You can use either i or j in equations — Mathcad always understands both. The selection you make here tells Mathcad which one to use when it gives you a complex answer. See Chapter 7, "Variables and Constants," for more information on how to type complex numbers.

Trailing Zeros

Check this box to make all displayed results have as many digits to the right of the decimal point as required by the current choice of Displayed Precision. For example, with Displayed Precision set to 3, Mathcad displays 5 as 5.000.

Display as Matrix

Check this box to suppress the use of scrolling output tables. Vectors and matrices having more than nine rows or columns are displayed as scrolling output tables unless this box is checked. See page 192 for more information on scrolling output tables.

Displayed Precision

Enter an integer between 0 and 15. This indicates how many decimal places to show in computed results. The default is 3. Numbers are rounded for display only. Mathcad maintains 15 digits of precision internally.

Exponential Threshold

Enter an integer n between 0 and 15. Mathcad shows computed results of magnitude greater than 10^n or smaller than 10^{-n} in exponential notation. When the threshold is 3, numbers like 30,000 are displayed as $3 \cdot 10^4$ instead of 30,000. The default is 3.

Complex Tolerance

Enter an integer n between 0 and 63. If the ratio between the real and imaginary part of a complex number is less than 10^{-n} or greater than 10^n, then the smaller part is not shown. The default setting is 10. This means that numbers like $1 + 10^{-12} i$ will appear simply as 1. Mathcad rounds only the displayed values. No change is made in the internally stored values.

Zero Tolerance

Enter an integer n between 0 and 307. Numbers less than 10^{-n} are shown as zero. The default setting is 15. This means numbers of magnitude less than 10^{-15} appear as zero. Mathcad changes the displayed values only. No change is made in the internally stored values.

Changing the global result format affects only the worksheet you were in when you made the change. Any other worksheets that may have been open at the time retain their own global result formats.

If you want to use your global result formats every time you start Mathcad, choose **Save Configuration** from the **File** menu once they are all set to your liking. See Chapter 3 for more on configuration files.

All of these formatting options affect only the display of a number. Mathcad continues to carry out all calculations in full precision regardless of formatting options. If you copy a result by choosing **Copy** from the **Edit** menu, Mathcad copies the answer to the precision displayed.

To see the number as it is stored internally:

■ Click anywhere on the result.

■ Press [**Ctrl**]**F**

Mathcad displays the number in full precision on the message line as shown in Figure 1.

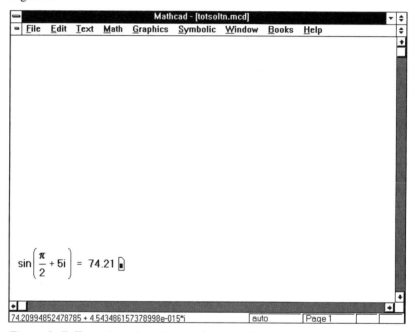

Figure 1: Full precision is maintained internally.

Setting local result format

You can set the format for a single result — a number, table, vector, or matrix — independently of the global result format. This is called setting the *local result format.* To change the format with which a particular result is displayed, you must:

■ Click anywhere in the equation whose result you want to format.

$$\pi \cdot 10^5 = 3.142 \cdot 10^5 \quad ■$$

- Choose **Numerical Format** from the **Math** menu. Alternatively, double-click on the equation itself. The dialog box shown on the right appears. Note that the option button "Local" is already selected.

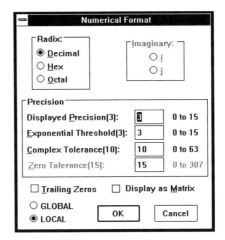

- Change the desired settings. See the previous section to learn what the various settings do and what their allowed values are. To display the six decimal places shown below, you would change "Displayed Precision" from 3 to 6.

- Click "OK." Mathcad redisplays the result using the new format.

$$\pi \cdot 10^5 = 3.141593 \cdot 10^5 \ \blacksquare$$

You can also apply local formats to all tables, vectors, or matrices. Just click on the table, vector, or matrix and choose **Numerical Format** from the **Math** menu. When you click on "OK," Mathcad applies the selected format to all the numbers in the table, vector, or matrix. It is not possible to individually format these numbers.

When you click the button labelled "Local," Mathcad disables the Imaginary Unit and Zero Tolerance settings. These settings can only be set globally, not locally.

To redisplay a result using the global result format settings:

- Click on the "=" to place a selection box around the entire equation. Alternatively, click anywhere in the equation and press [↑] repeatedly until the selection box encloses the equation.

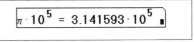

$$\pi \cdot 10^5 = 3.141593 \cdot 10^5 \ \blacksquare$$

- Press [**BkSp**] to delete the equals sign.

$$\pi \cdot 10^5 |$$

- Press = to replace the equals sign. The result is formatted using the global result format settings.

$$\pi \cdot 10^{5} = 3.142 \cdot 10^{5}$$

Figure 2 shows the same number formatted several different ways.

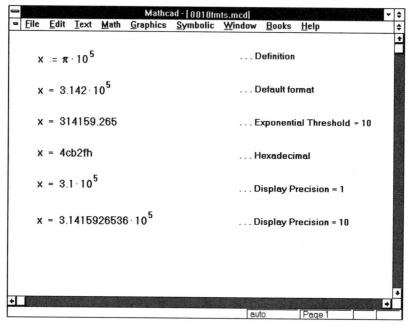

Figure 2: Several ways to format the same number.

Mathcad's default font for all variables and plots is 10-point Times Roman. To change this:

■ Click on any variable and choose **Font Tag** from the **Math** menu. The dialog box shown below.

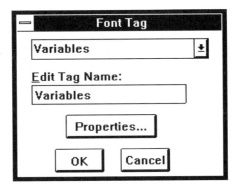

■ To change the font associated with that variable's font tag, click on "Properties." You'll see the usual Windows dialog box for changing fonts.

■ Click the "OK" button. Mathcad changes the font of all variables in the worksheet.

If you change the variable's font, you may also want to change the font used for numbers so that the two look good together. To do so, click on a number. The font tag window should now say "Constants". Then follow the procedure for variables.

You can also use the font bar to change font, size, or style of variables. To do so, click on a variable, then click on the appropriate font bar button to make variables bold, italic or underlined or to specify the font or point size in the scrolling lists.

The font, size, and style you choose for variables affects not only the appearance of equations, but the appearance of the entire worksheet. Mathcad's line-and-character grid does not depend on the font size. Therefore, changing font characteristics, particularly font sizes, may cause regions to overlap. You can separate these regions by choosing **Separate Regions** from the **Edit** menu.

You may wish to have your math regions colored differently from text to avoid mixing the two up. To change the color of all equations in your worksheet:

■ Choose **Change Colors** from the **Window** menu.

■ Pull right (or left if necessary) and choose **Equation Color** to bring up a dialog box containing a palette of colors.

■ Click on the appropriate color.

Font tags

Whenever you type a variable name, Mathcad:

- Assigns to it a font tag named "Variables."

- Looks up the font, size, and style associated with that particular font tag. By default, this is 10 point Times Roman.

- Displays the variable name using the font characteristics associated with the font tag named "Variables."

Similarly, when you type a constant, Mathcad:

- Assigns to it a font tag named "Constants."

- Looks up the font, size, and style associated with that particular font tag. By default, this is 10 point Times Roman.

- Displays the constant using the font characteristics associated with the font tag named "Constants."

This means that when you change a font, you are not changing the font for the string itself. Instead, you are changing the font for the font tag assigned to that, and possibly many other strings. This mechanism allows you to easily change the font for many strings at once.

To see what font tag is currently assigned to a name or number, click on the name or number and look at the font tag window on the font bar.

Alternatively, you can click on the name or number and choose **Font Tag** from the **Math** menu. You'll see the dialog box shown in the last section. The font tag associated with whatever you clicked on will appear in the drop-down list.

In Figure 3, the selected string is assigned the "Variables" font tag. Note that this font tag name is also shown in the leftmost text box on the font bar.

By default, variables are tagged with "Variables," and numbers are tagged with "Constants." Answers displayed on the right of an equals sign are always tagged as "Constants." These two tag names cannot be changed.

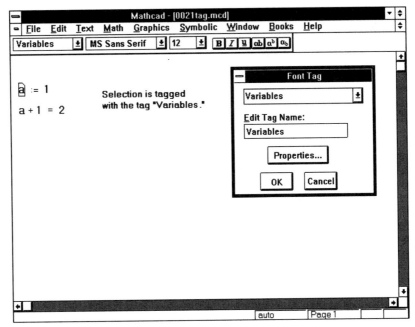

Figure 3: Scrolling list shows font tag of selected string.

If you click on the button to the right of "Variables", you'll see a drop-down list of available font tags. If you now choose "User 1" and click "OK," the variable selected in Figure 3 gets retagged and its font changes accordingly. Figure 4 shows the result.

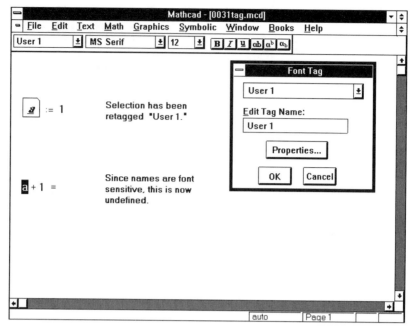

Figure 4: First variable name from Figure 3 has been retagged. Note change in font.

Applications of Font Tags

The notion of tagging strings becomes useful when you need to make many changes in your worksheet. You may have already encountered the concept if you've ever used *style sheets* to tag paragraphs in word processing or desktop publishing software. By making changes to the style sheets rather than the paragraphs themselves, you can make sweeping and strikingly uniform changes in the way a worksheet looks. You can get this same kind of leverage by judicious use of Mathcad's font tags.

For example, many math books show vectors in Times bold underlined, and matrices to be Times bold. If you want to use this convention without having to scroll through the worksheet and changing the font characteristics for every string in it, do the following:

- Choose **Font Tag** from the **Math** menu.

- Click the down arrow beside the name of the current font tag to see a drop-down list of available font tags.

- Click on an unused font tag like "User1" to select it.

- The name "User1" should now appear in the "Edit Tag Name" text box. Click in this text box and change the name to something like "Vectors."

- Change the font, size and style of this font tag to 10 point Times bold underlined.

This creates a font tag called "Vectors" with the desired font. Proceed in a similar way to create a font tag named "Matrices" with 10 point Times bold as its font. When you're done defining both font tags, click "OK."

Now rather than individually changing the font, size and style for names of vectors and matrices, you can simply change their font tags. To do so, do the following:

- Click on the name of the vector or matrix. The font tag assigned to that name appears on the font bar. By default, this is "Variables."

- Click on the arrow beside the font bar window and Scroll down to the font tag "Vectors". The font tag changes to "Vectors" and the font changes to Times bold underlined, because that's the font assigned to the Vectors font tag.

Repeat the previous two steps for all vectors in the worksheet. For matrices, choose the newly created font tag "Matrices" instead. Note that you can tag only one name at a time.

If after having done this you decide to remove all the underlines from the vectors, you can simply:

- Choose **Font Tag** from the **Math** menu.

- Choose "Vectors" from the drop-down list of font tags at the top of the dialog box.

- Click on the underline check box.

Once you click on the "OK" button, the underlines will be removed from every vector in the worksheet.

Note that this procedure changes the font for the *names* of vectors and matrices, not the individual elements themselves. The individual elements continue to be tagged as "Variables" or "Constants."

Saving font tags

Once you've completed a set of font tags that you like, you need not repeat the process for other worksheets. You can save font tag information by choosing **Save Configuration** from the **File** menu.

To apply font tag information to another worksheet, choose **Execute Configuration File** from the **File** menu.

For more information, see the section "Configuration files" in Chapter 3.

Font sensitivity

All names, whether function names or variable names, are font sensitive. This means that x and x refer to different variables, and $\mathbf{f}(x)$ and $f(x)$ refer to different functions.

In deciding whether two variable names are the same, Mathcad actually checks *font tags* rather than fonts. To avoid having distinct variables that look identical, don't create a font tag with exactly the same font, size and style as another font tag.

Highlighting equations

To highlight an equation so that it stands out from the rest of the equations and text in your worksheet:

- Click in the equation you want to highlight.

- Choose **Highlight Equation** from the **Math** menu.

Mathcad draws a box around the equation and fills it with a color light enough so you can see the equation. This is a purely cosmetic change with no effect on the equation other than rendering it more conspicuous.

The appearance of a highlighted equation on printing will depend very much on the capabilities of your printer. Some printers will render a color as black, obscuring the equation in the process. Others will render the exact same color as just the right gray to highlight the equation without obscuring it.

To solve this problem, you should change the background color of a highlighted equation by doing the following:

- Choose **Change Colors** from the **Window** menu.

- Pull right and choose **Highlighted Equation Color** to bring up a dialog box containing a palette of colors.

- Click on the appropriate color.

Computational Features

Chapter 6
Equations and Computation

This chapter describes how to define and evaluate variables and functions. This chapter discusses only numerical equations. To learn how to use Mathcad's symbolic processing features, turn to Chapter 17, "Symbolic Calculation."

The following sections make up this chapter:

Defining variables and functions

How to define variables and functions. How the relative placement of equations affects calculations.

Evaluating expressions

How to get a numerical answer.

Copying numerical results

How to copy numerical results from one worksheet to another or from Mathcad to other Windows applications.

Controlling calculations

How to suppress the way Mathcad automatically updates the worksheet.

Disabling equations

Turning calculation on and off for individual equations.

Error messages

What to do when Mathcad displays an error message.

Defining variables and functions

Whenever you type an equation into a worksheet, you are doing one of two things:

- You could be typing an expression and asking Mathcad to give you the answer. This is discussed in the next section, "Evaluating expressions."

- You could be typing a variable or function name and assigning some value to it. The remainder of this section discusses how to do this.

Defining a variable

A variable definition defines the value of a variable everywhere below the definition. To define a variable, you must follow these three steps:

- Type the variable name to be defined. Chapter 7 contains a description of valid variable names.

$$KE|$$

- Press the colon (:) key. The definition symbol (:=) appears.

$$KE := \blacksquare$$

- Type an expression to complete the definition. This expression can include numbers and any previously defined variables and functions.

$$KE := \frac{1}{2} \cdot m \cdot v^2|$$

Figure 1 shows several examples of a variable definition. The left hand side of a ":=" can contain any of the following:

- A simple variable name like x.

- A subscripted variable name like v_i.

- A matrix whose elements are any of the above. For example:

$$\begin{pmatrix} x \\ y_1 \end{pmatrix}$$

- A function name with an argument list of simple variable names. For example, $f(x, y, z)$. This is described further in the next section.

- A superscripted variable name like $\mathbf{M}^{<1>}$.

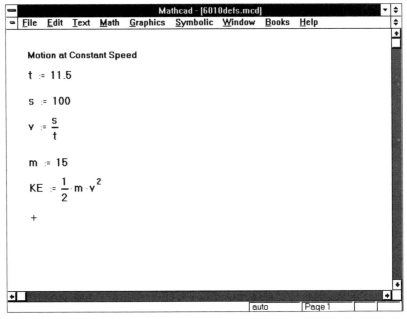

Figure 1: Defining variables.

Defining a function

You can also define your own functions in Mathcad. Unlike a variable, the value of a function depends on the values of its arguments.

You define a function in much the same way you define a variable. The name goes on the left, a ":=" goes in the middle, and an expression goes on the right. The main difference is that the name includes an *argument list*. The example below shows how to define a function called dist(*x, y*) which returns the distance between the point (*x, y*) and the origin.

To type such a function definition:

■ Type the function name.

    dist|

■ Type a left parenthesis followed by one or more names separated by commas. Complete this argument list by typing a right parenthesis.

    dist (x, y)

It makes no difference whether or not the names in the argument list have been defined or used elsewhere in the worksheet. What is important is that these arguments *must be names*. They cannot be more complicated expressions.

■ Press the colon (:) key. You see the definition symbol (:=).

Defining variables and functions   139

- Type an expression to define the function. In this example, the expression involves only the names in the argument list. In general though, the expression can contain any previously defined functions and variables as well.

$$\text{dist}(x, y) := \sqrt{x^2 + y^2}$$

Once you have defined a function, you can use it anywhere below the definition, just as you would use a variable.

When you use a function in an equation, Mathcad:

- evaluates the arguments you place between the parentheses,

- replaces the dummy arguments in the function definition with the actual arguments you place between the parentheses,

- performs whatever arithmetic is specified by the function definition, and

- returns the result as the value of the function.

Figure 2 shows an example.

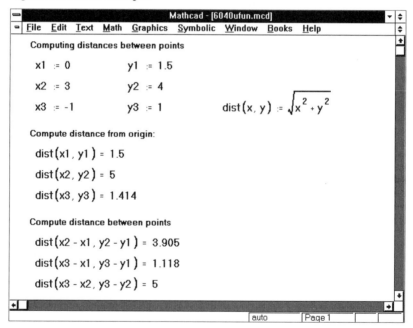

Figure 2: A user-defined function to compute the distance to the coordinate origin.

The arguments of a user function can represent scalars, vectors, or matrices. For example, you could define the distance function as

$$dist(\mathbf{v}) := \sqrt{v_0^2 + v_1^2}$$

This is an example of a function that accepts a vector as an argument, and returns a scalar result. See the section on "Arrays and user functions" at the end of Chapter 9 for more information.

Note that function names are font sensitive. This means that the function $\mathbf{f}(x)$ is different from the function f(x). Figure 3 shows an example.

Mathcad's built-in functions are defined for all fonts (except the Symbol font), sizes and styles. This means that $\mathbf{sin}(x)$, sin(x), and $\mathtt{sin}(x)$ all refer to the same function.

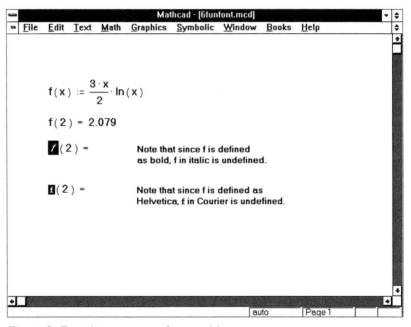

Figure 3: Function names are font sensitive.

Variables in user functions

When you define a function, you don't have to define any of the names in the argument list. This is because when you define a function, you are telling Mathcad *what to do* with the arguments, not what they are. When you define a function, Mathcad doesn't even have to know whether the arguments are scalars, vectors or matrices. All it needs to know is how many arguments there are and what to do with them. It is only when Mathcad actually *uses* a function that it needs to know what the arguments really are.

However, if in the process of defining a function you use a variable name that *is not* in the argument list, you must define that variable name above the function definition. The value of that variable at the time you make the function definition then becomes a permanent part of the function. This is illustrated in Figure 4.

When you evaluate a function, Mathcad:

- evaluates the arguments,
- substitutes their values on the right side of the function definition,
- evaluates the values of the other variables *at the point where the function is defined*,
- computes and returns a result.

If you want a function to depend on the value of a variable, you must include that variable as an argument. If not, Mathcad will just use that variable's fixed value at the point in the worksheet where the function is defined.

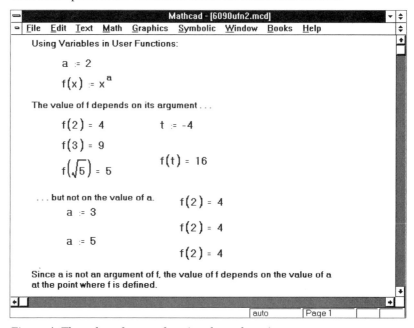

Figure 4: The value of a user function depends on its arguments.

How Mathcad scans a worksheet

Mathcad scans a worksheet the same way you read it: left to right and top to bottom. This means that a variable or function definition involving a "**:=**" affects everything below and to the right of it.

To determine whether one equation is above or below another, Mathcad compares their *anchor points*. To see these anchor points, choose **Regions⇒View Regions** from the **Edit** menu. Mathcad will display blank space in gray and leave regions white (or whatever your background color happens to be). Each region's anchor point will appear as a dot on the left.

Figure 5 shows an example of how not to place equations in a worksheet. In the first evaluation, both *x* and *y* are shown in reverse video to indicate that they are undefined. This is because the definitions for *x* and *y* lie below where they are used. Because Mathcad scans from top to bottom, when it gets to the first equation, it has no idea what numbers to substitute for *x* and *y*.

The second evaluation, on the other hand, is below the definitions of *x* and *y*. By the time Mathcad gets to this equation, it has already assigned values to both *x* and *y*.

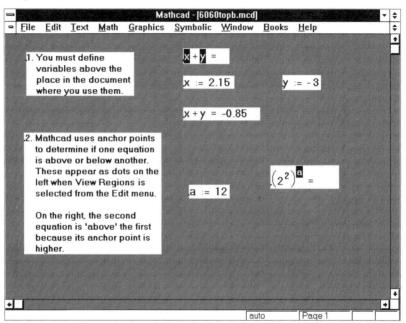

Figure 5: Mathcad evaluates equations from top to bottom in a worksheet. Note the anchor points.

You can define a variable twice in the same worksheet. Mathcad will simply use the first definition for all expressions below the first definition and above the second. For expressions below the second definition, Mathcad uses the second definition. Figure 6 illustrates a worksheet in which some variables are defined twice.

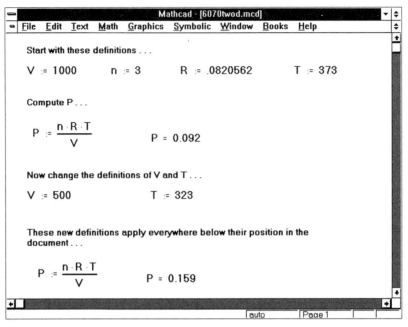

Figure 6: A worksheet in which V and T are both defined twice.

Global definitions

Global definitions are exactly like local definitions except that they are evaluated before any local definitions. If you define a variable or function with a global definition, that variable or function is available to all local definitions in your worksheet, regardless of whether the local definition appears above or below the global definition.

To type a global definition, follow these steps:

- Type a variable name or function to be defined.

- Press the tilde (~) key. The global definition symbol appears.

- Type an expression. The expression can involve numbers or other globally defined variables and functions.

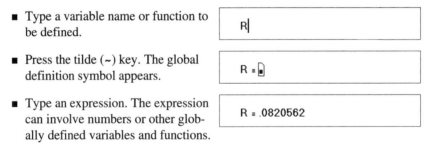

You can use global definitions for functions, subscripted variables, and anything else that normally uses the definition symbol ":=". Just type a tilde instead of a colon, and Mathcad will show the global definition symbol "≡" in place of ":=" .

This is the algorithm that Mathcad uses to evaluate all definitions, global and otherwise:

- First, Mathcad takes one pass through the entire worksheet from top to bottom. During this first pass, Mathcad evaluates global definitions only.

- Mathcad then makes a second pass through the worksheet from top to bottom. This time, Mathcad evaluates all definitions made with ":=" as well as all equations containing "=".

Figure 7 shows the results of a global definition for the variable R which appears at the bottom of the figure.

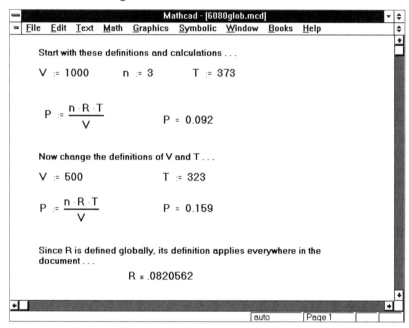

Figure 7: Using the global definition.

Although global definitions are evaluated before any local definitions, Mathcad evaluates global definitions the same way it evaluates local definitions: top to bottom and left to right. This means that whenever you use a variable to the right of a "≡":

- that variable must also have been defined with a "≡," *and*

- the variable must have been defined *above* the place where you are trying to use it.

Otherwise, the variable is marked in reverse video to indicate that it is undefined.

It is good practice to allow only one definition for each global variable. Although you can do things like define a variable with two different global definitions or with one global and one local definition, this is never necessary and usually serves only to make your worksheet difficult to understand.

To evaluate an expression, follow these steps:

- Type an expression containing any valid combination of numbers, variables and functions. Any variables or functions in this expression should be defined earlier in the worksheet.

$$\frac{1}{2} \cdot m \cdot v^2|$$

- Press the "=" key. Mathcad computes the value of the expression and shows it after the equals sign.

$$\frac{1}{2} \cdot m \cdot v^2| = 629.71\blacksquare$$

Figure 8 shows some calculations using the definitions from Figure 1.

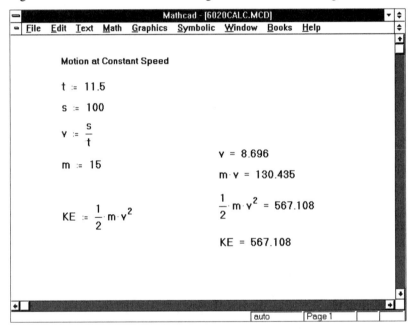

Figure 8: Calculations based on the variables defined in Figure 1.

Whenever you evaluate an expression, Mathcad shows a final placeholder at the end of the equation. You can use this placeholder for unit conversions, as explained in Chapter 8, "Units and Dimensions." As soon as you click outside the region, Mathcad hides the placeholder.

Copying numerical results

You can copy a numerical result and paste it either elsewhere in your worksheet or into another Windows application. This allows you to copy an array of numbers directly from a spreadsheet or database into Mathcad where you can take advantage of its free-form interface and its advanced mathematical tools, and vice versa. Once you've performed the necessary computations, you can paste the resulting array of numbers back to where it came from or even into another Windows application.

Copying a single number

To copy a single number appearing to the right of an equal sign:

- Click on the result to the right of the equal sign. A selection box should enclose the entire result.

- Choose **Copy** from the **Edit** menu. This places the result on the clipboard.

- Click wherever you want to paste the result. If you're pasting into another application, choose **Paste** from that application's **Edit** menu. If you're pasting into a Mathcad worksheet, choose **Paste** from Mathcad's **Edit** menu.

The **Copy** command will copy the numerical result to the precision displayed. You can preview the result in full precision by clicking in the result, pressing [Ctrl]F and looking on the message line. Note that **Copy** will not copy units and dimensions from a numerical result.

When you paste a numerical result into a Mathcad worksheet, it appears as:

- a math region consisting of a number if you paste it into empty space,

- a text string if you paste it into a text,

- a number if you paste it into a placeholder in a math region or if you paste it into text using the **Embed Math** command on the **Text** menu.

Copying an array of numbers

To copy an array (vector or matrix) appearing to the right of an equal sign:

- Click on the array to the right of the equal sign. A selection box should enclose the entire array.

- Choose **Copy** from the **Edit** menu. This places the array on the clipboard.

- Click wherever you want to paste the result. If you're pasting into another application, choose **Paste** from that application's **Edit** menu. If you're pasting into a Mathcad worksheet, choose **Paste** from Mathcad's **Edit** menu.

When you paste an array into a Mathcad worksheet, it appears as:

- a vector or matrix if you paste it into empty space,

- a text string if you paste it into text,

- a vector or matrix if you paste it into a placeholder in a math region or if you paste it into text using the **Embed Math** command on the **Text** menu.

The **Copy** command will copy the numerical result to the precision with which it is displayed. You can view the current display settings by double-clicking on the result you want to copy and examining the dialog box. See Chapter 5 to learn more about formatting numbers for display. Note that **Copy** will not copy units and dimensions.

Copying numbers from a scrolling output table

When you display results in a scrolling output table as described on page 192, you may want to copy some of the numbers from the table and use them elsewhere.

To copy just one number from a scrolling output table, simply click on the number and choose **Copy** from the **Edit** menu. To copy more than one number from a scrolling output table:

- Click on the first number you want to copy.

- Drag the mouse in the direction of the other values you want to copy while holding the mouse button down.

- Choose **Copy** from the **Edit** menu.

To copy all the values in a row or column, click on the column or row number shown to the left of the row or at the top of the column. All the values in the row or column will be selected. Then choose **Copy** from the **Edit** menu.

After you have copied one or more numbers from a scrolling output table, you can paste them into another part of your worksheet or into another Windows application. Figure 9 shows an example of a new matrix created by copying and pasting numbers from a scrolling output table. Note that if you copied and pasted more than nine rows or columns of numbers from the table, they will be displayed as a new scrolling output table.

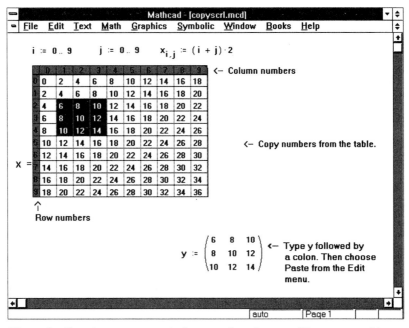

Figure 9: Creating a new matrix from numbers in a scrolling output table.

Controlling calculations

When you start Mathcad, you are in "automatic mode." This means that Mathcad updates results in the worksheet window automatically. You can tell you're in automatic mode because the word "auto" appears in the message line.

If you don't want to wait for Mathcad to make computations as you edit, disable automatic mode by choosing **Automatic Mode** from the **Math** menu or by clicking the light bulb on the toolbar. The word "auto" disappears from the message line and the checkmark beside **Automatic Mode** disappears to indicate that automatic mode is now off.

Automatic window update

The word "auto" on the message line indicates that you are in automatic mode. This means that:

■ As soon as you press the equals sign, Mathcad displays a result.

■ As soon as you click outside of an equation having a ":=" or a "≡, " Mathcad performs all calculations necessary to make the assignment statement.

When you process a definition in automatic mode by clicking outside the equation region, this is what happens:

- Mathcad evaluates the expression on the right side of the definition and assigns it to the name on the left.

- Mathcad then takes note of all other equations in the worksheet that are in any way affected by the definition you just made.

- Finally, Mathcad updates any of the affected equations that are currently visible in the worksheet window.

Although the equation you altered may affect equations throughout your worksheet, Mathcad performs only those calculations necessary to insure that whatever you can see in the window is up-to-date. This optimization makes sure you don't have to wait for Mathcad to evaluate expressions that are not visible.

In automatic mode, if you print or move to the end of the worksheet, Mathcad automatically updates the whole worksheet.

Whenever Mathcad needs time to complete computations, the mouse pointer changes its appearance and the word "WAIT" appears on the message line. This can occur when you enter or calculate an equation, when you scroll, during printing, or when you enlarge a window to reveal additional equations. In all these cases, Mathcad evaluates pending calculations from earlier changes.

As Mathcad evaluates an expression, it covers it with a green cross-hatched rectangle. This makes it easy to follow the progress of a calculation.

To force Mathcad to recalculate all equations throughout the worksheet, choose **Calculate Worksheet** from the **Math** menu.

Manual window update

In manual mode, Mathcad does not compute equations or display results until you specifically request it to recalculate. This means that you don't have to wait for Mathcad to calculate as you enter equations or scroll around a worksheet.

Mathcad keeps track of pending computations while you're in manual mode. As soon as you make a change that requires computation, the words "calc F9" appear on the message line. This is to remind you that the results you see in the window are not up-to-date and that you must recalculate them before you can be sure they are updated.

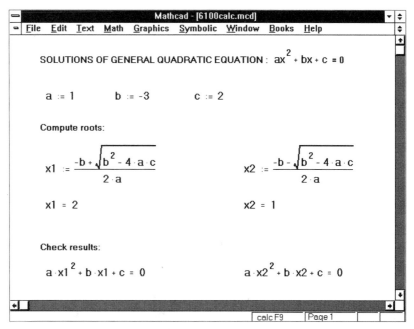

SOLUTIONS OF GENERAL QUADRATIC EQUATION : $ax^2 + bx + c = 0$

$a := 1$ $b := -3$ $c := 2$

Compute roots:

$$x1 := \frac{-b + \sqrt{b^2 - 4 \cdot a \cdot c}}{2 \cdot a} \qquad x2 := \frac{-b - \sqrt{b^2 - 4 \cdot a \cdot c}}{2 \cdot a}$$

$x1 = 2$ $x2 = 1$

Check results:

$$a \cdot x1^2 + b \cdot x1 + c = 0 \qquad a \cdot x2^2 + b \cdot x2 + c = 0$$

Figure 10: The words "calc F9" on the message line indicate that recalculation is required.

You can update the screen either by choosing **Calculate** from the **Math** menu or by pressing [**F9**]. These actions are equivalent. Mathcad performs whatever computations are necessary to update all results visible in the worksheet window. When you move down to see more of the worksheet, the words "calc F9" reappear on the message line to indicate that you must recalculate to see up-to-date results.

To process the whole worksheet, including those portions not visible in the worksheet window, choose **Calculate Worksheet** from the **Math** menu.

To switch back to automatic mode, choose **Automatic Mode** from the **Math** menu. Mathcad updates the entire worksheet and displays the word "auto" on the message line.

When you print a worksheet in manual calculation mode, the results on the printout are not necessarily up-to-date. When you're in manual mode, make sure to choose **Calculate Worksheet** from the **Math** menu before you print.

Interrupting calculations

To interrupt a computation in progress:

- Press [**Esc**]. The dialog box shown below will appear.

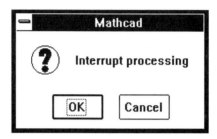

- Click "OK" to stop the calculations or "Cancel" to resume calculations.

If you click "OK, " Mathcad displays a message on the message line to indicate that processing has been interrupted. The equation that was being processed when you pressed [**Esc**] is marked with the error message "*Interrupted*." To resume an interrupted calculation, first click in the equation with the error message, then choose **Calculate** from the **Math** menu, press [**F9**], or click on the equals button on the tool bar.

If you find yourself frequently interrupting calculations to avoid having to wait for Mathcad to recalculate as you edit your worksheet, you may wish to switch to manual mode. To do so, disable automatic mode by choosing **Automatic Mode** from the **Math** menu. This will remove the checkmark from the menu. In manual mode, Mathcad recalculates only when you press [**F9**], choose **Calculate** from the **Math** menu, or click on the equals button on the tool bar.

Starting in manual mode

If you often work in manual calculation mode, you may find it useful to start Mathcad in manual mode rather than having to disable automatic calculation each time you start up. To make Mathcad always start up in manual mode, do the following:

- Double click on the Mathcad icon in the program manager window.

- Choose **Automatic Mode** from the **Math** menu. This command puts Mathcad into manual mode. The checkmark beside this menu item should now be gone.

- Choose **Save Configuration** from the **File** menu.

- Click "OK" in the Save Configuration dialog box.

Mathcad saves the current configuration, including the fact that it is in manual calculation mode, in a file called `mcad.mcc`. From this point on, Mathcad will always start in in manual mode.

Disabling equations

You can disable calculation for a single equation by selecting it and choosing **Toggle Equation** from the **Math** menu. With this feature, you can use Mathcad's equation editing, formatting, and display capabilities without having to worry about error messages.

To disable calculation for an equation, follow these steps:

- Click on the equation you want to disable.

- Choose **Toggle Equation** from the **Math** menu.

Mathcad shows a small rectangle after the equation to indicate that it is disabled. An example is shown on the right.

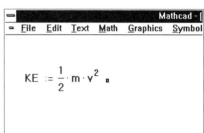

You can edit a disabled equation just as you would any other equation. However, a disabled equation does not affect any other calculations, nor does it reflect changes you make to other equations in the worksheet.

To re-enable calculation for a disabled equation:

- Click on the equation to select it.

- Choose **Toggle Equation** from the **Math** menu.

Mathcad removes the small rectangle beside the equation.

Note: If you disable a plot or an output table, Mathcad freezes the display for the plot or table. Changes you make to other parts of the worksheet will not affect the plot or table. If you move a disabled equation that happens to be displaying a result, the result will disappear. If you move a graph, whatever is inside the graph will disappear.

Error messages

Mathcad may encounter an error when evaluating an expression. When it does, it marks the offending expression with an error message. Figure 11 shows a worksheet with several errors.

Mathcad cannot process an expression containing an error. If the expression is a definition, the variable or function it is supposed to define will remain undefined. This can cause any expressions that reference that variable to be undefined as well. Mathcad indicates undefined variables and functions by displaying their names in reverse video. Figure 11 shows how an error in the definition of $x1$ causes a variable to be undefined in three different places.

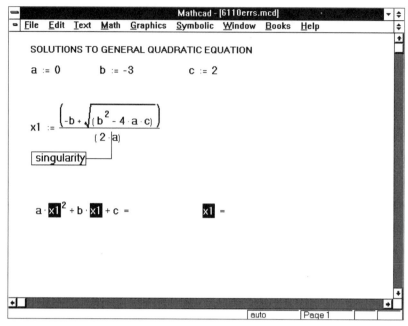

Figure 11: A worksheet containing an error message and several undefined variables (shown in reverse video.)

The error message describes what the problem is. A line points from each error message to the operator, name, or number to which Mathcad has attributed the error. You can get on-line help about an error message by clicking on it and pressing [**F1**].

Note that in an expression with zero as a pre-factor or numerator ($0 \cdot x$ or $0/x$), Mathcad computes the result as zero, without evaluating or checking for errors in the x expression.

Fixing errors

If your worksheet contains several expressions with errors, as in Figure 11, this is what to do:

- Make sure the error messages do not obscure the equations you need to read. If you need to, drag the equations to a spot where you can read them.

- If necessary, switch to manual mode. You may want to do this if your calculations are time-consuming. This will allow you to make as many changes as necessary without waiting for Mathcad to recalculate. When you are ready to recalculate, press [**F9**].

- Determine which expression with an error is closest to the top of the worksheet. This error is probably the cause of many of the other errors.

- If necessary, consult Appendix B for information on the error message. Alternatively, press [**Shift**][**F1**] and click on the error for help.

Once you have determined which expression caused the error, edit that expression to fix the error, or change the variable definitions that led to the error. When you click in the expression and begin editing, Mathcad removes the error message. When you click outside the equation (or in manual calculation mode, when you recalculate), Mathcad recomputes the expression. If you have fixed the error, Mathcad then recomputes the other expressions affected by the expression you changed.

Note that the expression marked in error need not be the root cause of the error. The error may depend on functions or variables defined farther up in the worksheet. Edit these other definitions to fix the error.

In Figure 11, the problem is a division by zero. To fix this problem, change the definition of *a*, as shown in Figure 12. When you click outside the definition of *a*, Mathcad is able to evaluate all the expressions.

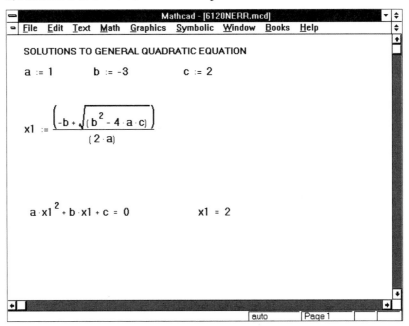

Figure 12: Changing the definition of the variable "a" fixes the errors.

A note about function definitions

When you define a function, Mathcad does not try to evaluate it until you use it later on in the worksheet. If there is an error, the use of the function is marked in error, even though the real problem may be in the definition of the function itself. Figure 13 shows an example of this.

When a user-defined function is marked in error, be sure to check the function definition to find the actual source of error.

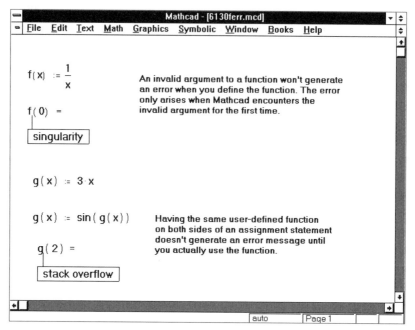

Figure 13: When an error message points to a function, go back and check the way the function was defined.

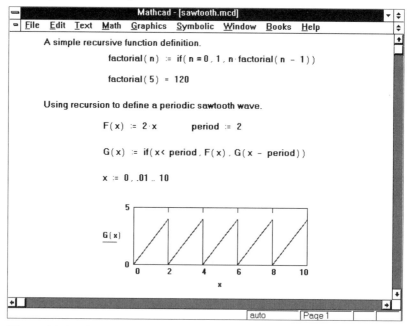

Figure 14: Mathcad allows recursive function definitions. These let you easily define arbitrary periodic functions.

Chapter 7
Variables and Constants

This chapter describes valid Mathcad variable names, function names, and numbers, including predefined variables like π.

Mathcad handles imaginary and complex numbers as easily as it does real numbers. Mathcad variables can have imaginary or complex values, and most Mathcad built-in functions can take complex arguments. This chapter describes how to use complex numbers in Mathcad.

The following sections make up this chapter:

Names
  Valid variable and function names; how to type Greek letters.

Predefined variables
  List of variables that have values when you start Mathcad.

Numbers
  Real, imaginary, hexadecimal, and octal numbers; dimensional values.

Complex numbers
  How to use complex numbers in Mathcad.

This section describes valid Mathcad variable and function names.

Names in Mathcad can contain any of the following characters:

- Uppercase and lowercase letters.

- The digits 0 through 9.

- The underscore (_).

- a prime symbol (′). Note that this is not the same as an apostrophe. You'll find the prime symbol on the same key as the tilde (~).

- percent (%).

- Greek letters. To insert a Greek letter, type the equivalent roman letter and press [Ctrl]G. The section "How to type Greek letters." contains a table of equivalent roman letters.

- The infinity symbol ∞, generated by typing [Ctrl]Z.

Variable and function names cannot include spaces or any characters other than those listed above.

The following restrictions apply to variable names:

- A name cannot start with one of the digits 0 through 9, an underscore (_), a prime symbol (′), or a percent (%).

- The infinity symbol, ∞, can only appear as the first character in a name.

- Any characters you type after a period (.) will appear as a subscript. This is discussed in the section "Literal subscripts" later in this chapter.

- All characters in a name must be in the same font, have the same pointsize and be in the same style (italic, bold, etc.). Greek letters can, however, appear in any variable name.

- Mathcad does not distinguish between variable names and function names. Thus, if you define $f(x)$, and later on you define the variable f, you will find that you cannot use $f(x)$ anywhere below the definition for f.

- Certain names are already used by Mathcad for built-in constants, units, and functions. Although you can redefine these names, keep in mind that their built-in meanings will no longer exist after the definition. For example, if you define a variable *mean*, Mathcad's built-in function mean(**v**) can no longer be used.

Mathcad distinguishes between uppercase and lowercase letters. For example, *diam* is a different variable from *DIAM*. Mathcad also distinguishes between names in different fonts. Thus, *DIAM* is also a different variable from *DIAM*. The following are examples of valid names:

`alpha`	`b`
`xyz700`	`A1_B2_C3_D4%%%`
`F1'`	`a%%`

How to type Greek letters

There are three ways to type a Greek variable name in Mathcad:

- Type the roman equivalent from the table on the following page. Then press [`Ctrl`]G.

- Type the roman equivalent from the table on the following page. Then choose **Change to Greek Variable** from the **Math** menu.

- Click on the appropriate letter on Greek letter palette. To see this palette, click on the button labelled "αβ" on the strip of buttons just below the menu commands.

Note that although many of the uppercase Greek letters look like ordinary capital letters, they are *not* the same. Mathcad distinguishes between Greek and roman letters. If you use a Greek letter in place of the corresponding roman letter in a variable or function name, Mathcad will not recognize the two as equivalent.

Note: Because it is used so frequently, the Greek letter π can also be typed by pressing [`Ctrl`]P.

The table on the following page lists all the Greek letters and their roman equivalents. These are the same roman equivalents used in the Windows Symbol font. To insert an uppercase Greek letter, use the uppercase roman equivalent. To insert a lowercase Greek letter, use the lowercase roman equivalent.

Name	Uppercase	Lowercase	Roman equivalent
alpha	A	α	A
beta	B	β	B
chi	X	χ	C
delta	Δ	δ	D
epsilon	E	ε	E
eta	H	η	H
gamma	Γ	γ	G
iota	I	ι	I
kappa	K	κ	K
lambda	Λ	λ	L
mu	M	μ	M
nu	N	ν	N
omega	Ω	ω	W
omicron	O	o	O
phi	Φ	ϕ	F
phi(alternate)		φ	J
pi	Π	π	P
psi	Ψ	ψ	Y
rho	P	ρ	R
sigma	Σ	σ	S
tau	T	τ	T
theta	Θ	θ	Q
theta(alternate)	ϑ		J
upsilon	Y	υ	U
xi	Ξ	ξ	X
zeta	Z	ζ	Z

Literal subscripts

If you include a period in a variable name, Mathcad displays whatever follows the period as a subscript. You can use these *literal subscripts* to create variables with names like vel_{init} and u_{air}.

To create a literal subscript, follow these steps:

- Type the portion of the name that appears before the subscript.

  vel|

- Type a period, followed by the portion of the name that is to become the subscript.

  vel_{init}|

Do not confuse literal subscripts with array subscripts. Although they appear identical, they are quite different. A literal subscript, created by typing a period, is really just part of a variable name. An array subscript represents a reference to an array element. Array subscripts are generated with the left bracket key ([ ). See Chapter 9 for a description of how to use subscripts with arrays.

Predefined variables

Mathcad includes eight variables that, unlike ordinary variables, are already defined when you start Mathcad. These variables are called *predefined* or *built-in variables*. Predefined variables either have a conventional value, like π and e, or are used as system variables to control how Mathcad works, like ORIGIN and TOL.

Here is a complete list of Mathcad's predefined variables and their default values:

Variable = default value	Definition and use
$\pi = 3.14159...$	Pi. Mathcad uses the value of π to 15 digits in numerical calculations. In symbolic calculations, π is exact. To type π, press [Ctrl]P.
$e = 2.71828...$	The base of natural logarithms. Mathcad uses the value of e to 15 digits in numerical calculations. In symbolic calculations, e is exact.
$\infty = 10^{307}$	Infinity. In numerical calculations, this is an actual number of finite magnitude. In symbolic calculations, this represents a true infinity. To type ∞, press [Ctrl]Z.
$\% = 0.01$	Percent. Use this in expressions like $10 \cdot \%$ or as a scaling unit in the placeholder at the end of an equation with an equals sign.
$TOL = 10^{-3}$	Numerical tolerance for the various approximation algorithms (integrals, equation solving, etc.). For more information, see the section on the specific operation in question.
$ORIGIN = 0$	Array origin. Specifies the index of the first element of an array.
$PRNCOLWIDTH = 8$	Column width used when writing files with the WRITEPRN function.
$PRNPRECISION = 4$	Number of significant digits used when writing files with the WRITEPRN function.
$FRAME = 0$	Used to drive animation. Set to zero when no animation is in progress.

Although these variables already have values when you start Mathcad, you can still redefine them. For example, if you want to use a variable called e with a value other than the one Mathcad provides, enter a new definition, like $e := 2$. The variable e takes on the new value everywhere in the worksheet below the new definition.

Mathcad's predefined variables are defined for all fonts, sizes and styles. This means that if you redefine *e* as shown on the previous page, you can still use **e**, or e as the base for natural logarithms. Note however that Greek letters are not included. This means that "ε", although it is typed as "e" in the Symbol font, is not the same number as *e*.

You can control the values of TOL, ORIGIN, PRNPRECISION, and PRNCOL-WIDTH without having to explicitly define them in your worksheet. To do so, choose **Built-In Variables** from the **Math** menu. The Built-in Variables dialog box appears, as shown below.

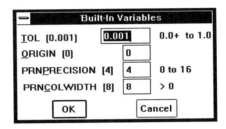

To set new starting values for any of these variables, enter a new value in the appropriate text box and click "OK." Then choose **Calculate Document** from the **Math** menu to ensure that all existing equations take the new values into account.

The numbers in brackets to the right of the variable name represent the default values for those variables. Those to the right of the text box represent valid values of the variables.

Numbers

This section describes the various types of numbers that Mathcad uses and how to enter them into equations.

Types of numbers

Mathcad interprets anything beginning with a digit as a number. A digit can be followed by:

- other digits

- a decimal point

- digits after the decimal point

- one of the letters **h** or **o**, for hex and octal numbers, **i** or **j** for imaginary numbers, and **M**, **L**, **T**, **Q** or **K** for numbers carrying units. These are discussed in more detail below.

Note that Mathcad uses the period (.) to signify the decimal point. The comma (,) is used both to show iteration and to separate values in an input table. These topics are discussed in Chapter 10, "Range Variables."

Imaginary numbers

To enter an imaginary number, follow it with i or j, for example, 1i or 2.5j. You cannot use i or j alone to represent the imaginary unit. You must always type 1i or 1j. If you don't, Mathcad will think you are referring to a variable named either i or j. See "Complex numbers" later in this chapter.

Dimensional values

Dimensional values are numbers associated with one of the Mathcad dimensions: *mass*, *length*, *time*, *charge*, and *temperature*. Mathcad uses these dimensions to keep track of units for dimensional analysis and unit conversions. To enter a dimensional value, type a number followed by an upper or lowercase M for mass, L for length, T for time, Q for charge, or K for temperature. For example, 4.5m represents 4.5 mass units. For more detailed information on units and dimensions, see Chapter 8, "Units and Dimensions."

Octal integers

To enter a number in octal, follow it with the upper or lowercase letter O. For example, 25636o represents 11166 in decimal. Octal numbers must be integers less than 2^{31}.

Hexadecimal integers

To enter a number in hexadecimal, follow it with the upper or lowercase letter H. For example, 2b9eh represents 11166 in decimal. To represent digits above 9, use the upper or lowercase letters A through F. To enter a hexadecimal number that begins with a letter, you must begin it with a leading zero. If you don't, Mathcad will think it's a variable name. For example, use 0a3h rather than a3h to represent the decimal number 163 in hexadecimal. Hexadecimal numbers must be integers less than 2^{31}.

Exponential notation

To enter very large or very small numbers in exponential notation, just multiply a number by a power of 10. For example, to represent the number $3 \cdot 10^{8}$, type 3*10^8.

Combining types of numbers

You can freely combine all types of numbers with various operators. Figure 1 shows some examples.

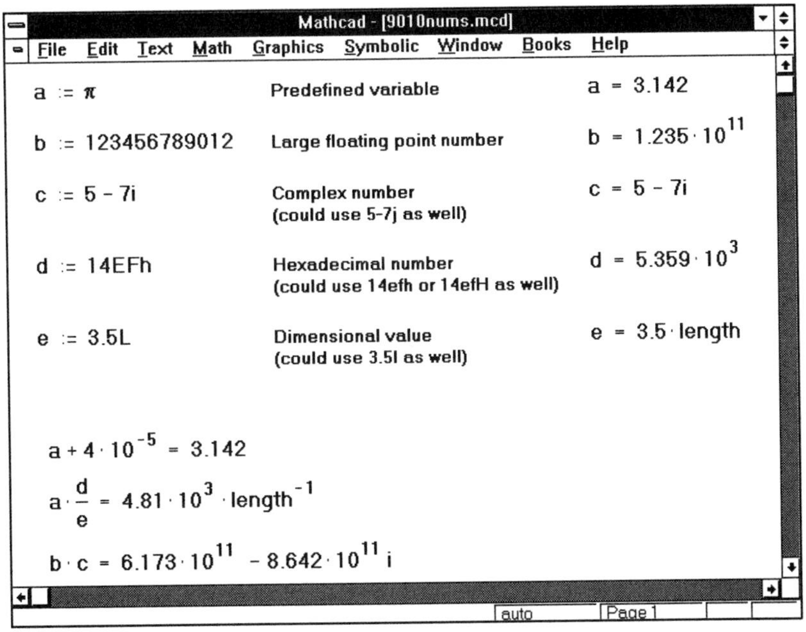

Mathcad - [9010nums.mcd]

File   Edit   Text   Math   Graphics   Symbolic   Window   Books   Help

$a := \pi$ Predefined variable $a = 3.142$

$b := 123456789012$ Large floating point number $b = 1.235 \cdot 10^{11}$

$c := 5 - 7i$ Complex number $c = 5 - 7i$
(could use 5-7j as well)

$d := 14EFh$ Hexadecimal number $d = 5.359 \cdot 10^{3}$
(could use 14efh or 14efH as well)

$e := 3.5L$ Dimensional value $e = 3.5 \cdot \text{length}$
(could use 3.5l as well)

$$a + 4 \cdot 10^{-5} = 3.142$$

$$a \cdot \frac{d}{e} = 4.81 \cdot 10^{3} \cdot \text{length}^{-1}$$

$$b \cdot c = 6.173 \cdot 10^{11} - 8.642 \cdot 10^{11} i$$

auto   Page 1

Figure 1: Combining different types of numbers.

Complex numbers

As described in the preceding section, Mathcad accepts complex numbers of the form $a + bi$, where a and b are ordinary numbers. You can use j instead of i if you prefer that notation.

Complex numbers can also arise if you enter an expression with a complex result. Even a Mathcad expression that involves only real numbers can have a complex value. For example, if you evaluate $\sqrt{-1}$, Mathcad will return i.

Although you can enter imaginary numbers followed by either i or j, Mathcad normally displays them followed by i. To have Mathcad display imaginary numbers with j, choose **Numerical Format** from the **Math** menu, click on the Global option button, and set "Imaginary" to j. See Chapter 5, "Equation and Result Formatting," for a full description of this dialog box.

When typing complex numbers, remember that you cannot use i or j alone to represent the imaginary unit. You must always type `1i` or `1j`. If you don't, Mathcad will interpret the i or j as a variable. When the cursor is outside an equation that shows $1i$ or $1j$, Mathcad hides the superfluous 1.

Complex operators and functions

Mathcad has the following special functions and operators for working with complex numbers:

Re(z)   Real part of a number z.

Im(z)   Imaginary part of a number z.

arg(z)   Angle in complex plane from real axis to z. This returns a result between $-\pi$ and π radians.

|z| The magnitude of the number z. To take the magnitude of an expression, enclose it in a selection box and press the vertical-bar key " | ".

$\overline{z}$ Complex conjugate of z. To apply the conjugate operator to an expression, select the expression, then press double-quote ("). The conjugate of the complex number $a + b{\cdot}i$ is $a - b{\cdot}i$.

Figure 2 shows some examples of how to use complex numbers in Mathcad.

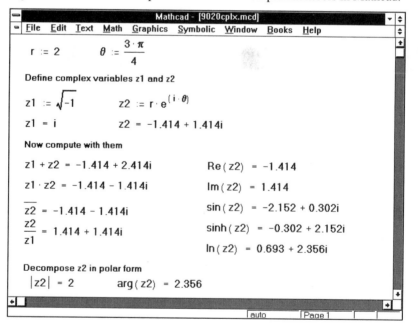

Figure 2: Complex numbers in Mathcad.

Multivalued functions

When complex numbers are available, many functions and operators we think of as returning unique results become multivalued. The impact of this on logarithmic and exponential functions is discussed more fully on page 269.

As a general rule, when a function or operator is multivalued, Mathcad always returns the value making the smallest positive angle relative to the positive real axis in the complex plane. This is the principal value.

For example, when asked to evaluate $(-1)^{1/3}$, Mathcad will return $.5 + .866i$ despite the fact that we commonly think of the cube root of -1 as being 1. This is because the number $.5 + .866i$ makes an angle of only 60 degrees from the positive real axis. The number -1, on the other hand, is all the way on the other side, 180 degrees from the positive real axis.

The single exception to this rule is the nth root operator described on page 241. This operator always returns a real root whenever one is available. Figure 3 compares these two alternatives.

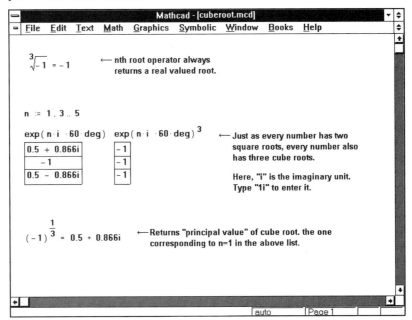

Figure 3: Finding real valued roots of a negative number.

Chapter 7 Variables and Constants

Chapter 8
Units and Dimensions

Units of measurement, while not required in Mathcad equations, can help detect errors and enhance the display of computed results. Mathcad's unit capabilities take care of many of the usual chores associated with using units and dimensions in scientific calculation. Once you enter the appropriate definitions, Mathcad automatically performs unit conversions and flags incorrect and inconsistent dimensional calculations.

This chapter describes how to use units and dimensions in Mathcad, including unit conversions, dimensional checking, and changing dimension names.

The following sections make up this chapter.

Computing with units

How to use units in an equation and how Mathcad catches any dimensional inconsistencies.

Displaying units of results

How Mathcad displays units and how to convert from one unit to another.

Built-in units

Choosing a system of units, defining your own units in terms of fundamental dimensions.

Changing dimension names

How to change the names of Mathcad's five fundamental dimensions.

Computing with units

When you first start Mathcad, a complete set of units is available for your calculations. You can treat these units just like built-in variables. To assign units to a number, just multiply it by the name of the unit. For example:

```
mass:75*kg
acc:100*m/sec^2
acc_g:9.8*m/sec^2
F:mass*(acc + acc_g)
```

Figure 1 shows how these equations appear in a worksheet.

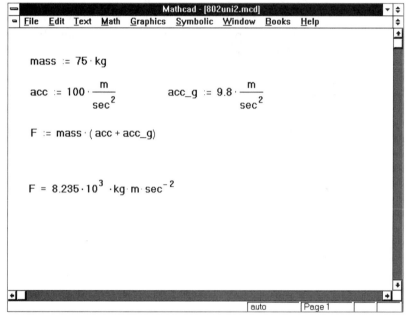

Figure 1: Equations using units.

Mathcad will recognize most units by their common abbreviations. Appendix C lists all of Mathcad's built-in units.

You can also use the Insert Unit dialog box to insert one of Mathcad's built-in units into any placeholder. The Insert Unit dialog box offers the following advantages:

- You won't have to remember the abbreviation Mathcad uses for a unit.

- You'll see at a glance all available units appropriate to the result you've clicked on.

- You can't make any typing mistakes.

To use the Insert Unit dialog box:

- Click in the empty placeholder and choose **Units⇒Insert Units** from the **Math** menu. Mathcad opens a dialog box with two scrolling lists.

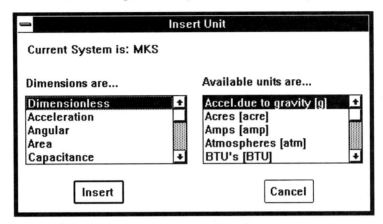

- The right-hand scrolling list shows built-in units corresponding to whatever physical quantity is selected in the left-hand scrolling list. For convenience, when "Dimensionless" is selected on the left, a list of all available built-in units shows on the right.

- If necessary, use the left scrolling list to display only those units corresponding to a particular physical quantity. This makes it easier to find a particular unit or to see what choices are appropriate.

- In the right scrolling list, double-click on the unit you want to insert. Mathcad inserts that unit into the empty placeholder.

Note that Mathcad performs some dimensional analysis by trying to match the dimensions of your result with one of the common physical quantities in the left scrolling list. If it finds a match, you'll see all the built-in units corresponding to the highlighted physical quantity in the left-hand scrolling list. If nothing matches, Mathcad simply lists all available built-units on the right.

Dimensional checking

Whenever you enter an expression involving units, Mathcad checks it for dimensional consistency. If you add or subtract values with incompatible units, or violate other principles of dimensional analysis, Mathcad displays an appropriate error message.

For example, suppose you had defined *acc* as 100·m/sec instead of 100·m/sec^2 as shown in Figure 2. Since *acc* is in units of velocity and *acc_g* is in units of acceleration, it is inappropriate to add them together. When you attempt to do so, Mathcad displays the error message "*incompatible units*".

Unit errors are usually caused by one of the following:

- An incorrect unit conversion,

- A variable with the wrong units as shown in Figure 2,

- Units in exponents or subscripts (for example $v_{3 \cdot acre}$ or $2^{\,3 \cdot ft}$),

- Units as arguments to inappropriate functions (for example, $\sin(0 \cdot henry)$).

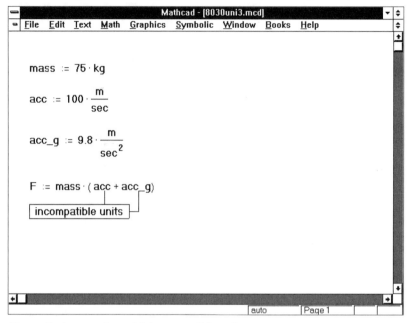

Figure 2: An equation with incompatible units.

Defining your own units

Although Mathcad recognizes many common units, you may need to define your own unit if:

- that unit isn't in the list of built-in units in Appendix C, or

- you prefer to use your own abbreviation instead of that shown in Appendix C.

You define your own units in terms of existing units in exactly the same way you would define a variable in terms of an existing variable. Figure 3 shows how to define new units as well as how to redefine existing units.

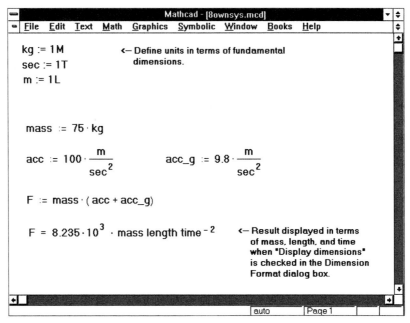

Figure 3: Defining your own units.

Since units behave just like variables, you may run into unexpected conflicts. For example, if you define the variable *m* in your worksheet, you won't be able to use the built-in unit *m* for meters anywhere below that definition.

Displaying units of results

Mathcad automatically displays results in terms of the fundamental units: *m*, *kg*, *sec*, *coul*, and *K* (degrees Kelvin). You can have Mathcad redisplay a particular result in terms of any of Mathcad's built-in units. To do so:

- Click in the result. You'll see an empty placeholder to its right. This is the *units placeholder*.

- Click on the units placeholder and choose **Units⇒Insert Units** from the **Math** menu. Mathcad opens the Insert Unit dialog box. This is described in detail on page 171.

- Double-click on the unit in terms of which you want to display the result. Mathcad inserts this unit in the units placeholder.

Another way to insert a unit is to type it directly into the units placeholder. This method is more general since it works not only for built-in units but for units you've defined yourself and for combinations of units.

For example, in Figure 1, F is displayed in terms of the fundamental units kg, m and sec. To change this to *dyne:*

- Click in a displayed result to see the units placeholder to its right. Then click on this units placeholder.

$$F = 8.235 \cdot 10^3 \cdot kg \cdot m \cdot sec^{-2} \ \blacksquare$$

- In the units placeholder, type **dyne**.

$$F = 8.235 \cdot 10^3 \cdot kg \cdot m \cdot sec^{-2} \ dyne|$$

- Click outside the equation. Mathcad displays the answer in terms of the units you entered.

$$F = 8.235 \cdot 10^8 \cdot dyne$$

Unit conversions

There are two ways to convert from one set of units to another:

- By using the Insert Units dialog box, or

- By typing the new units in the units placeholder itself.

If you want to display the result in terms of one of Mathcad's built-in units, the simplest method is to use the Insert Units dialog box:

- Click on the unit you want to replace.

- Choose **Units**⇒**Insert Units** from the **Math** menu.

- In the scrolling list of units, double-click on the unit in terms of which you want to display the result.

If you want to display the result in terms of something not available through the Insert Unit dialog box, for example a unit you defined yourself or an algebraic combination of units, you can edit the units placeholder directly. For example, to express the result in the previous example in terms of force-pounds rather than dynes:

- Click in the name of the unit you want to replace.

$$F = 8.235 \cdot 10^8 \cdot dyne|$$

- Delete the unit name. The calculated result disappears since Mathcad no longer knows what units to display it in.

$$F = \blacksquare \cdot \blacksquare$$

- Type in the name of the new unit and click outside the equation.

$$F = 1.851 \cdot 10^3 \cdot lbf$$

Figure 4 shows F displayed both in terms of its fundamental MKS units and in terms of several combinations of units.

When you enter an inappropriate unit in the units placeholder, Mathcad will display whatever combination of *kg, m, sec, coul,* or *K* makes the result have the right units. For example, in the last equation in Figure 4, you see that $kW \cdot sec$ is not a unit of force. Mathcad therefore inserts m^{-1} to cancel the extra length dimension.

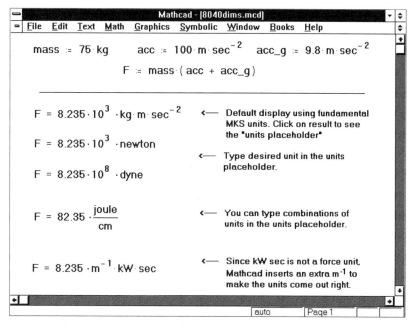

Figure 4: A calculated result displayed in terms of different units.

Whenever you enter units in the units placeholder, Mathcad divides the value to be displayed by whatever you enter in the units placeholder. This ensures that the complete displayed result — the number *times* the expression you entered for the placeholder — is a correct value for the equation.

Conversions involving an offset in addition to a multiplication, for example gauge pressure to absolute pressure, cannot be performed directly with Mathcad's unit conversion mechanism.

In particular, when working with temperature, keep in mind that you cannot use Mathcad's unit conversions to convert between Fahrenheit and Centigrade. You can, however, perform conversions of this type by defining suitable functions. See Chapter 6 for more on defining your own functions.

Scaling results

The techniques described in this chapter are not restricted to units. You can put any variable, constant or expression in a units placeholder. Mathcad will then redisplay the result in terms of the value of whatever is in the units placeholder. Just remember that whenever you type something in the units placeholder, Mathcad will change the calculated result so that the complete displayed result — the number *times* the expression you entered in the placeholder — is correct.

For example, you can use the units placeholder to display a result as a multiple of π. To do so:

- Click on the units placeholder to put a selection box around it.

$$\frac{4509}{11750} = 0.384 \; \blacksquare$$

- Click on π on the symbol palette. Then click outside the equation. Mathcad shows the result in terms of π.

$$\frac{4509}{11750} = 0.122 \cdot \pi$$

You can also use the units placeholder for dimensionless units like degrees and radians. To convert a number in degrees to radians, multiply it by the built-in unit *rad.* You can also type *deg* into the units placeholder to convert the result from radians to degrees. Figure 5 shows some examples of these techniques with *deg.*

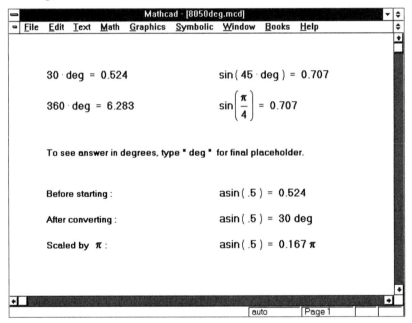

Figure 5: Using dimensionless units in placeholders.

When you start Mathcad, the MKS system of units is automatically loaded. This means that when you use the equal sign to display a result having units, Mathcad will display those units in terms of some combination of *m*, *kg*, *sec*, *coul*, and *K*. You can of course, as discussed on page 174, convert this combination of *m*, *kg*, *sec*, *coul*, and *K* into a different unit by typing that unit into the units placeholder. However, until you do so, Mathcad will use the MKS fundamental units to display your result.

You can have Mathcad display results in terms of the fundamental CGS or the fundamental US units. To do so, choose **Units⇒Change System of Units** from the **Math** menu. You will see the dialog box shown below:

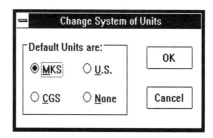

Click on the button corresponding to the default units in which you want to display results. The table below summarizes what each button does.

MKS	Displays results in terms of *m*, *kg*, *sec*, *coul*, and *K*.
CGS	Displays results in terms of *cm*, *gm*, *sec*, *coul*, and *K*.
US	Displays results in terms of *ft*, *lb*, *sec*, *coul*, and *K*.
none	Displays results in terms of fundamental dimensions of *length*, *mass*, *time*, *charge*, and absolute *temperature*. All built-in units are disabled.

Most units are available in all three systems of units. For example, when CGS is selected, you'll still be able to use *kg* and *lb* even though these are not, strictly speaking, part of the CGS system of units. A small minority of units are not available across all three systems of units. For a listing of which units are available in each system, see Appendix C.

If you click "none" in the Change System of Units dialog box, there will be no built-in units at all. You can, however, still define and use your own units as described on page 172. To do so, you use the special built-in constants: *1L*, *1M*, *1T*, *1Q*, and *1K*. These represent the dimensions *length*, *mass*, *time*, *charge*, and absolute *temperature*. When you click "none," Mathcad will display answers in terms of the fundamental dimensions of *length*, *mass*, *time*, *charge*, and *temperature* rather in terms of any system of units. Figure 6 shows how to define units using these built-in constants and how to carry out the analysis in Figure 1 after having done so.

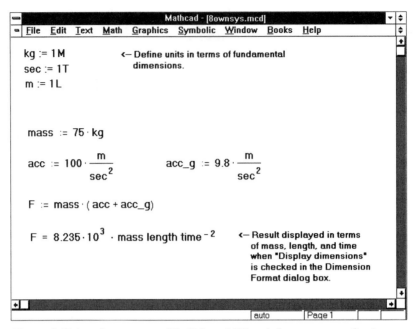

Figure 6: Using the constants 1L, 1M, and 1T to define a system of units.

Changing dimension names

The previous section showed how you can display a result in terms of the fundamental units of either of three systems of units or in terms of the fundamental physical dimensions of *mass*, *length*, *time*, *charge* and *temperature*. This section describes how to go even further and actually change the names of the fundamental dimensions altogether.

This may be useful if the nature of your work makes another set of fundamental dimensions more appropriate. Thus, a commodities trader may prefer to use *bushels* and *currency* rather than *charge* and *temperature*; a car salesman might define *trucks* and *sedans* rather than *length* and *mass*. In short, a dimension is nothing more than a way of tagging numbers so you can keep better track of them. It just so happens that in physical problems, it's convenient to name these dimensions *mass*, *length*, *time*, *charge* and *temperature*.

To change the names of the dimensions:

- Choose **Units⇒Dimensional Format** from the **Math** menu. This brings up the Dimensional Format dialog box shown below.

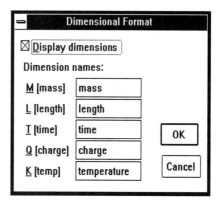

- Click on the check box beside Display dimensions.

- To change a dimension name, edit the name shown in the appropriate text box.

Renaming the dimensions in this dialog box changes the dimension names only for the Mathcad worksheet you are working on. To make these dimension names a permanent part of your Mathcad configuration, choose **Save Configuration** from the **File** menu and click "OK" in the dialog box. See Chapter 3 for more on configuration files.

Chapter 9
Vectors and Matrices

This chapter describes Mathcad arrays. While ordinary variables (scalars) hold a single value, arrays hold many values.

As is customary in linear algebra, arrays having only one column will often be referred to as vectors. All others are matrices. The following sections make up this chapter.

Creating a vector or matrix

How to create or edit vectors and matrices

Computing with arrays

Defining variables as arrays and using them in expressions.

Subscripts and superscripts

Referring to individual array elements and columns.

Displaying vectors and matrices

How Mathcad displays answers involving matrices and vectors.

Limits on array sizes

Limits on the sizes of arrays to be stored, displayed, or entered.

Vector and matrix operators

Operators designed for use with vectors and matrices.

Vector and matrix functions

Built-in functions designed for use with vectors and matrices.

Doing calculations in parallel

Using Mathcad's "vectorize" operator to speed calculations.

Simultaneous definitions

Using vectors to define several variables simultaneously.

Arrays and user-defined functions

Using arrays as arguments to user defined functions.

Nested arrays

Arrays in which the elements are themselves arrays.

A single number in Mathcad is called a *scalar*. A column of numbers is a *vector*, and a rectangular array of numbers is called a *matrix*. The general term for a vector or matrix is an *array*.

There are three ways to create an array:

- By filling in an array of empty placeholders as discussed in this section. This technique is useful for arrays that are not too large.

- By using range variables to fill in the elements as discussed in the following chapter on range variables. This technique is useful when you have some explicit formula for the elements in terms of their indices.

- By reading them in from a datafile as discussed in Chapter 18.

You may wish to distinguish between the names of matrices, vectors and scalars by font. For example, in many math and engineering books, names of vectors are set in bold while those of scalars are set in italic. The section "Math fonts" in Chapter 5, "Equation and Result Formatting" describes how to do this.

Creating a vector

A vector is an array or matrix containing one column. To create a vector in Mathcad, follow these steps:

- Click in either a blank space or on a placeholder.

- Choose **Matrices** from the **Math** menu, or press [**Ctrl**]**M**. A dialog box appears, as shown on the right.

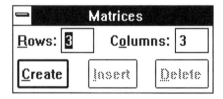

- Enter the number of elements in the text box beside "Rows." For example, to create a three-element vector, type **3**.

- Enter **1** in the text box beside "Columns." Then click "Create." Mathcad inserts a vector of placeholders.

The next step is to fill in these placeholders with scalar expressions. To do so, follow these steps:

- Click on the top placeholder and type **2**.

- Move the selection box to the next placeholder. You can do this either with the [Tab] key, or by clicking directly on the second placeholder.

- Type **3** on the second placeholder. Then move the selection box to the third placeholder and type **4**.

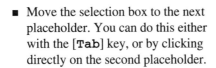

If you're going to need several vectors in your calculation, you can leave the Matrices dialog box up for later use.

Once you have created a vector, you can use it in calculations just as you would a number. For example, to add another vector to this vector, follow these steps:

- Press the [↑] several times or click on either of the vector's brackets. The selection box now encloses the entire vector. This ensures that the plus sign you type next will apply to the whole vector rather than to one of its elements.

$$\begin{pmatrix} 2 \\ 3 \\ 4 \end{pmatrix}$$

- Type the plus key (**+**). Mathcad shows a placeholder for the second vector.

$$\begin{pmatrix} 2 \\ 3 \\ 4 \end{pmatrix} + \blacksquare$$

- Use the Matrices dialog box to create another three-element vector.

$$\begin{pmatrix} 2 \\ 3 \\ 4 \end{pmatrix} + \begin{pmatrix} \blacksquare \\ \blacksquare \\ \blacksquare \end{pmatrix}$$

- Fill in this vector by clicking in each placeholder and typing in the numbers shown on the right. You can also use the [Tab] to move from one element to another.

$$\begin{pmatrix} 2 \\ 3 \\ 4 \end{pmatrix} + \begin{pmatrix} 0 \\ -1 \\ 1 \end{pmatrix}$$

- Press the equals sign (**=**) to see the result.

$$\begin{pmatrix} 2 \\ 3 \\ 4 \end{pmatrix} + \begin{pmatrix} 0 \\ -1 \\ 1 \end{pmatrix} = \begin{pmatrix} 2 \\ 2 \\ 5 \end{pmatrix} \blacksquare$$

Addition is just one of Mathcad's vector and matrix operations. Mathcad also includes matrix subtraction, matrix multiplication, dot product, integer powers, determinants, and many other operators and functions for vectors and matrices. Complete lists appear in the sections "Vector and matrix operators" and "Vector and matrix functions," later in this chapter.

If you're using Mathcad PLUS, you'll also be able to carry out many symbolic operations with matrices. See Chapter 17 for more details.

Creating a matrix

To create a matrix, first click in a blank space or on a placeholder. Then:

- Choose **Matrices** from the **Math** menu, or press [**Ctrl**]**M**. The dialog box shown on the right appears.

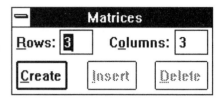

- Enter a number of rows and a number of columns in the appropriate boxes. In this example, there are two rows and three columns. Then click on "Create." Mathcad inserts a matrix of placeholders.

$$\begin{pmatrix} \blacksquare & \bullet & \bullet \\ \bullet & \bullet & \bullet \end{pmatrix}$$

- Fill in the placeholders to complete the matrix as described in the previous section for vectors.

$$\begin{pmatrix} 2 & 5 & 17 \\ 3.5 & 3.9 & -12.9 \end{pmatrix}$$

You can use this matrix in equations, just as you would a number or vector.

Throughout this manual, the term "vector" refers to a column vector. A column vector is identical to a matrix with one column. You can also create a *row vector* by creating a matrix with one row and many columns. Operators and functions which expect vectors always expect column vectors. They do not apply to row vectors. To change a row vector into a column vector, use the transpose operator [**Ctrl**]1.

Changing the size of a matrix

You can change the size of a matrix by inserting and deleting rows and columns. To do so, follow these steps:

- Click on one of the matrix elements to enclose it in a selection box. Mathcad will begin inserting or deleting with this element.

$$\begin{pmatrix} 2 & 5 & 17 \\ 3.5 & 3.9 & -12.9 \end{pmatrix}$$

- Choose **Matrices** from the **Math** menu. The dialog box as shown on the right appears.

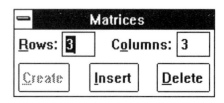

- Type the number of rows and/or columns you want to insert or delete. Then click on either "Insert" or "Delete." For example, to delete the column that currently holds the selected element, type **1** in the box next to "Columns," **0** in the box next to "Rows," and click on "Delete."

$$\begin{pmatrix} 5 & 17 \\ 3.9 & -12.9 \end{pmatrix}$$

Here's how Mathcad inserts or deletes rows or columns based on what you type in the dialog box:

- If you insert rows, Mathcad creates rows of empty placeholders below the selected element. If you insert columns, Mathcad creates columns of empty placeholders to the right of the selected element.

- To insert a row above the top row or a column to the left of the first column, first enclose the whole matrix in a selection box by clicking inside and pressing [↑] several times. Then select **Matrices** and proceed as you would normally.

- If you delete rows or columns, Mathcad begins with the row or column occupied by the selected element. Mathcad deletes rows from that element downward and columns from that element rightward.

- If you type 0 as the number for "Rows," Mathcad neither inserts nor deletes rows. If you type 0 as the number for "Columns," Mathcad neither inserts nor deletes columns.

Note that when you delete rows or columns, Mathcad discards the information in the rows or columns you eliminate.

To delete an entire matrix or vector, enclose it in a selection box and choose **Cut** from the **Edit** menu.

Computing with arrays

Variables can represent arrays as well as scalars. Defining a variable as an array is very much like defining a scalar. First type a variable name and a colon as you would with any other definition. Then create an array (vector or matrix) on the other side of the equation.

For example, to define a vector **v**, follow these steps:

- Click in empty space and type **v**, followed by the colon key (**:**).

$$v := \blacksquare$$

- Choose **Matrices** from the **Math** menu to bring up a dialog box. Type **3** in the box next to "Rows" and **1** in the box next to "Columns."

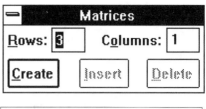

- Press "Create" and fill in the elements.

$$v := \begin{pmatrix} 2 \\ 3 \\ 4 \end{pmatrix}$$

You can now use the name **v** in place of the actual vector in any equation. Figure 1 demonstrates that the variable name **v** and the vector itself are interchangeable. Once you have defined a vector, you can of course define other vectors in terms of that vector, just as if you were doing mathematics on paper.

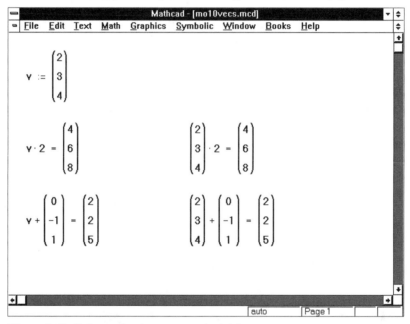

Figure 1: Defining and using a vector variable.

Do not use the same name for a scalar variable and a vector variable. This will simply redefine the variable.

Subscripts and superscripts

You can refer to individual array elements by using subscripts. You can also refer to an entire column of an array by using a superscript. To type a subscript, use the left bracket key " [" and put an integer or a pair of integers in the placeholder. To insert a superscript operator, press [Ctrl]6 and place an integer in the placeholder.

Vector and matrix elements are ordinarily numbered starting with row zero and column zero. To change this, change the value of the built-in variable ORIGIN. See "Changing the ORIGIN," later in this chapter.

Subscripts and vector elements

The top equation in Figure 1 defines the vector **v**. To see the zeroth (top) element of the vector **v**:

- Type **v[0=**

$$v_0 = 2 \, \blacksquare$$

You can also define individual vector elements by using a subscript on the left side of a definition. To change v_2 to 6:

- Type **v[2:6**

$$v_2 := 6$$

Figure 2 shows how this changes the value of **v**.

When you define vector elements, you may leave gaps in the vector. For example, if **v** is undefined and you define v_3 as 10, v_0, v_1, and v_2 are all undefined. Mathcad fills these gaps with zeros until you enter specific values for them, as shown in Figure 3. Be careful of inadvertently creating very large vectors and matrices by doing this.

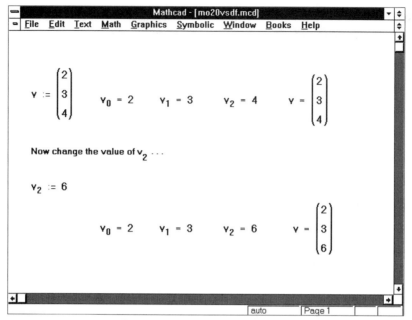

Figure 2: Defining a vector element.

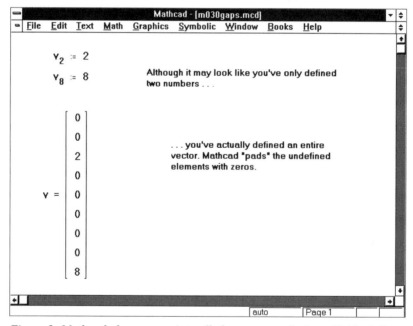

Figure 3: Mathcad places zeros into all elements you don't explicitly define.

Subscripts and matrix elements

To view or define a matrix element, use two subscripts separated by a comma. In general, to refer to the element in the ith row, j^{th} column of matrix **M**, type:

```
M[i,j
```

Note that the subscripts, like division and exponentiation, are "sticky." Whatever you type after `[` remains in the subscript until you press [**Space**] to leave.

If you want to add more to the equation, press [**Space**] to enclose the entire matrix element name, $M_{i,j}$, in a selection box.

Figure 4 shows some examples of how to define individual matrix elements and how to view them. Notice that, as with vectors, Mathcad fills unspecified matrix elements with zeros.

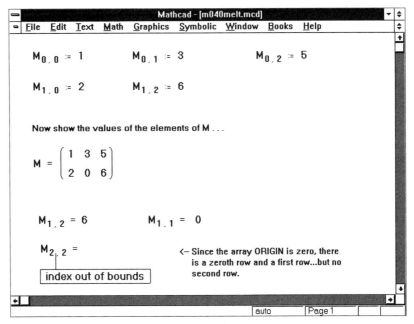

Figure 4: Defining and viewing matrix elements.

You can also define the elements of a vector or matrix with a definition like $v_i := i$, where i is a *range variable*. See the next chapter, "Range Variables."

Superscripts with matrix columns

To refer to an entire column of an array, press [**Ctrl**]**6** and place the column number in the resultant placeholder. Figure 5 below shows how to place the third column of the matrix **M** in the vector **v**.

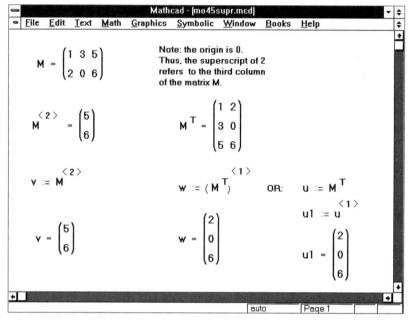

Figure 5: Using the superscript operator to extract a column from a matrix.

You can also extract a single row from a matrix by extracting a column from the transposed matrix. This is shown on the right-hand side of Figure 5.

Changing the ORIGIN

By default, Mathcad arrays begin at element zero. To change this, change the value of the built-in variable ORIGIN. When you use subscripts to refer to array elements, Mathcad assumes the arrays begin at the current value of ORIGIN.

For example, suppose you want all your arrays to begin with element one. There are two ways to change the value of ORIGIN for the whole worksheet:

- Choose the **Built-In Variables** command from the **Math** menu and change the value of ORIGIN.

- Enter a global definition for ORIGIN anywhere in your worksheet. For example, to change the ORIGIN to one, type: **ORIGIN~1**.

If you change ORIGIN to one, Mathcad no longer maintains an element zero for vectors or a zeroth row and column for matrices. Figure 6 shows a worksheet with the ORIGIN set to 1. Note that when you try to refer to v_0, Mathcad now delivers the error message "*index out of bounds.*"

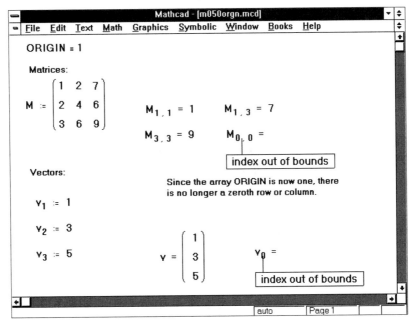

File   Edit   Text   Math   Graphics   Symbolic   Window   Books   Help

ORIGIN ≡ 1

Matrices:

$$M := \begin{pmatrix} 1 & 2 & 7 \\ 2 & 4 & 6 \\ 3 & 6 & 9 \end{pmatrix}$$

$M_{1,1} = 1$ $M_{1,3} = 7$

$M_{3,3} = 9$ $M_{0,0} =$

> index out of bounds

Since the array ORIGIN is now one, there is no longer a zeroth row or column.

Vectors:

$v_1 := 1$

$v_2 := 3$

$v_3 := 5$

$$v = \begin{pmatrix} 1 \\ 3 \\ 5 \end{pmatrix}$$ $v_0 =$

> index out of bounds

auto   Page 1

Figure 6: Arrays beginning at element one instead of at element zero.

When you redefine ORIGIN in a worksheet, keep in mind the following suggestions:

- If you define ORIGIN with a definition in the worksheet rather than using the **Built-in Variables** menu command, use a single global definition. Although you can redefine ORIGIN with a " **: =**" this will invariably lead to confusion. Changing ORIGIN in the middle of a worksheet can cause confusing effects. Array elements will seem to have shifted *n* positions, where *n* is the difference between the old ORIGIN and the new ORIGIN.

- Don't forget to type ORIGIN in capital letters. Mathcad variable names are case-sensitive. Because ORIGIN is a built-in variable, its name is not font sensitive. It is however, still case-sensitive.

- When you define an array, Mathcad assigns zero to any undefined elements. See Figure 3 in this chapter for an example.

- If you inadvertently define an array starting with element one when ORIGIN is set to its default value of zero, you will get unexpected answers with array functions like *mean* and *fft*. This is because Mathcad will automatically define $x_0 = 0$ for all these arrays. This extra element distorts the values returned by array functions. To avoid this problem, choose **Built-In Variables** from the **Math** menu and set ORIGIN to 1 in the Built-In Variable dialog box.

- When you set ORIGIN in the Built-In Variable dialog box, its value applies to all array variables. It is not possible to have some variables use one ORIGIN and others use a different ORIGIN.

Subscripts and superscripts   191

- You can use ORIGIN to define variables with negative subscripts. If you set ORIGIN to –10, all arrays will begin with element –10.

- If you reference an array element with a subscript less than ORIGIN, Mathcad marks the array reference with the error message "*index out of bounds.*"

Displaying vectors and matrices

After computing with arrays in Mathcad, your resulting arrays may be large and unwieldy when displayed. Mathcad therefore displays matrices and vectors having more than nine rows or columns as scrolling output tables rather than as matrices or vectors. Figure 7 shows an example.

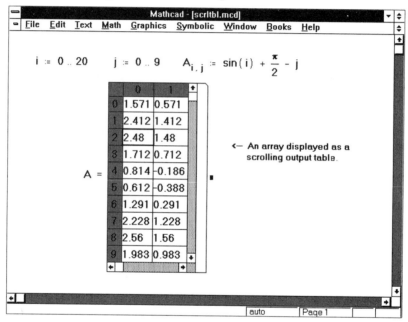

Figure 7: Displaying results in a scrolling output table.

A scrolling output table displays a portion of an array. To the left of each row and at the top of each column, there is a number indicating the index of the row or column. Use these row and column headers to determine the index of a particular value in the table.

If your results extend beyond the table, a scroll bar will appear along the appropriate edge of the table. You can scroll through the table using these scroll bars just as you would scroll through any window.

Another way to view more of a resulting array is to enlarge the table. To resize a scrolling output table:

■ Click the mouse just outside the equation region in which the scrolling output table appears. This anchors one corner of the selection rectangle.

■ Press and hold down the left mouse button. With the button still held, drag the mouse across the scrolling output table. A selection rectangle emerges from the anchor point.

■ When the selection rectangle just encloses the equation region, let go of the mouse button.

■ Move the mouse pointer to the right or bottom edge of the selection rectangle. It will change to a double headed arrow.

■ Press and hold down the mouse button. With the mouse button still pressed, move the mouse. The scrolling output table will be stretched in the direction of the motion.

■ Once the scrolling output table is the right size, let go of the mouse button. Click outside the selection rectangle to deselect the equation region.

In addition to being able to resize and scroll through a scrolling output table, you can copy one or more values from it and paste them into another part of your worksheet or into another Windows application. For information on copying results from a scrolling output table, see page 148.

Changing the display of arrays

Although matrices and vectors having more than nine rows or columns are automatically displayed as scrolling output tables, you can have Mathcad display them as matrices. To do so:

■ Click on the scrolling output table.

■ Choose **Numerical Format** from the **Math** menu.

■ Click on the box beside "Display as Matrix." The box should now be checked.

■ Click the "OK" button.

To display all the matrices and vectors of results in your worksheet as matrices regardless of their size:

■ Click on an empty part of your worksheet.

■ Choose **Numerical Format** from the **Math** menu.

■ Click on the box beside "Display as Matrix."

■ Make sure the "Global" radio button is filled and click "OK".

Graphical display of matrices

In addition to looking at the actual numbers making up an array, you can also see a graphical representation of those same numbers. There are three ways to do this:

- For an arbitrary array, you can use the various three dimensional plot types discussed starting at Chapter 21, "Surface plots."

- For an array of integers between 0 and 255, you can look at a gray scale image by choosing **Create Picture** from the **Graphics** menu and entering the array's name in the placeholder.

- For three arrays of integers beyween 0 and 255 representing the red, green and blue components of an image, by choosing **Create Picture** from the **Graphics** menu and entering the array's names, separated by commas, in the placeholder.

You'll find numerous examples of three dimensional plots of matrices beginning with Chapter 21, "Surface plots." An example of viewing a matrix as a gray scale image is shown in the last Figure of Chapter 14, "Programming."

Limits on array sizes

Mathcad has the following limits on the sizes of arrays to be defined, entered, or displayed:

Limit on input arrays

You cannot use the **Matrices** command on the **Math** menu to create an array having more than 100 elements. This limitation applies whether you attempt to create a new array or add to an existing array. You can however, create larger arrays by either using the *augment* or *stack* functions to join arrays together, by using range variables, or by reading the numbers in directly from a disk file. An example of how to use the *augment* function is shown in Figure 8. The use of range variables to create arrays is discussed in Chapter 10, "Range Variables." Reading files directly from a disk is discussed in Chapter 18 "Data Files."

Limit on displayed arrays

If an array has more than nine rows or columns, Mathcad automatically displays it as a scrolling output table. You can enlarge the table or use the scroll bars provided in order to view all of the array. If, however, you change the local result format such that Mathcad displays it as an array rather than as a scrolling output table, Mathcad displays only the first two hundred rows or columns. Mathcad uses an ellipsis to indicate that rows and columns are present but not displayed. Although Mathcad does not display these rows or columns, it does continue to keep track of them internally.

Limit on array size

The effective array size limit depends on the memory available on your system. For most systems, it will usually be at least 1 million elements. In no system will it be higher than 8 million elements. If you try to define an array larger than your system will accomodate, you'll see an error message stating "*not enough memory.*" The elements can be distributed among any combination of rows and columns. When only limited memory is available and you define several very large arrays, the array size limit may decrease.

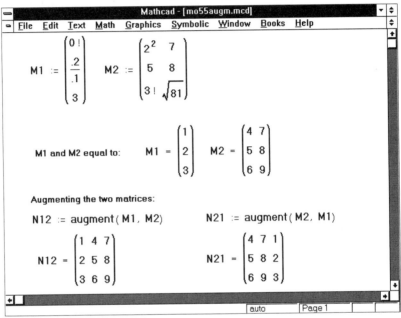

Figure 8: Using the augment function to combine two matrices.

Vector and matrix operators

Some of Mathcad's operators have special meanings for vectors and matrices. For example, the multiplication symbol means multiplication when applied to two numbers, but it means dot product when applied to vectors, and matrix multiplication when applied to matrices.

The table on the next page describes Mathcad's vector and matrix operations. Many of these operators are available from the symbol palette. Note that operators which expect vectors always expect column vectors rather than row vectors. To change a row vector into a column vector, use the transpose operator [Ctrl]1.

Operators not listed in this table will not work for vectors and matrices. If you attempt to use such an operator with a vector or matrix Mathcad will mark it with the error message *"illegal array operation"* or *"non-scalar value."* You can, however, use the "vectorize" operator to perform any scalar operation or function element by element on a vector or matrix. See the section "Doing calculations in parallel," later in this chapter. Figure 9 shows some ways to use vector and matrix operations.

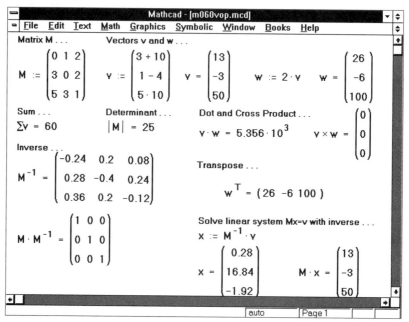

Figure 9: Vector and matrix operations.

Chapter 9 Vectors and Matrices

In the following table,

- **A** and **B** represent arrays, either vector or matrix.

- **u** and **v** represent vectors.

- **M** represents a square matrix.

- u_i and v_i represent the individual elements of vectors **u** and **v**.

- z represents a scalar.

- m and n represent integers.

Operation	Appearance	Keystroke	Description
Scalar multiplication	$\mathbf{A} \cdot z$	*	Multiplies each element of **A** by the scalar z.
Dot product	$\mathbf{u} \cdot \mathbf{v}$	*	Returns a scalar: $\Sigma\, u_i v_i$. The vectors must have the same number of elements.
Matrix multiplication	$\mathbf{A} \cdot \mathbf{B}$	*	Returns the matrix product of **A** and **B**. The number of columns in **A** must match the number of rows in **B**.
Vector/Matrix multiplication	$\mathbf{A} \cdot \mathbf{v}$	*	Returns the product of **A** and **v**. The number of columns in **A** must match the number of rows in **v**.
Scalar division	$\dfrac{\mathbf{A}}{z}$	/	Divides each element of the array **A** by the scalar z.
Vector and matrix addition	$\mathbf{A} + \mathbf{B}$	+	Adds corresponding elements of **A** and **B**. The arrays **A** and **B** must have the same number of rows and columns.
Scalar addition	$\mathbf{A} + z$	+	Adds z to each element of **A**.
Vector and matrix subtraction	$\mathbf{A} - \mathbf{B}$	–	Subtracts corresponding elements of **A** and **B**. The arrays **A** and **B** must have the same number of rows and columns.
Scalar subtraction	$\mathbf{A} - z$	–	Subtracts z from each element of **A**.
Negative of vector or matrix	$-\mathbf{A}$	–	Returns an array whose elements are the negatives of the elements of **A**.
Powers of matrix, matrix inverse	$\mathbf{M}^n$	^	n^{th} power of square matrix **M** (using matrix multiplication). n must be an integer. $\mathbf{M}^{-1}$ represents the inverse of **M**. Other negative powers are powers of the inverse. Returns a matrix.

Operation	Appearance	Keystroke	Description
Magnitude of vector	$\|v\|$	I	Returns $\sqrt{\mathbf{v} \cdot \overline{\mathbf{v}}}$ where $\overline{\mathbf{v}}$ is the complex conjugate of $\mathbf{v}$.
Determinant	$\|M\|$	I	$\mathbf{M}$ must be square matrix. Returns a scalar.
Transpose	$\mathbf{A^T}$	[Ctrl]1	Interchanges row and columns of $\mathbf{A}$.
Cross product	$\mathbf{u} \times \mathbf{v}$	[Ctrl]8	$\mathbf{u}$ and $\mathbf{v}$ must be three-element vectors; result is another three-element vector.
Complex conjugate	$\overline{\mathbf{A}}$	"	Takes complex conjugate of each element of $\mathbf{A}$.
Sum	Σv	[Ctrl]4	Sum elements in $\mathbf{v}$.
Vectorize	$\overrightarrow{\mathbf{A}}$	[Ctrl]–	Treat all operations in $\mathbf{A}$ element by element. See the section "Doing calculations in parallel" later in this chapter for a complete description.
Superscript	$\mathbf{A}^{<n>}$	[Ctrl]6	n^{th} column of array $\mathbf{A}$. Returns a vector.
Vector subscript	v_n	[	n^{th} element of a vector.
Matrix subscript	$A_{m,n}$	[	$(m, n)^{th}$ element of a matrix.

Vector and matrix functions

Mathcad includes functions for manipulating arrays in ways that are common in linear algebra. These functions are intended for use with vectors and matrices. If a function is not explicitly set up to take a vector or matrix argument, it is inappropriate to supply one to it as an argument. Note that functions which expect vectors always expect column vectors rather than row vectors. To change a row vector into a column vector, use the transpose operator [Ctrl]1.

If you're using Mathcad PLUS, you'll also have several additional functions that accept vector arguments. These functions are intended for data analysis rather than for matrix manipulation matrices. They are discussed in Chapter 12, "Built-in Functions."

The following tables list Mathcad's vector and matrix functions. In these tables,

- $\mathbf{A}$ and $\mathbf{B}$ are arrays, either vector or matrix.

- $\mathbf{v}$ is a vector.

- $\mathbf{M}$ and $\mathbf{N}$ are square matrices.

- z is a scalar expression.

■ Names beginning with *m*, *n*, *i* or *j* are integers.

Size and scope of an array

Mathcad provides several functions that return information about the size of an array and its elements. Figure 10 shows how these functions are used.

Function Name	Returns...
rows(**A**)	Number of rows in array **A**. If **A** is a scalar, returns 0.
cols(**A**)	Number of columns in array **A**. If **A** is a scalar, returns 0.
length(**v**)	Number of elements in vector **v**.
last(**v**)	Index of last element in vector **v**.
max(**A**)	Largest element in array **A**. If **A** has complex elements, returns the largest real part plus *i* times the largest imaginary part.
min(**A**)	Smallest element in array **A**. If **A** has complex elements, returns the smallest real part plus *i* times the smallest imaginary part.

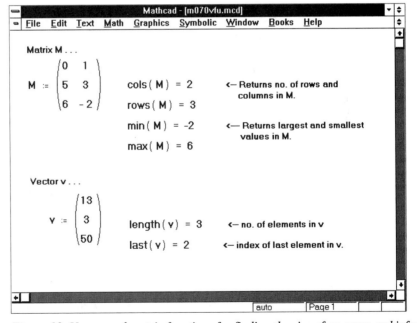

Figure 10: Vector and matrix functions for finding the size of an array and information about its elements.

Special types of matrices

You can use the following functions to derive from an array or scalar a special type or form of a matrix. The functions *rref, diag,* and *geninv* are available only with Mathcad PLUS.

Function Name	Returns...
identity(n)	An $n \times n$ matrix of 0's with 1's on the diagonal.
Re(**A**)	An array of the same size as **A** but with the imaginary parts of each element set to 0.
Im(**A**)	An array of the same size as **A** but with the real parts of each element set to 0.
⊕ diag(**v**)	A diagonal matrix containing on its diagonal the elements of **v**.
⊕ geninv(**A**)	The left inverse matrix **L** of **A**, such that **L·A** = **I**, where **I** is the identity matrix having the same number of columns as **A**. Matrix **A** is an $m \times n$ real-valued matrix, where $m \geq n$.
⊕ rref(**A**)	The reduced-row echelon form of **A**.

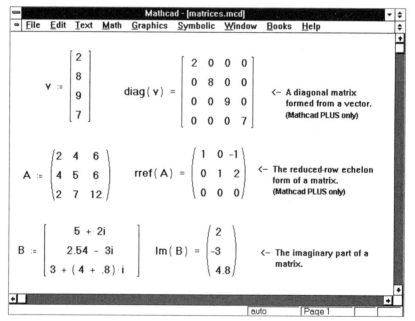

Figure 11: Functions for transforming arrays. Note that the functions diag and rref are available only with Mathcad PLUS.

Special characteristics of a matrix

You can use the functions in the following table to find the trace, rank, norms, and condition numbers of a matrix. Except for *tr*, these functions are available only in Mathcad PLUS.

Function Name	Returns...
tr(**M**)	The sum of the diagonal elements, otherwise known as the *trace*, of **M**.
⊕ rank(**A**)	The rank of the real-valued matrix **A**.
⊕ norm1(**M**)	The L_1 norm of the matrix **M**.
⊕ norm2(**M**)	The L_2 norm of the matrix **M**.
⊕ norme(**M**)	The Euclidean norm of the matrix **M**.
⊕ normi(**M**)	The infinity norm of the matrix **M**.
⊕ cond1(**M**)	The condition number of the matrix **M** based on the L_1 norm.
⊕ cond2(**M**)	The condition number of the matrix **M** based on the L_2 norm.
⊕ conde(**M**)	The condition number of the matrix **M** based on the Euclidean norm.
⊕ condi(**M**)	The condition number of the matrix **M** based on the infinity norm.

Forming new matrices from existing ones

Mathcad provides two functions for joining matrices together, either side by side, or one on top of the other. Mathcad also provides a function for extracting a smaller matrix from a larger one. Figures 12 and 13 show some examples.

Function Name	Returns...
augment(**A**, **B**)	An array formed by placing **A** and **B** side by side. The arrays **A** and **B** must have the same number of rows.
stack(**A**, **B**)	An array formed by placing **A** above **B**. The arrays **A** and **B** must have the same number of columns.
submatrix(**A**, ir, jr, ic, jc)	A submatrix of **A** consisting of all elements contained in rows ir through jr and columns ic through jc. To maintain order of rows and/or columns, make sure $ir \le jr$ and $ic \le jc$, otherwise order of rows and/or columns will be reversed.

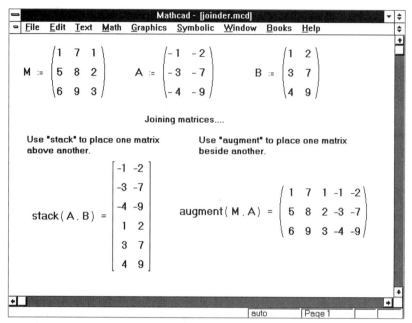

Figure 12: Joining matrices together with the stack and augment functions.

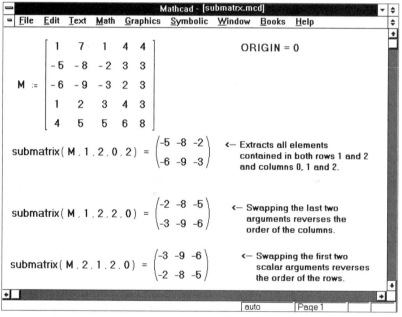

Figure 13: Extracting a submatrix from a matrix using the submatrix function.

Chapter 9 Vectors and Matrices

Eigenvalues and eigenvectors

Mathcad provides the *eigenval* and *eigenvec* functions for finding the eigenvalues and eigenvectors of a matrix. Mathcad PLUS also comes with the *eigenvecs* function for obtaining all the eigenvectors at once. If you're using Mathcad PLUS, you'll also have access to *genvals* and *genvecs* for finding the generalized eigenvalues and eigenvectors. Figure 14 shows how some of these functions are used.

Function Name	Returns...
eigenvals($\mathbf{M}$)	A vector containing the eigenvalues of the matrix $\mathbf{M}$.
eigenvec($\mathbf{M}$, z)	A matrix containing the normalized eigenvector corresponding to the eigenvalue z of the square matrix $\mathbf{M}$.
⊕ eigenvecs($\mathbf{M}$)	A matrix containing normalized eigenvectors corresponding to the eigenvalues of the square matrix $\mathbf{M}$. The nth column of the matrix returned is an eigenvector corresponding to the nth eigenvalue returned by *eigenvals*.
⊕ genvals($\mathbf{M}$, $\mathbf{N}$)	A vector $\mathbf{v}$ of computed eigenvalues each of which satisfies the generalized eigenvalue problem $\mathbf{M}\cdot\mathbf{x} = v_i\cdot\mathbf{N}\cdot\mathbf{x}$. Matrices $\mathbf{M}$ and $\mathbf{N}$ contain real values. Vector $\mathbf{x}$ is the corresponding eigenvector. $\mathbf{M}$ and $\mathbf{N}$ are square matrices having the same number of columns.
⊕ genvecs($\mathbf{M}$, $\mathbf{N}$)	A matrix containing the normalized eigenvectors corresponding to the eigenvalues in $\mathbf{v}$, the vector returned by *genvals*. The nth column of this matrix is the eigenvector $\mathbf{x}$ satisfying the generalized eigenvalue problem $\mathbf{M}\cdot\mathbf{x} = v_n\cdot\mathbf{N}\cdot\mathbf{x}$. Matrices $\mathbf{M}$ and $\mathbf{N}$ are real valued square matrices having the same number of columns.

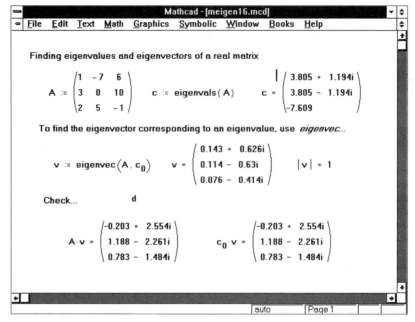

Figure 14: Finding eigenvalues and eigenvectors.

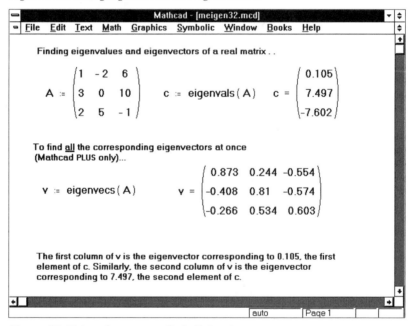

Figure 15: Using eigenvecs to find all the eigenvectors at once.

Decomposition

If you're using Mathcad PLUS, you'll have access to some additional functions for performing the cholesky decomposition, the QR decomposition, the LU decomposition, and the singular value decomposition of a matrix. Some of these functions return two or three matrices joined together as one large matrix. Use *submatrix* to extract these two or three smaller matrices. Figure 16 shows an example.

Function Name	Returns...
⊕ cholesky(**M**)	A lower triangular matrix **L** such that $\mathbf{L} \cdot \mathbf{L}^T = \mathbf{M}$. This uses only the upper triangular part of **M**. The upper triangular of **M**, when reflected about the diagonal, must form a positive definite matrix.
⊕ qr(**A**)	A matrix whose first *n* columns contain the square, orthonormal matrix **Q**, and whose remaining columns contain the upper triangular matrix, **R**. Matrices **Q** and **R** satisfy the equation $\mathbf{A} = \mathbf{Q} \cdot \mathbf{R}$, where **A** is a real-valued array.
⊕ lu(**M**)	One matrix containing the three square matrices **P**, **L**, and **U**, all having the same size as **M** and joined together side by side, in that order. These three matrices satisfy the equation $\mathbf{P} \cdot \mathbf{M} = \mathbf{L} \cdot \mathbf{U}$. **L** and **U** are lower and upper triangular respectively.
⊕ svd(**A**)	One matrix containing two stacked matrices **U** and **V**, where **U** is the upper $m \times n$ submatrix and **V** is the lower $n \times n$ submatrix. Matrices **U** and **V** satisfy the equation $\mathbf{A} = \mathbf{U} \cdot \text{diag}(\mathbf{s}) \cdot \mathbf{V}^T$, where **s** is a vector returned by svds(**A**). **A** is an $m \times n$ array of real values, where $m \geq n$.
⊕ svds(**A**)	A vector containing the singular values of the $m \times n$ real-valued array **A**, where $m \geq n$.

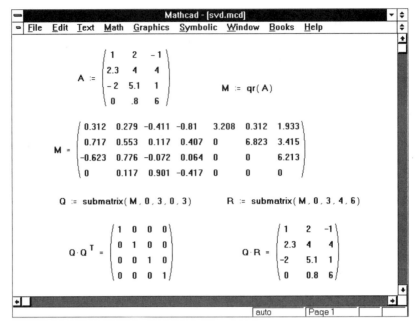

Figure 16: Using the submatrix function to extract the results from the rq function. Use submatrix in a similar way to extract results from the lu and svd functions. Note that these functions are only available with Mathcad PLUS.

Solving a linear system of equations

If you're using Mathcad PLUS you'll be able to use the *lsolve* function to solve a linear system of equations. Figure 17 shows an example. Note that the argument **M** for *lsolve* must be a matrix that is neither singular nor nearly singular. A matrix is singular if its determinant is equal to zero. A matrix is nearly singular if it has a high condition number. You may want to use one of the functions described on page 201 to find the condition number of a matrix.

Function Name	Returns...
⊕ lsolve($\mathbf{M}$, $\mathbf{v}$)	A solution vector $\mathbf{x}$ such that $\mathbf{M}\cdot\mathbf{x} = \mathbf{v}$.

If you're not using Mathcad PLUS, you can still solve a system of linear equations by using matrix inversion as shown in the lower right corner of Figure 9.

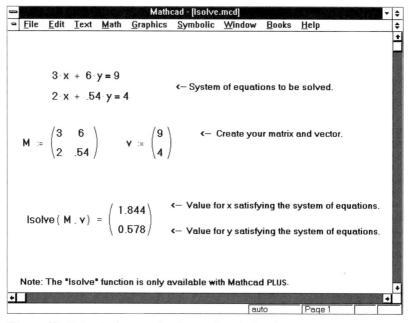

Figure 17: Using lsolve to solve 2 equations in 2 unknowns.

Doing calculations in parallel

Any calculation Mathcad can perform with single values, it can also perform with vectors or matrices of values. There are two ways to do this:

- By iterating over each element using range variables as described in the next chapter "Range Variables."

- By using the "vectorize" operator described in this chapter.

Mathcad's vectorize operator allows it to perform the same operation efficiently on each *element* of a vector or matrix.

Mathematical notation often shows repeated operations with subscripts. For example, to define a matrix **P** by multiplying corresponding elements of the matrices **M** and **N**, you would write:

$$\mathbf{P}_{i,j} = \mathbf{M}_{i,j} \cdot \mathbf{N}_{i,j}$$

Note that this is not matrix multiplication, but multiplication element by element. It *is* possible to perform this operation in Mathcad using subscripts, as described in the next chapter, but it is much faster to perform exactly the same operation with a vectorized equation.

How to apply the vectorize operator to an expression

Here's how to apply the vectorize operator to an expression like $\mathbf{M} \cdot \mathbf{N}$:

- Select the whole expression by clicking inside and pressing [↑] until the right-hand side is enclosed by the selection box.

$$P := \boxed{\mathbf{M} \cdot \mathbf{N}}$$

- Press [**Ctrl**]– to apply the vectorize operator. Mathcad puts an arrow over the top of the selected expression.

$$P := \overrightarrow{(\mathbf{M} \cdot \mathbf{N})}$$

How the vectorize operator changes the meaning of an expression

The vectorize operator changes the meaning of the operators and functions to which it applies. The vectorize operator tells Mathcad to apply the operators and functions with their scalar meanings, element by element.

Here are some examples of how the vectorize operator changes the meaning of expressions with vectors and matrices:

- If $\mathbf{v}$ is a vector, $\sin(\mathbf{v})$ is an illegal expression. But if you apply the vectorize operator, Mathcad applies the sine function to every element in $\mathbf{v}$. The result is a new vector whose elements are the sines of the elements in $\mathbf{v}$.

- If $\mathbf{M}$ is a matrix, $\sqrt{\mathbf{M}}$ is an illegal expression. But if you apply the vectorize operator, Mathcad takes the square root of every element of $\mathbf{M}$ and places the results in a new matrix.

- If $\mathbf{v}$ and $\mathbf{w}$ are vectors, then $\mathbf{v} \cdot \mathbf{w}$ means the dot product of $\mathbf{v}$ and $\mathbf{w}$. But if you apply the vectorize operator, the result is a new vector whose i^{th} element is obtained by multiplying v_i and w_i. This is *not* the same as the dot product.

These properties of the vectorize operator let you use scalar operators and functions with array operands and arguments. In this manual, this is referred to as "vectorizing" an expression. For example, suppose you want to apply the quadratic formula to three vectors containing coefficients a, b, and c. Figure 18 shows how to do this when a, b, and c are just scalars. Figure 19 shows how to do the same thing when $\mathbf{a}$, $\mathbf{b}$, and $\mathbf{c}$ are vectors.

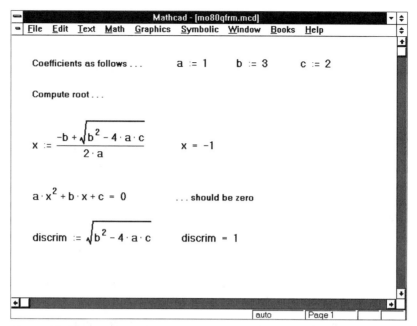

Figure 18: The quadratic formula.

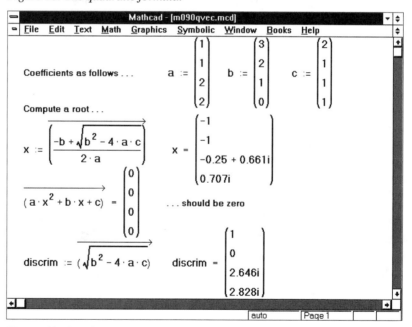

Figure 19: Quadratic formula with vectors and the vectorize operator.

The vectorize operator appears as an arrow above the quadratic formula in Figure 19. Its use is essential in this calculation. Without it, Mathcad would interpret **a·c** as a vector dot product and also flag the square root of a vector as illegal. But with the vectorize operator, both **a·c** and the square root are performed element by element.

Here are the properties of the vectorize operator:

- The vectorize operator changes the meaning of the other *operators* and *functions* to which it applies. It does not change the meaning of the actual names and numbers. If you apply the vectorize operator to a single name, it simply draws an arrow over the name. You can use this arrow just for cosmetic purposes.

- Since operations between two arrays are performed element by element, all arrays under a vectorize operator must be the same size. Operations between an array and a scalar are performed by applying the scalar to each element of the array. For example, if **v** is a vector and *n* is a scalar, applying the vectorize operator to $\mathbf{v}^n$ returns a vector whose elements are the nth powers of the elements of **v**.

- You cannot use any of the following matrix operations under a vectorize operator: dot product, matrix multiplication, matrix powers, matrix inverse, determinant, or magnitude of a vector. The vectorize operator will transform these operations into element-by-element scalar multiplication, exponentiation, or absolute value, as appropriate.

- The vectorize operator has no effect on operators and functions that *require* vectors or matrices: transpose, cross product, sum of vector elements, and functions like *mean*. These operators and functions have no scalar meaning.

- The vectorize operator applies only to the final, scalar arguments of *interp* and *linterp*. The other arguments are unaffected. See "Interpolation functions" in Chapter 13, "Statistical Functions."

Simultaneous definitions

You can use vectors and matrices to define several variables at once. You do this by placing an array of variable names on the left side of a **:=**, and a corresponding array of values to the right. Mathcad assigns the values on the right to the corresponding names on the left. Figure 20 shows two such definitions.

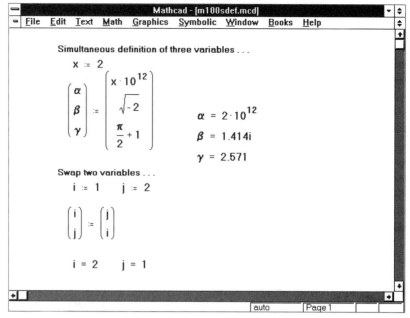

Figure 20: Simultaneous definitions.

The left side of a simultaneous definition is a vector or matrix whose elements are either names or subscripted variable names. The right side must be a vector or matrix expression having the same number of rows and columns as the left side. Mathcad defines each variable on the left side with the value of the expression in the corresponding position on the right side.

Mathcad evaluates all elements on the right hand side before assigning any of them to the left hand side. Because of this, nothing on the right hand side of an expression can depend on what is on the left hand side. You also cannot have a variable appear more than once on the left hand side.

Simultaneous definitions are useful for iterating several equations simultaneously. Several examples are described in Chapter 10, "Range Variables."

Arrays and user-defined functions

The arguments in a function definition need not be scalar variables. They can also be vectors or matrices. Functions can return values that are scalars, vectors, or matrices.

Figure 21 shows some examples of functions with vector and matrix arguments and results.

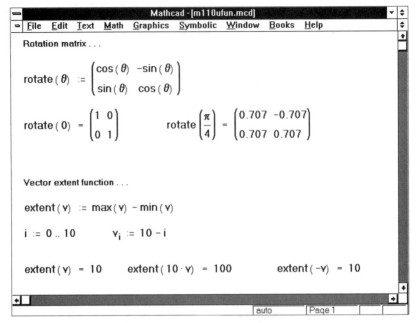

Rotation matrix . . .

$$\text{rotate}(\theta) := \begin{pmatrix} \cos(\theta) & -\sin(\theta) \\ \sin(\theta) & \cos(\theta) \end{pmatrix}$$

$$\text{rotate}(0) = \begin{pmatrix} 1 & 0 \\ 0 & 1 \end{pmatrix} \qquad \text{rotate}\left(\frac{\pi}{4}\right) = \begin{pmatrix} 0.707 & -0.707 \\ 0.707 & 0.707 \end{pmatrix}$$

Vector extent function . . .

$$\text{extent}(v) := \max(v) - \min(v)$$

$$i := 0 .. 10 \qquad v_i := 10 - i$$

$$\text{extent}(v) = 10 \qquad \text{extent}(10 \cdot v) = 100 \qquad \text{extent}(-v) = 10$$

Figure 21: User functions used with vectors and matrices.

Note that if a function expects a vector or a matrix for an argument, it will not work on a scalar argument. In the example in Figure 21, trying to evaluate *extent*(3) will flag the equation with the message "*must be array.*"

If a function returns a vector or matrix as a result, you use the subscript and superscript operators to extract specific numbers. For example, in Figure 21, you could evaluate:

$$\text{rotate}(0)_{1,0} = 0$$

$$\text{rotate}(0)^{<1>} = \begin{pmatrix} 0 \\ 1 \end{pmatrix}$$

Nested arrays

An array element need not be a scalar. It's possible to make an array element itself be another array. This allows you to create arrays within arrays.

These arrays behave very much like arrays whose elements are all scalars. However there are some distinctions:

■ You cannot use the **Matrices** menu command to insert an array into a placeholder that's already inside an array.

■ You cannot display the entire nested array. You will instead see a string like "{3,2}" to indicate that a 3×2 array is present in a particular array location.

- Most math operators and functions do not make sense in the context of nested arrays.

The following sections explore these differences in some detail.

Defining a nested array

You define a nested array in much the same way you would define any array. The only difference is that you cannot use the **Matrices** command from the **Math** menu when you've selected a placeholder within an existing array. You can, however, click on a placeholder in an array and type the *name* of another array as shown in Figure 22.

Figure 22 shows three ways to define a matrix of matrices: using range variables, element by element, and with the **Matrices** command from the **Math** menu.

In addition to those methods shown in Figure 22, you can also use the *READPRN* function in the array of empty placeholders created using the **Matrices** command. Keep in mind, however, that you can't use *READPRN* on the same file more than once in a given matrix. The *READPRN* function is discussed more fully in chapter 18, "Data Files."

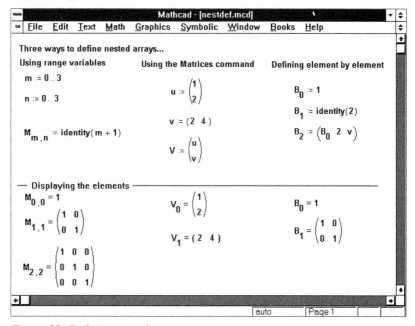

Figure 22: Defining nested arrays.

Displaying nested arrays

When you display a nested array using the equal sign, you won't actually see every element in every nested array. Such a display would be very cumbersome, especially when you consider that an array inside an array may itself contain arrays within it.

Instead, whenever an array element is itself an array, Mathcad indicates this by showing the number of rows and columns rather than the array itself. Figure 23 shows how the arrays created in Figure 22 would appear when displayed. Each array element is displayed either:

- As a number when the array element is simply a number, or

- As an ordered pair m, n where m and n are the number of rows and columns in the array which occupying that array element.

Note that the **B** array contains an element, B_2, which is itself a nested array. To view this array, you would simply nest your subscripts as shown in the lower-right corner of Figure 22.

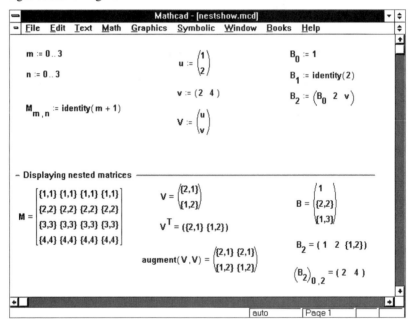

Figure 23: Displaying nested arrays.

Operators and functions for nested arrays

Most operators and functions do not work with nested arrays. This is because there is no universally accepted definition of what correct behavior would be in this context. For example, there is no clear definition of what it means to "invert" such an array. When you attempt to perform the usual arithmetic operations on nested arrays, you will most likely get either an error message such as "*overflow*" or a meaningless result. For the most part, nested arrays are designed for storing and accessing data in a convenient way.

Some operators and functions are nevertheless useful and appropriate for nested arrays. For example, transpose does something meaningful as shown at the bottom of Figure 23. Operators which make sense in the context of nested arrays are:

Operation	Appearance	Keystroke	Description
Transpose	A^T	[Ctrl]1	Interchanges row and columns of A.
Superscript	$A^{<n>}$	[Ctrl]6	n^{th} column of array A. Returns a vector.
Vector subscript	v_n	[	n^{th} element of a vector.
Matrix subscript	$A_{m,n}$	[	$(m, n)^{th}$ element of a matrix.
Boolean equals	$w = z$	[Ctrl]=	Boolean equals. Returns 1 if the two nested arrays, along with all nested arrays contained within them, are identical; otherwise returns 0.

Useful functions for nested arrays tend to be those having to do with the number of rows and columns in an array or those used for joining or dividing arrays. In particular, you can use the *rows* and *cols* functions to distinguish between scalar array elements and array elements which are themselves arrays. Both these functions return a zero in the former case and the appropriate number in the latter. The functions you'll find useful when working with nested arrays are:

Function Name	Returns...
rows($\mathbf{A}$)	Number of rows in matrix $\mathbf{A}$.
cols($\mathbf{A}$)	Number of columns in matrix $\mathbf{A}$.
length($\mathbf{v}$)	Number of elements in vector $\mathbf{v}$.
last($\mathbf{v}$)	Index of last element in vector $\mathbf{v}$.
augment($\mathbf{A}$, $\mathbf{B}$)	An array formed by placing $\mathbf{A}$ and $\mathbf{B}$ side by side. The arrays $\mathbf{A}$ and $\mathbf{B}$ must have the same number of rows.
stack($\mathbf{A}$, $\mathbf{B}$)	An array formed by placing $\mathbf{A}$ above $\mathbf{B}$. The arrays $\mathbf{A}$ and $\mathbf{B}$ must have the same number of columns.
submatrix($\mathbf{A}$, ir, jr, ic, jc)	A submatrix of $\mathbf{A}$ consisting of all elements contained in rows ir through jr and columns ic through jc. To maintain order of rows and/or columns, make sure $ir \leq jr$ and $ic \leq jc$, otherwise order of rows and/or columns will be reversed.

Chapter 10
Range Variables

A range variable is a variable that takes on a range of values each time you use it. Range variables greatly extend Mathcad's capabilities by allowing you to iterate, or loop, through repetitive calculations.

This chapter describes range variables and shows how to use them to perform iterative calculations, display tables of numbers, and facilitate the entry of many data values into a table.

The following sections make up this chapter.

Range variables

How to step through a range of numbers by defining a range variable.

Output tables

How to display a table of numbers.

Entering a table of numbers

How to use range variables to enter a table of numbers.

Iterative calculations

How to perform iteration with one or two range variables.

Seeded iteration

How to perform iteration when values in one step depend on the values in the previous step. Recursive techniques such as this provide the foundation for solving difference equations with Mathcad.

Vector notation

When to use the "vectorize" operator rather than subscripts.

Range variables

All iterative processes in Mathcad depend on *range variables*. Except for the way it's defined, a range variable looks just like a conventional variable. The difference is that a conventional variable takes on only one value. A range variable, on the other hand, takes on a range of values separated by uniform steps. For example, you could define a range variable to go from –4 through 4 in steps of 2. If you now use this range variable in an expression, Mathcad evaluates that expression five times, once for each value taken by the range variable.

Range variables are crucial to exploiting Mathcad's capabilities to their fullest. This section shows how to define and use range variables to perform iteration.

Defining and using range variables

To define a range variable, type the variable name followed by a colon and a range of values. For example, here's how to define the variable j ranging from 0 to 15:

- Type **j** and then press the colon key (**:**). The empty placeholder indicates that Mathcad expects a definition for j. At this point, Mathcad does not know whether j is to be a conventional variable or a range variable.

$$j := \square$$

- Type **0**. Then press the semicolon key (**;**). This tells Mathcad that you are defining a range variable. Mathcad shows the semicolon as two periods ".." to indicate a range. Complete the range variable definition by typing **15** in the remaining placeholder.

$$j := 0 \ .. \ 15|$$

This definition indicates that j now takes on the values 0, 1, 2 ... 15. To define a range variable that changes in steps other than 1, see the section "Types of ranges" later in this chapter.

Once you define a range variable, it takes on its complete range of values *every time you use it*. If you use a range variable in an equation, for example, Mathcad must evaluate that equation once for each value of the range variable.

You must define a range variable exactly as shown above. There must be:

- a variable name on the left,
- either a ":=" or a "≡" in the middle, and
- a valid range on the right.

In particular, you cannot define a variable in terms of a range variable. For example, if after having defined j as shown you now define $i := j + 1$, Mathcad assumes you are trying to set a scalar variable equal to a range variable and marks the equation with the error "*non-scalar value.*"

One application of range variables is to fill up the elements of a vector or matrix. You can define vector elements by using a range variable as a subscript. For example, to define x_j for each value of j:

- Type **x[j:j^2[Space]+1.**

$$x_j := j^2 + 1|$$

Figure 1 shows the vector of values computed by this equation. Since j is a range variable, the entire equation is evaluated once for each value of j. This defines x_j for each value of j from 0 to 15. The effect is exactly the same as if you had typed

$$x_0 := 0^2 + 1$$
$$x_1 := 1^2 + 1$$

$$.$$
$$.$$
$$.$$

$$x_{15} := 15^2 + 1$$

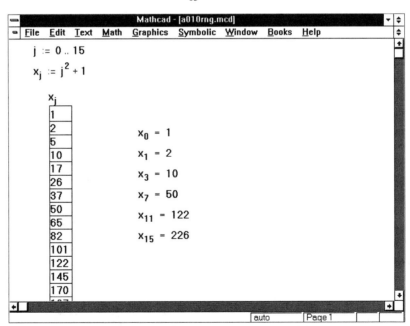

Figure 1: Using a range variable to define the values of the vector x.

To understand how Mathcad computes with range variables, keep in mind this fundamental principle:

If you use a range variable in an expression, Mathcad evaluates the expression once for each value of the range variable.

This principle sums up the difference between expressions with and without range variables. Expressions that involve no range variables have only one value. Expressions that involve range variables take on many values, one for each value of each range variable.

If you use two or more range variables in an equation, Mathcad evaluates the equation once for each value of each range variable. The section "Iterative calculations" later in this chapter discusses this in more detail.

Mathcad takes longer to compute equations with ranged expressions since there are many computations for each equation. While Mathcad is computing, the mouse pointer changes its appearance. To interrupt a calculation in progress, press [**Esc**]. To restart the calculation, click in the interrupted equation and press [**F9**].

Types of ranges

The definition of j in the previous section, ranging from 0 to 15, is the simplest type of range definition. Mathcad permits range variables with values ranging from any value to any other value, using any constant increment or decrement.

To define an arbitrary range variable, type an equation of this form:

$$\texttt{k:1,1.1;2}$$

This appears in your document window as:

$$k := 1, 1.1 \ .. \ 2$$

In this range definition:

- The variable k is the name of the range variable itself. It must be a simple name. No subscripts or function definitions are allowed.

- The number 1 is the first value taken by the range variable k.

- The number 1.1 is the second value in the range. Note that this is *not* the stepsize. The stepsize in this example is 0.1, the difference between 1.1 and 1. If you omit the comma and the 1.1, Mathcad assumes a step size of one in whatever direction (up or down) is appropriate.

- The number 2 is the last value in the range. In this example, the range values are constantly increasing. If instead you had defined $k := 10 \ .. 1$, then k would count down from 10 to 1. Even if the third number in the range definition is not an even number of increments from the starting value, the range will not go beyond it. For example, if you define $k := 10, 20 \ .. 65$, k will take values $10, 20, 30 \ldots 60$.

You can use arbitrary scalar expressions in place of 1, 1.1, and 2. However, these values must always be real numbers. Complex numbers do not make sense in range variable definitions because given two complex numbers, there is an infinite number of paths connecting them. Figure 2 shows the results of various range variable definitions.

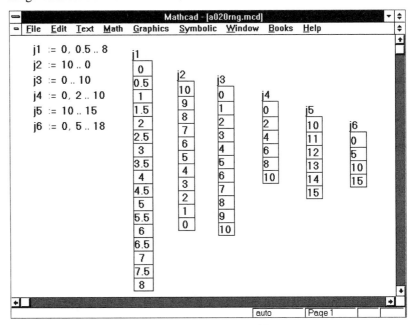

Figure 2: Some valid definitions for range variables.

Note that if you use a fractional increment for a range variable, you will not be able to use that range variable as a subscript. This is because subscripts must be integers.

Output tables

Whenever you type "=" after an expression involving range variables, Mathcad shows the computed values in an *output table*. Figure 2 shows the values of several range variables displayed as output tables.

Figure 3 shows some output tables for slightly more complicated expressions involving range variables.

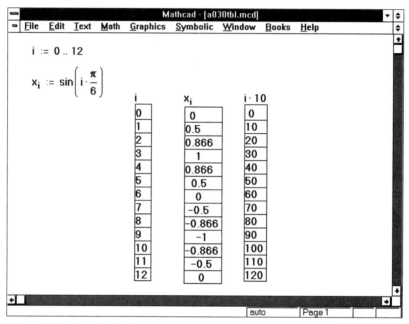

Figure 3: Typing "=" after an expression with range variables gives an output table.

To create the three tables in Figure 3, first define the range variable. Then type these equations:

$$i=$$
$$x[i=$$
$$i*10=$$

Whenever you type an expression followed by "=" Mathcad displays:

- a number, if the result is a scalar (a single number).

- a vector or a matrix, if the result is a vector or a matrix *and* the expression to the left of the "=" contains no range variables.

- a table like that shown in Figure 3 if the expression to the left of the "=" contains range variables.

- A scrolling output table if the result is a vector or a matrix, the expression to the left of the "=" contains no range variables, *and* the result has more than nine rows or columns. Scrolling output tables are discussed on page 192.

Since both **x=** and **x[i=** display the same numbers, you can think of tables as another way of viewing the contents of a vector. Tables are particularly convenient for viewing selected parts of a vector. For example, if you've defined a vector **v**, you can view every other element of that vector by typing:

$$i := 0, 2 \,.. \text{last}(\mathbf{v})$$

$$v_i =$$

Here are some facts about output tables in Mathcad:

- Mathcad shows only the first 50 values of a ranged expression in a table. For example, even if i ranges from 1 to 100, typing **i^2=** will show only the values from 1^2 up to 50^2 in a table. To see more than 50 values, use several range variables and several tables. You could, for example, define $j1$ from 1 to 50 and $j2$ from 51 to 100, and then show tables for **j1^2=** and **j2^2=**, side by side.

- To format the numbers in a table, click in the table and choose **Numerical Format** from the **Math** menu. Then specify your formatting preferences in the dialog box as you would for an equation with a single numeric result. For more information on number formatting, see Chapter 5, "Equation and Result Formatting."

- There are three ways to show the values in a vector. If you use a vector name *with* a subscript like $x_j =$, Mathcad shows an output table. If instead you type a vector name *without* a subscript like $x =$, Mathcad shows the vector as a vector rather than as an output table. If you type a vector name without a subscript and the vector has more than nine elements, you see a scrolling output table as described on page 192. Keep in mind that these are just three different ways of looking at the same thing: an ordered collection of numbers.

- You cannot use units with a table as you would with a single scalar answer. If the results in a table have dimensions, Mathcad shows the dimensions *on each value in the table*. To avoid this display, divide the ranged expression by the desired units. Figure 4 shows an example.

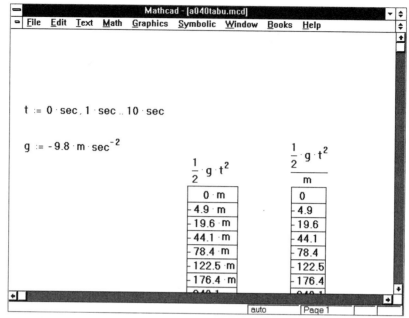

Figure 4: Units in a table.

Entering a table of numbers

When you enter a table of numbers, you are actually assigning elements to a vector. This section discusses how to do this using *input tables* and range variables. To enter an input table, enter a definition with a subscripted variable on one side and a sequence of values separated by commas on the other. For example:

- To define i to run through four values, type **i:1;4**. Note that i must take integer values only. Otherwise it can't be used as a subscript in the next step.

$$i := 1 .. 4$$

- Click in a new spot and type **x[i:** The placeholder indicates that Mathcad is expecting a value for x_1.

$$x_i := \blacksquare$$

- Type **3** and press the comma key. Mathcad shows another placeholder to indicate that Mathcad now expects a value for x_2.

$$x_i :=$$
$$\boxed{3}$$
$$\boxed{\blacksquare}$$

- Type **5,15,20** to supply values for x_2, x_3 and x_4.

Once you have created an input table, you can do any of the following:

- **Insert a value in the middle of a table**. Click on the value immediately above wherever you want to insert the new value. Then type a comma. Under the selected value in the table, Mathcad creates a placeholder surrounded by a box. To enter another number, just type it into this placeholder.

- **Extend the table to hold additional values**. Click on the last value in the table and follow the steps above for inserting a value in the table.

- **Replace or delete a value from the table**. Enclose the value you want to replace or delete in a selection box, then press [**Del**]. Mathcad replaces the value with an empty placeholder. Type a new value in this placeholder to replace the old one. To delete the value completely and decrease the array length by one in the process, press [**Del**] again. This will delete the placeholder itself.

Some notes about input tables:

- Each value in an input table must be either a number or an expression that returns a number, the name of an array or an expression that returns an array. Expressions involving range variables and expressions created by using the **Matrices** command on the **Math** menu are not permitted.

- All expressions in an input table must have the same dimensions if any. If you want each expression to be in meters, for example, you may have to include the abbreviation for meters in each table entry. A shortcut is to enter the numbers without units and redefine the vector with units by typing something like $x := x \cdot \text{m/sec}^2$.

- An input table ordinarily has one entry for each value of the range variable used in defining it. If the table has too few entries, Mathcad will define only as many values as are present. If the table has too many entries, the extra entries will be ignored.

- Input tables assign values *only to those elements specified by the range variable*. If in the previous example, the range variable definition had been $i := 10, 20 \ldots 40$, Mathcad would have assigned values to x_{10}, x_{20}, x_{30} and x_{40}. Mathcad would then pad the unassigned entries, namely x_0 through x_9, x_{11} through x_{19}, and so on, with zeros. You will see these zeros if you display the vector by typing "**x=**." It is possible to inadvertently create large tables this way.

- Input tables are limited to 50 elements. If you want to enter more than 50 elements, enter them using several tables. You could, for example, define $j1$ from 1 to 50 and $j2$ from 51 to 100, type **x[j1:** followed by the first fifty numbers, then type **x[j2:** followed by the second fifty numbers.

- When confronted with a very large number of data values, consider reading them in from a data file stored on your disk as an alternative to typing them in with input tables. Chapter 18 on data files discusses this in more detail.

Figure 5 shows some input tables. Note how typing **x=** and **y=** displays the elements of x and y in vector form. Mathcad ignores the last number in the input table for y since this entry would have index 5 and the range variable i stops at 4. Contrast this with typing **x[i=** as shown in Figure 3 of the previous section.

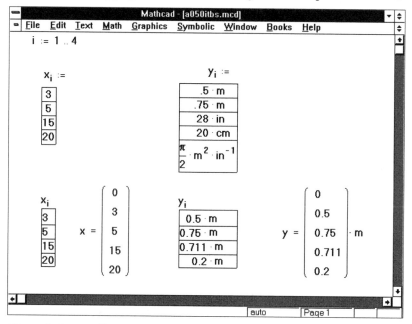

Figure 5: Input tables.

Note that the first element of both vectors is zero. This is because Mathcad's array origin is set to zero by default. Since the range variable i starts at 1, the zeroth element is never explicitly defined. In the absence of an explicit definition, Mathcad assumes a value of zero.

Iterative calculations

This section shows how to use range variables to perform iteration.

Iteration over a range

The simplest kind of iteration in Mathcad is just a generalization of scalar calculations. Any calculation you can perform once, you can perform over a range of values.

For example, suppose you want to create a list of x and y values for points on the polar curve $r = \cos(\theta) + 1$. The basic idea is as follows:

- θ should take on values between 0 and 2π.

- For each θ, the corresponding r is given by $r = \cos(\theta) + 1$.

- For each r and θ, there is a corresponding x and y given by $x = r \cdot \cos(\theta)$ and $y = r \cdot \sin(\theta)$.

The strategy for solving this problem is simple: create a range variable i and then compute θ, r, x, and y for each value of i. The formula for θ_i defines θ to run from 0 to 2π in steps of $2\pi/N$. To create the other formulas, just put the subscript i on each variable in the formula. Figure 6 shows the result.

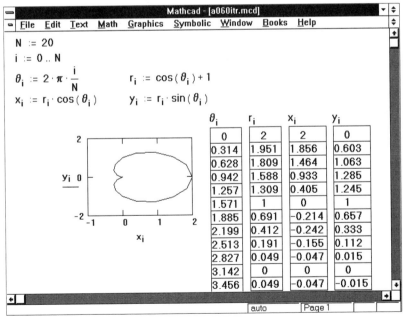

Figure 6: Using iteration to create a draw a polar curve using an X-Y plot.

Notice that in this example i, not θ, is defined as the range variable. Since i takes on only whole-number values, it is a valid subscript. On the other hand, θ takes on fractional values. It therefore cannot be used as a subscript. In many cases, you can avoid this extra step by using functions instead of vectors. Figure 7 shows how to generate the cardioid shown in Figure 6 with functions instead of vectors.

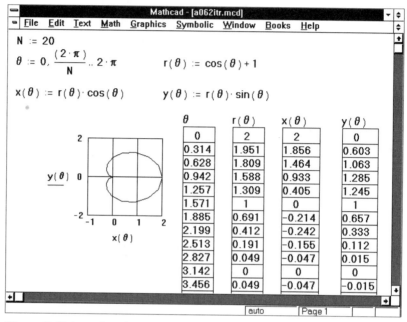

Figure 7: Using a function to do the same thing as shown in Figure 6.

By using vector notation and the vectorize operator, you can eliminate the use of a subscript in the last three equations in Figure 6. Figure 8 shows an example of how to do this.

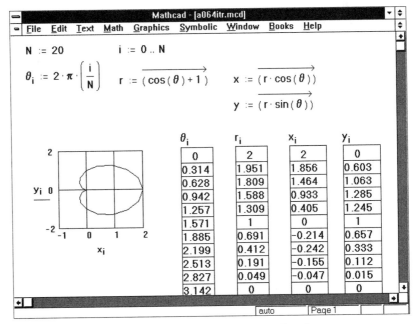

Figure 8: Using the vectorize operator to create a polar plot.

Equations that use vector notation instead of subscripts typically compute much more quickly. For more information, see Chapter 9, "Vectors and Matrices."

Multiple range variables and double subscripts

If you use two range variables in an equation, Mathcad runs through each value of each range variable. This is useful for defining matrices. For example, to define a 5×5 matrix whose ij^{th} element is $i + j$, type these equations:

$$i:0;4$$
$$j:0;4$$
$$x[i,j:i+j$$

Note that you don't need to type [**Space**] to leave the subscript in this case. Typing **:** leaves the subscript and creates the definition symbol.

Figure 9 shows the result of typing the above equations. It is usually best to display the matrix in the form shown in Figure 9. If instead of typing **x=** you were to type **x[i,j=**, Mathcad would show one long output table with 25 numbers. Such a table is often difficult to interpret. A similar problem arises when you use a pair of range variables in a graph.

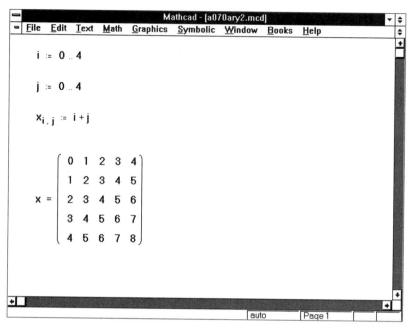

File   Edit   Text   Math   Graphics   Symbolic   Window   Books   Help

$i := 0 .. 4$

$j := 0 .. 4$

$x_{i,j} := i + j$

$$x = \begin{pmatrix} 0 & 1 & 2 & 3 & 4 \\ 1 & 2 & 3 & 4 & 5 \\ 2 & 3 & 4 & 5 & 6 \\ 3 & 4 & 5 & 6 & 7 \\ 4 & 5 & 6 & 7 & 8 \end{pmatrix}$$

auto   Page 1

Figure 9: Defining a matrix.

The $x_{i,j}$ equation is evaluated for each value of each range variable, for a total of 25 evaluations. The result is the matrix shown at the bottom, with 5 rows and 5 columns. The element in the ith row and j^{th} column of this matrix is $i + j$.

Note that if the two range variables have m and n values, respectively, then an equation using both range variables will calculate $m \cdot n$ results. If you try to use two range variables in an output table, Mathcad will show these $m \cdot n$ results in a long table with one entry for each result. If you use two range variables in a graph, Mathcad will plot one point for each of the $m \cdot n$ results.

Seeded iteration is a recursive technique for solving difference equations such as those that arise in compound interest problems, Markov processes, and many state variable equations. It can also be used for obtaining approximate solutions for certain differential equations. In a seeded iteration, you specify the first element of an array and then compute successive elements based on the first element. This section describes three types of seeded iteration: iterating a single variable, iterating multiple variables, and iterating a vector.

Seeded iteration on one variable

The classical method for estimating square roots arithmetically is as follows:

- To find $\sqrt{a}$, begin with a guess value.

- Compute a new guess based on the old guess, with this formula:

$$NewGuess = \frac{OldGuess + a/OldGuess}{2}$$

- Continue until the guesses converge to an answer.

Figure 10 shows how to implement this method in Mathcad.

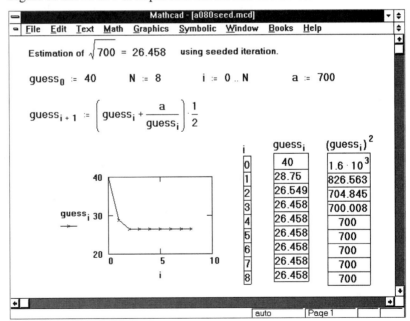

Figure 10: Using seeded iteration to estimate a square root.

The important characteristics of this example are:

- The seed value is defined as the zeroth element of the array, $guess_0$.

- Each $guess_{i+1}$ is defined in terms of a previously computed element.

It is this dependence of array elements on previously computed array elements that distinguishes seeded iteration from the more straightforward iteration discussed in the previous section.

Seeded iteration on several variables

You can use Mathcad's vector notation to iterate several variables simultaneously. This variation on simple seeded iteration is a powerful method for solving a system of simultaneous difference equations.

When you iterate several variables, each step computes the value of the variables from all of their previous values. You can't accomplish this with several equations because when Mathcad sees an equation with range variables, it attempts to evaluate it for *each* value of the range variable before going on to the next equation. You must, therefore, create one equation that performs all the iterations simultaneously.

For example, consider an infection model with four variables: i for the number of individuals infected, s for the number susceptible, d for the number deceased, and r for the number recovered and hence immune. The four equations that relate these four variables over time are:

$$i_{t+1} = 0.0001 \cdot s_t \cdot i_t$$

$$s_{t+1} = s_t - 0.0001 \cdot s_t \cdot i_t$$

$$d_{t+1} = d_t + 0.55 \cdot i_t$$

$$r_{t+1} = r_t + 0.45 \cdot i_t$$

Figure 11 shows how to perform a simultaneous iteration using these equations.

The single most important thing about this example is that all the $t + 1$ subscripts are on the left-hand side of the matrix equation. The right-hand side contains only the subscript t. Mathcad evaluates all the expressions on the right-hand side before performing any assignments to the left-hand side. This means that nothing on the right-hand side can depend on something on the left-hand side.

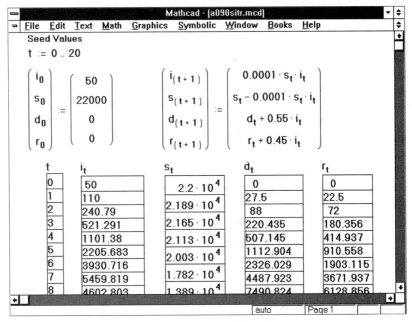

Figure 11: Simultaneous iteration to model an infection.

Seeded iteration on a vector

You can also perform seeded iteration starting with a vector and computing a new vector each time. This type of iteration uses a seed vector and Mathcad's superscript operator.

A *Markov process* is an example of a problem that involves iteration on a vector. A Markov process begins with a vector **v** that represents the starting values of some quantities, for example, the number of voters planning to vote for different candidates, the number of trucks at regional offices of a truck rental company, or the market share of different companies. Each step in the Markov process computes a new vector by multiplying the previous vector by a "state transition" matrix **A**.

Figure 12 shows how to set up a Markov process. This technique uses *superscripts* to index an entire column of a matrix at once. To create a superscript, press [**Ctrl**]**6**. This generates a placeholder between angle brackets: <>.

Here's how to enter the equations in Figure 12:

- First, define the state transition matrix **A**. Type **A**, press the colon key (**:**), and create a 3×3 matrix. To create a matrix, choose **Matrices** from the **Math** menu.

$$A := \begin{pmatrix} .5 & 0 & .2 \\ .25 & .9 & .1 \\ .25 & .1 & .7 \end{pmatrix}$$

- Click to the right of the matrix and type **v**. Then press [Ctrl]6. Type 0 in the placeholder for the superscript.

$$\mathbf{v}^{\langle 0|\rangle}$$

- Now complete the definition of the initial vector. First press the colon key (:). Then choose **Matrices** from the **Math** menu. Specify that you want to create a matrix with three rows and one column. Then fill in the matrix entries.

$$\mathbf{v}^{\langle 0 \rangle} := \begin{pmatrix} 10 \\ 25 \\ 15 \end{pmatrix}$$

- Type **k:1;8**. This defines a range variable k to count eight iterations.

$$k := 1 .. 8$$

- To define the kth vector in terms of the $(k-1)^{th}$, type **v[Ctrl]6 k**. Then type a colon (:) for the definition symbol. Complete the equation by typing this expression after the definition symbol: **A*v[Ctrl]6 k-1**

$$\mathbf{v}^{\langle k \rangle} := A \cdot \mathbf{v}^{\langle k-1 \rangle}$$

- To see the eighth (last) column of the matrix, type **v [Ctrl]6 8 =** .

$$\mathbf{v}^{\langle 8 \rangle} = \begin{pmatrix} 6.017 \\ 29.124 \\ 14.859 \end{pmatrix}$$

- To see all the vectors as columns of a matrix, type **v=** . Note that not all the columns are displayed in the picture to the right.

$$\mathbf{v} = \begin{pmatrix} 10 & 8 & 7.1 & 6.65 & 6.398 \\ 25 & 26.5 & 27.4 & 27.985 & 28.386 \\ 15 & 15.5 & 15.5 & 15.365 & 15.217 \end{pmatrix}$$

The superscript operator actually retrieves or defines one column in a matrix. When you define $\mathbf{v}^{\langle k \rangle}$ in terms of $\mathbf{v}^{\langle k-1 \rangle}$, you are actually defining each column of a matrix in terms of the preceding column. The last equation in Figure 12 shows the matrix composed from these columns.

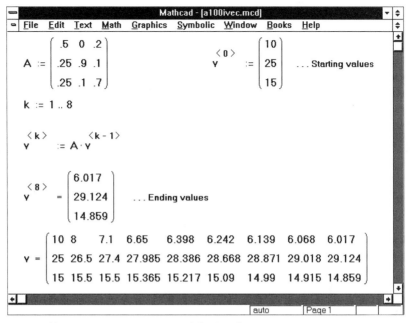

Figure 12: Iterating a vector to model a Markov process.

Vector or subscript notation

This chapter has shown many examples using subscript notation and range variables. Chapter 9, "Vectors and Matrices," showed many examples using vector notation without subscripts. This distinction is important. If you use subscripts when they are not required, or vice versa, you probably won't get the answer you're looking for.

Subscripts refer to individual array elements. When you use range variables as subscripts like $M_{i,j}$, Mathcad runs through the individual elements of the array one at a time.

Without subscripts, the variable name refers to the whole array.

Here are some rules of thumb for when to use subscripts:

- To refer to an individual array element, use numbers as subscripts. For example, to see matrix element (2,3), type `M[2,3=`.

- To refer to an array as a whole, use the array name without subscripts. (The term array means either a vector or a matrix.) The array name with no subscripts is appropriate for multiplying one matrix by another, applying the *mean* function to an array, or viewing a whole vector or matrix — all cases where you want to treat the array as a whole. For example, to view the whole matrix **M** in Figure 13, type `M=`.

- To refer to each of the array elements in succession, use the array name with a range variable subscript. This is useful when defining the matrix elements using some sort of formula. For example, to define the matrix **M** in Figure 13, type three equations:

```
i:0;3
j:0;3
M[i,j:i*j
```

Figure 13 shows some examples of using array names with and without subscripts.

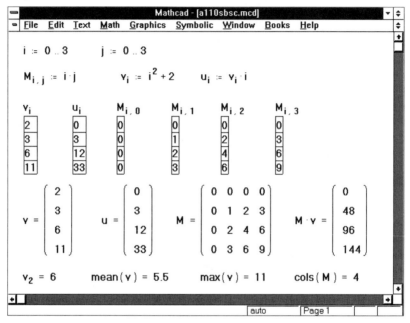

Figure 13: Array names with and without subscripts.

Iterative calculations with and without subscripts

It's often faster to use vector operations to perform iterative calculations than it is to do them element by element with a range variable. This is discussed in more detail in the section "Doing calculations in parallel" in Chapter 9. Unfortunately, not all iterative calculations can be done as vector operations. For example, the seeded iteration technique discussed earlier in this chapter cannot be done with vector operations.

To tell if an equation with subscripts could be rewritten using vector notation and the vectorize operator, check the following:

- If all the subscripts in the calculation are the same, then the calculation can probably be done quickly using vector operations. For example, consider this equation:

$$x_i := r_i \cdot \cos(\theta_i)$$

Since this equation contains no subscript other than i, it can be rewritten with the vectorize operator ([Ctrl][-]) instead of with subscripts:

$$x := \overrightarrow{(r \cdot \cos(\theta))}$$

- If the subscripts in a calculation vary or if there is arithmetic involved in computing the subscript, then the calculation probably cannot be done using vector operations. For example, seeded iteration involves the subscripts i and $i-1$ in the same equation. Since the subscripts are not the same, and since the second subscript involves arithmetic, this calculation cannot be done using vector operations.

- If the range variable appears anywhere in an equation other than in a subscript, the equation cannot be written using vector operations. For example, the variable θ below cannot be defined using the vectorize operator. Although the range variable appears on the left side as a subscript, its presence in an expression on the right disqualifies the entire equation.

$$\theta_i := 0.1 \cdot i$$

Figure 14 shows the polar coordinate conversions from Figure 6 computed two ways: using subscripts and using vector operations. The second method is much faster in Mathcad.

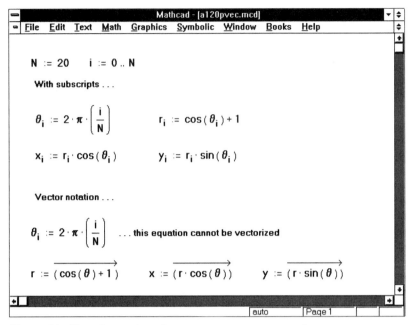

Figure 14: Changing an iterative process to vector operations.

Chapter 11
Operators

Mathcad includes ordinary operators like + and /, matrix operators like transpose and determinant, and special operators like iterated sum, iterated product, integrals, and derivatives.

This chapter contains a list of Mathcad operators and describes how to enter and use the special operators.

This chapter contains the following sections:

List of operators

List of Mathcad's operators in order of precedence.

Summations and products

How to use Mathcad's summation and product operators.

Derivatives

How to use Mathcad's derivative operators.

Integrals

How to use Mathcad's definite integral operator.

Boolean operators

How to use Mathcad's boolean operators such as ">" and "<."

Customizing operators

How to define your own operators just the way you define your own functions.

List of operators

This is a list of Mathcad operators in order of precedence. For information on array operators, see Chapter 9. Most of the following operators are available by clicking on one of the operator palettes. To open the operator palettes, click on the buttons on the button strip directly below the menu commands.

In this table:

- **A** and **B** represent arrays, either vector or matrix.

- **u** and **v** represent vectors with real or complex elements.

- **M** represents a square matrix.

- z and w represent real or complex numbers.

- x and y represent real numbers.

- m and n represent integers.

- i represents a range variable.

- t represents any variable name.

- f represents a function.

- X and Y represent variables or expressions of any type.

Operation	Appearance	Keystroke	Description
Parentheses	(X)	'	Grouping operator.
Vector Subscript	$\mathbf{v}_n$	[	Returns indicated element of a vector.
Matrix Subscript	$\mathbf{A}_{m,n}$	[	Returns indicated element of a matrix.
Superscript	$\mathbf{A}^{<n>}$	[Ctrl]6	Extracts column n from array **A**. Returns a vector.
Vectorize	$\vec{X}$	[Ctrl]–	Forces operations in expression X to take place element by element. All vectors or matrices in X must be the same size.
Factorial	$n!$	!	Returns $n \cdot (n-1) \cdot (n-2)\dots$ The integer n cannot be negative.
Complex conjugate	$\overline{X}$	"	Inverts the sign of the imaginary part of X.
Transpose	$\mathbf{A}^{\mathsf{T}}$	[Ctrl]1	Returns a matrix whose rows are the columns of **A** and whose columns are the rows of **A**. **A** can be a vector or a matrix.
Power	z^w	^	Raises z to the power w.

Operation	Appearance	Keystroke	Description
Powers of matrix, matrix inverse	$\mathbf{M}^n$	^	n^{th} power of square matrix $\mathbf{M}$ (using matrix multiplication). n must be a whole number. $\mathbf{M}^{-1}$ is the inverse of $\mathbf{M}$. Other negative powers are powers of the inverse. Returns a square matrix.
Negation	$-X$	–	Multiplies X by -1.
Vector sum	$\Sigma\mathbf{v}$	[Ctrl]4	Sums elements of vector $\mathbf{v}$; returns a scalar.
Square root	$\sqrt{z}$	\	Returns positive square root for positive z; principal value for negative or complex z.
nth root	$\sqrt[n]{z}$	[Ctrl]\	Returns n^{th} root of z; returns a real valued root whenever possible.
Magnitude, Absolute value	$\lvert z \rvert$	|	Returns $\sqrt{\text{Re}(z)^2+\text{Im}(z)^2}$.
Magnitude of vector	$\lvert \mathbf{v} \rvert$	|	Returns the magnitude of the vector $\mathbf{v}$: $\sqrt{\mathbf{v}\cdot\mathbf{v}}$ if all elements in $\mathbf{v}$ are real. Returns $\sqrt{\mathbf{v}\cdot\overline{\mathbf{v}}}$ if any element in $\mathbf{v}$ is complex.
Determinant	$\lvert \mathbf{M} \rvert$	|	Returns the determinant of the square matrix $\mathbf{M}$. Result is a scalar.
Division	$\dfrac{X}{z}$	/	Divides the expression X by the non-zero scalar z. If X is an array, divides each element by z.
Multiplication	$X{\cdot}Y$	*	Returns the product of X and Y if both X and Y are scalars. Multiplies each element of Y by X if Y is an array and X is a scalar. Returns the dot product (inner product) if X and Y are vectors of the same size. Performs matrix multiplication if X and Y are conformable matrices.
Cross product	$\mathbf{u}\times\mathbf{v}$	[Ctrl]8	Returns cross-product (vector product) for the three-element vectors $\mathbf{u}$ and $\mathbf{v}$.
Summation	$\displaystyle\sum_{i=m}^{n} X$	[Ctrl] [Shift]4	Performs summation of X over $i = m, m+1, \ldots n$. X can be any expression. It need not involve i but it usually does. m and n must be integers.
Product	$\displaystyle\prod_{i=m}^{n} X$	[Ctrl] [Shift]3	Performs iterated product of X for $i = m, m+1, \ldots n$. X can be any expression. It need not involve i but it usually does. m and n must be integers.
Range sum	$\displaystyle\sum_{i} X$	$	Returns a summation of X over the range variable i. X can be any expression. It need not involve i but it usually does.

Operation	Appearance	Keystroke	Description
Range product	$\displaystyle\prod_i X$	#	Returns the iterated product of X over the range variable i. X can be any expression. It need not involve i but it usually does.
Integral	$\displaystyle\int_a^b f(t)\,dt$	&	Returns the definite integral of $f(t)$ over the interval $[a, b]$. a and b must be real scalars. All variables in the expression $f(t)$, except the variable of integration t, must be defined. The integrand, $f(t)$, cannot return an array.
Derivative	$\dfrac{d}{dt} f(t)$	?	Returns the derivative of $f(t)$ evaluated at t. All variables in the expression $f(t)$ must be defined. The variable t must be a scalar value. The function $f(t)$ must return a scalar.
nth Derivative	$\dfrac{d^n}{dt^n} f(t)$	[Ctrl]?	Returns the nth derivative of $f(t)$ evaluated at t. All variables in $f(t)$ must be defined. The variable t must be a scalar value. The function $f(t)$ must return a scalar. n must be an integer between 0 and 5 for numerical evaluation or a positive integer for symbolic evaluation.
Addition	$X + Y$	+	Scalar addition if X, Y, or both are scalars. Element by element addition if X and Y are vectors or matrices of the same size. If X is an array and Y is a scalar, adds Y to each element of X.
Subtraction	$X - Y$	–	Performs scalar subtraction if X, Y, or both are scalars. Performs element by element subtraction if X and Y are vectors or matrices of the same size. If X is an array and Y is a scalar, subtracts Y from each element of X.
Addition with line break	$X \ldots$ $+ Y$	[Ctrl][↵]	Same as addition. Line break is purely cosmetic.
Greater than	$x > y$	>	Returns 1 if $x > y$, 0 otherwise. x and y must be real scalars.
Less than	$x < y$	<	Returns 1 if $x < y$, 0 otherwise. x and y must be real scalars.
Greater than or equal	$x \geq y$	[Ctrl]0	Returns 1 if $x \geq y$, 0 otherwise. x and y must be real scalars.
Less than or equal	$x \leq y$	[Ctrl]9	Returns 1 if $x \leq y$, 0 otherwise. x and y must be real scalars.
Not equal to	$z \neq w$	[Ctrl]3	Returns 1 if $z \neq w$, 0 otherwise. z and w must be scalars.
Equal to	$X = Y$	[Ctrl]=	Returns 1 if $z = w$, 0 otherwise. Appears as a bold $=$ on the screen.

Help with typing operators

You can avoid having to remember the keystrokes that go with each operator by using the operator palettes. To open the operator palettes, click on the buttons on the strip just below the menus. Each button opens a palette of operators grouped loosely by function.

The icons on the operator palette buttons indicate what operator appears when you click on that button. You can also hold the mouse pointer momentarily over a button to see a balloon indicating what the button does.

To type any operator from the table on the previous pages, just click wherever you want to put the operator, then click on its button on the appropriate operator palette.

In general, operator palettes only work in math regions. To use the operator palettes in text, you must first click in the text and choose **Embed Math** from the **Text** menu. This will create a math placeholder in the text into which you can insert operators using the palettes.

Summations and products

The summation operator sums an expression over all values of an index. The iterated product operator works much the same way. It takes the product of an expression over all values of an index.

To create a summation operator in your worksheet:

- Click in a blank space. Then type [Ctrl][Shift]4. A summation sign with four placeholders appears.

- In the placeholder to the left of the equal sign, type a variable name. This variable is the index of summation. It is defined only within the summation operator and therefore has no effect on, and is not influenced by, variable definitions outside the summation operator.

- In the placeholder to the right of the equal sign, type an integer or any expression that evaluates to an integer.

- In the single placeholder above the sigma, type an integer or any expression that evaluates to an integer.

- In the remaining placeholder, type the expression you want to sum. Usually, this expression will involve the index of summation. If this expression has several terms, type an apostrophe (') to create a pair of parentheses around the placeholder.

Iterated products are similar. Just type [Ctrl][Shift]3 and fill in the placeholders as described earlier.

Figure 1 shows some examples of how to use the summation and product operators. You can use a summation or an iterated product just as you would any other expression.

To evaluate multiple summations, place another summation in the final placeholder of the first summation. An example of this appears at the bottom of Figure 1.

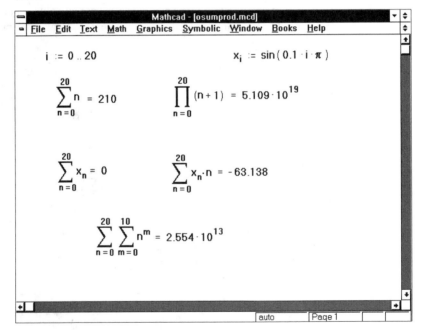

Figure 1: Summations and products.

When you use the summation operator shown in Figure 1, the summation must be carried out over integers and in steps of one. Mathcad provides more general versions of these operators that can use any range variable you define as an index of summation. To use these operators, first define a range variable. In the following example type `i:1,2;10`. Then do the following:

- Click in a blank space. Then type
  `$`. A summation sign with two
  placeholders appears.

- Click on the bottom placeholder
  and type the name of a range variable. The range variable you use
  here should already have been defined earlier in the worksheet.

- Click on the placeholder to the
  right of the summation sign and
  type an expression involving the
  range variable. If this expression
  has several terms, type an apostrophe (`'`) to create a pair of parentheses around the placeholder.

- Press the equals sign (=) to see the
  result.

$$\sum_i i^2 = 385$$

If you don't want to take the time to click in each placeholder, you can enter the previous expression by typing `i$i^2`.

A generalized version of the iterated product also exists. To use it, type `#`. Then fill in the two placeholders.

Figure 2 shows some examples of how to apply the range sum and range product operators. These operators, unlike the summation and product operators created with [Ctrl][Shift]4 and [Ctrl][Shift]3, cannot stand alone. They require the existence of a range variable. Note however, that a single range variable can be used with any number of these operators.

You can use summations and iterated products just as you would any other expression. To evaluate multiple summations, use two range variables as shown in Figure 2.

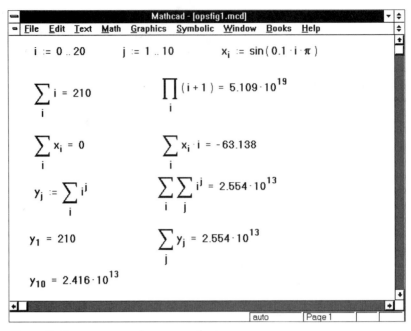

Figure 2: Range sums and range products.

Variable upper limit of summation

Mathcad's range summation operator runs through each value of the range variable you place in the bottom placeholder. It is possible, by judicious use of boolean expressions, to sum only up to a particular value. In Figure 3, the term $i \le x$ returns the value 1 whenever it is true and 0 whenever it is false. Although the summation operator still sums over each value of the index of summation, those terms for which $i > x$ are multiplied by 0 and hence do not contribute to the summation.

You can also use the four-placeholder summation and product operators to compute sums and products with a variable upper limit, but note that the upper limit in these operators must be an integer.

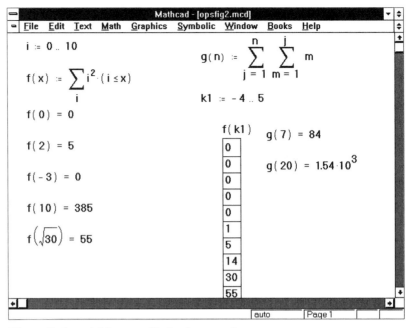

Figure 3: A variable upper limit of summation.

The vector-sum operator

The operation of summing the elements of a vector is so common that Mathcad provides a special operator for it. While the ordinary summation operator sums a ranged expression, the vector sum operator sums the elements of a vector without needing a range variable.

To sum all the elements of a vector **v** defined elsewhere in your worksheet, follow these steps:

- Click in blank space or on a placeholder. Then press [Ctrl]4.

- Type the name of a vector or vector-valued expression. Mathcad returns the sum of all the elements in the vector. In this example, the vector used is that shown in Figure 2.

Derivatives

You can use Mathcad's derivative operator to evaluate the derivative of a function at a particular point.

As an example, here's how you would evaluate the derivative of x^3 with respect to x at the point $x = 2$:

- First define the point at which you want to evaluate the derivative. Type **x:2** .

$$x := 2|$$

- Click below the definition of x. Then type **?**. A derivative operator appears, with a placeholder in the denominator and another to the right.

$$\frac{d}{d\blacksquare}\,\blacksquare$$

- Click on the bottom placeholder and type **x**. You are differentiating with respect to this variable.

$$\frac{d}{dx|}\,\blacksquare$$

- Click on the placeholder to the right of the d/dx and type **x^3** . This is the expression to be differentiated.

$$\frac{d}{dx}\,x^3|$$

- Press the equals sign = to see the derivative of the expression at the indicated point.

$$\frac{d}{dx}\,x^3| = 12\,\blacksquare$$

Figure 4 shows examples of differentiation in Mathcad.

With Mathcad's derivative algorithm, you can expect the first derivative to be accurate to within 7 or 8 significant digits, provided that the value at which you evaluate the derivative is not too close to a singularity of the function. The accuracy of this algorithm tends to decrease by one significant digit for each increase in the order of the derivative (refer to the subsection on higher order derivatives which follows).

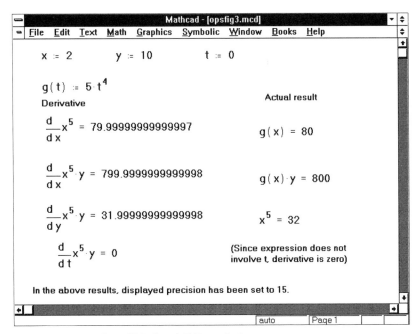

Figure 4: Examples of Mathcad differentiation.

Keep in mind that the result of differentiating is not a function, but a single number: the computed derivative at the indicated value of the differentiation variable. In the previous example, the derivative of x^3 is not the expression $3x^2$ but $3x^2$ evaluated at $x = 2$. If you want to evaluate derivatives symbolically, see Chapter 17, "Symbolic Calculation."

Although differentiation returns just one number, you can still define one function as the derivative of another. For example:

$$f(x) := \frac{d}{dx} g(x)$$

Evaluating $f(x)$ will return the numerically computed derivative of $g(x)$ at x.

You can use this technique to evaluate the derivative of a function at many points. An example of this is shown in Figure 5.

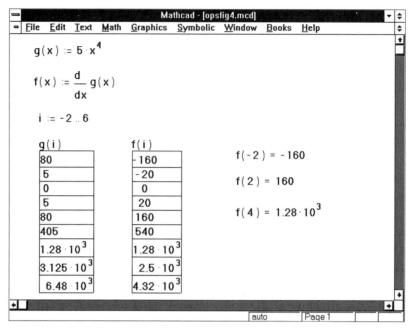

Figure 5: Evaluating the derivative of a function at several points.

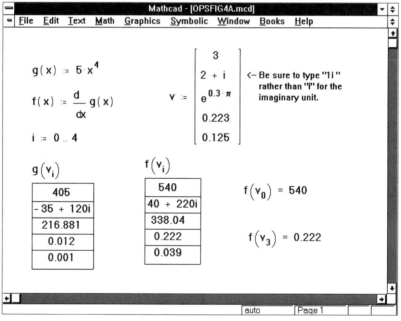

Figure 6: Evaluating the derivative of a function at several values stored as elements of a vector.

There are some important things to remember about differentiation in Mathcad:

- The expression to be differentiated can be either real or complex.

- The differentiation variable must be a single variable name. If you want to evaluate the derivative at several different values stored in a vector, use the technique illustrated in Figure 6.

Derivatives of higher order

Mathcad has an additional derivative operator for evaluating the nth order derivative of a function at a particular point.

As an example, here's how you would evaluate the third derivative of x^9 with respect to x at the point $x = 2$:

- First define the point at which you want to evaluate the derivative. Type **x:2**.

$$x := 2$$

- Click below the definition of x. Then type **[Ctrl]?**. A derivative operator appears, with two placeholders in the denominator, one in the numerator, and another to the right.

$$\frac{d^{\blacksquare}}{d\blacksquare}\blacksquare$$

- Click on the bottom placeholder and type **x**. You are differentiating with respect to this variable.

$$\frac{d^{\blacksquare}}{dx^{\blacksquare}}\blacksquare$$

- Click on the expression above and to the right of the previous placeholder and type **3**. This must be an integer between 0 and 5 inclusive. Note that the placeholder in the numerator automatically mirrors whatever you've typed.

$$\frac{d^3}{dx^3}\blacksquare$$

- Click on the placeholder to the right of the d/dx and type **x^9**. This is the expression to be differentiated.

$$\frac{d^3}{dx^3}x^9$$

- Press the equals sign = to see the third derivative of the expression at the indicated point.

$$\frac{d^3}{dx^3}x^9 = 3.226 \cdot 10^4$$

For $n = 1$, this operator gives the same answer as the first-derivative operator discussed above. For $n = 0$, it simply returns the value of the function itself.

You can use Mathcad's integral operator to numerically evaluate the definite integral of a function over some interval.

As an example, here's how you would evaluate the definite integral of $\sin(x)^2$ from 0 to $\pi/4$, follow these steps:

- Click in a blank space and type **&**. An integral appears, with placeholders for the integrand, the limits of integration, and the variable of integration.

$$\int_{\blacksquare}^{\blacksquare} \blacksquare \; d\blacksquare$$

- Click on the bottom placeholder and type **0**. Click on the top placeholder and type **[Ctrl]p/4**. These are the upper and lower limits of integration.

$$\int_{0}^{\frac{\pi}{4}} \blacksquare \; d\blacksquare$$

- Click on the placeholder between the integral sign and the "d." Then type **sin(x)^2**. This is the expression to be integrated.

$$\int_{0}^{\frac{\pi}{4}} \sin(x)^2 \; d\blacksquare$$

- Click on the remaining placeholder and type **x**. This is the variable of integration. Then press the equals sign (**=**) to see the result.

$$\int_{0}^{\frac{\pi}{4}} \sin(x)^2 \; dx = 0.143$$

Mathcad uses a numerical algorithm called Romberg integration to approximate the integral of an expression over an interval of real numbers.

There are some important things to remember about integration in Mathcad:

- The limits of integration must be real. The expression to be integrated can, however, be either real or complex.

- Except for the integrating variable, all variables in the integrand must have been defined elsewhere in the worksheet.

- The integrating variable must be a single variable name.

- If the integrating variable involves units, the upper and lower limits of integration must have the same units.

Like all numerical methods, Mathcad's integration algorithm can have difficulty with ill-behaved integrands. If the expression to be integrated has singularities, discontinuities, or large and rapid fluctuations, Mathcad's solution may be inaccurate.

Because Mathcad's integration method divides the interval into four subintervals and then successively doubles the number of points, it can return incorrect answers for periodic functions with having periods $1/2^n$ times the length of the interval. To avoid this problem, divide the interval into two uneven subintervals and integrate over each subinterval separately.

In some cases, you may be able to find an exact numerical value for your integral by using Mathcad's symbolic integration capability. You can also use this capability to evaluate indefinite integrals. See Chapter 17, "Symbolic Calculation."

Variable limits of integration

Although the result of an integration is a single number, you can always use an integral with a range variable to obtain results for many numbers at once. You might do this, for example, when you set up a variable limit of integration. Figure 7 shows how to do this.

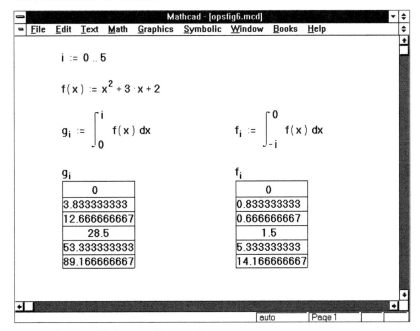

Figure 7: Variable limits of integration.

Keep in mind that calculations such as those shown in Figure 7 may require repeatedly evaluating an integral. This may take considerable time depending on the complexity of the integrals, the length of the interval, and the value of TOL (see the next section).

Changing the tolerance for integrals

Mathcad's numerical integration algorithm makes successive estimates of the value of the integral and returns a value when the two most recent estimates differ by less than the value of the built-in variable TOL. Figure 8 shows how changing TOL affects the accuracy of integral calculations. To display many digits of precision, see Chapter 5, "Equation and Result Formatting."

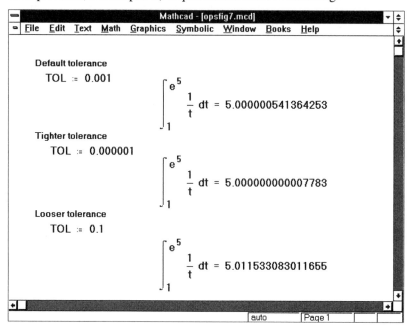

Figure 8: Effects of tolerance on integral calculations.

You can change the value of the tolerance by including definitions for TOL directly in your worksheet as shown on Figure 8. You can also change the tolerance by choosing **Built-In Variables** from the **Math** menu. To see the effect of changing the tolerance, choose **Calculate Document** from the **Math** menu to recalculate all the equations in the worksheet.

If Mathcad's approximations to an integral fail to converge to an answer, Mathcad marks the integral with the message "*not converging.*" This error can be caused by any function that has singularities or "spikes" in the interval or by an extremely long interval.

When you change the tolerance, keep in mind the tradeoff between accuracy and computation time. If you decrease (tighten) the tolerance, Mathcad will compute integrals more accurately. However, because this requires more work, Mathcad will take longer to return a result. Conversely, if you increase (loosen) the tolerance, Mathcad will compute more quickly, but the answers will be less accurate.

Contour integrals and double integrals

You can use Mathcad to evaluate complex contour integrals. To do so, first parametrize the contour. Then integrate over the parameter. If the parameter is something other than arc length, you must also include the derivative of the parametrization as a correction factor. Figure 9 shows an example. Note that the imaginary unit i used in specifying the path must be typed as 1i.

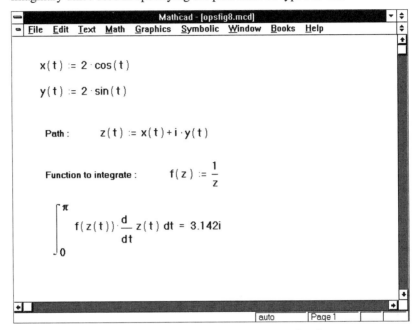

Figure 9: How to do a complex contour integral in Mathcad.

You can also use Mathcad to evaluate double or multiple integrals. To set up a double integral, press & twice. Fill in the integrand, the limits, and the integrating variable for each integral. Figure 10 shows an example.

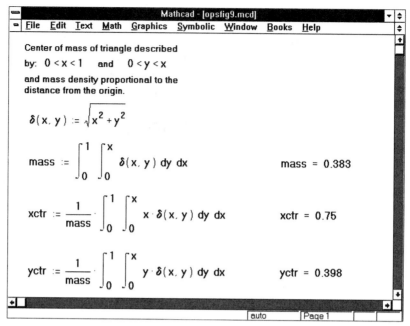

Figure 10: Double integrals.

Keep in mind that double integrals take much longer to converge to an answer than single integrals. Wherever possible, use an equivalent single integral in place of a double integral.

Boolean operators

Unlike other operators, the boolean operators can return only a zero or a one. Despite this, they can be very useful. You have already seen an example in Figure 3 showing how a boolean operator made a variable upper limit of summation possible. Figure 11 shows how a boolean operator makes it possible to determine the array index of a particular element. The *Treasury of Methods and Formulas*, an Electronic Book available from MathSoft, provides a wealth of examples illustrating this and other methods of getting the most out of Mathcad.

The following table lists the boolean operators:

Condition	How to type	Description
$w = z$	[Ctrl]=	Boolean equals. Returns 1 if expressions are equal; otherwise 0.
$x > y$	>	Greater than.
$x < y$	<	Less than.
$x \geq y$	[Ctrl]0	Greater than or equal to.
$x \leq y$	[Ctrl]9	Less than or equal to.
$w \neq z$	[Ctrl]3	Not equal to.

The four operators $>$, $<$, $\leq$, and $\geq$ cannot take complex numbers because the concepts of greater than and less than lose their meaning in the complex plane.

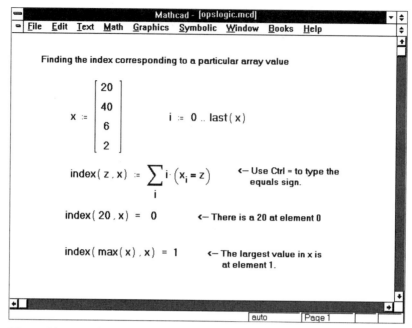

Finding the index corresponding to a particular array value

$$x := \begin{bmatrix} 20 \\ 40 \\ 6 \\ 2 \end{bmatrix} \qquad i := 0 .. \text{last}(x)$$

$$\text{index}(z, x) := \sum_i i \cdot \left(x_i = z\right) \qquad \text{<— Use Ctrl = to type the equals sign.}$$

$$\text{index}(20, x) = 0 \qquad \text{<— There is a 20 at element 0}$$

$$\text{index}(\max(x), x) = 1 \qquad \text{<— The largest value in x is at element 1.}$$

Figure 11: Using boolean operators.

Customizing operators

Mathcad
PLUS

You can think of operators and functions as really being the same thing. A function takes "arguments" and returns a result. An operator, likewise, takes "operands" and returns a result. The differences are merely cosmetic:

- Functions have names you can spell, like *tan* or *spline*; operators are generally symbols like "+" or "×".

- Arguments to a function are enclosed by parentheses, they come after the function's name, and they're separated by commas. Operands on the other hand, can appear elsewhere. For example, you'll often see "$f(x, y)$" but you'll rarely see "$x f y$". Similarly, you'll often find "$x + y$" but you'll rarely find "$+(x, y)$".

Since operators and functions are fundamentally the same, and since you can define your own functions, there's no reason why you can't define your own customized operators as well. If you are using Mathcad PLUS, you'll be able to do just that.

The first section describes how to define a new operator. This is followed by a section on how to use the operator you've just defined. The last section brings together these ideas by showing how functions can themselves be displayed as if they were operators.

Defining a custom operator

You define an operator just as if you were defining a function. You'd type the operator name followed by a pair of parentheses. The operands (two at the most) would go between the parentheses. On the other side of the ":=" you'd type an expression describing what you want the operator to do with its operands. These steps are described in detail in the section "Defining a function" on page 139.

Since operators tend to have names that aren't found on a keyboard, a problem arises when you try and type the name. For example, suppose you want to define a new division operator using "÷". You first have to know how to put a "÷" into your worksheet. There are three ways to do this.

- You can paste it in from the Windows Character Map, or

- If you know the ANSI code, you can hold down the [**Alt**] key while typing the ANSI code using the *numeric keypad* (the number keys on the main keyboard won't work).

- You can drag a symbol from the "Math Symbols" QuickSheet by choosing **QuickSheets** from the **Help** menu.

We recommend that you save your custom operators by dragging them into a QuickSheet. Choose **QuickSheets** from the **Help** menu and click on "Personal QuickSheets" at the bottom of the table of contents. Click on "My Operators". Then drag the definitions into the this QuickSheet. The next time you need them, you'll be able to drag them off the same QuickSheet rather than having to redefine them.

The simplest way to insert a character that isn't on your keyboard is to drag it from the "Math Symbols" QuickSheet. If the character you're looking for is not on this QuickSheet, use the Windows Character Map. This is usually in the "Accessories" group in your Program Manager's window. Double-clicking on the icon will open a window similar to the following:

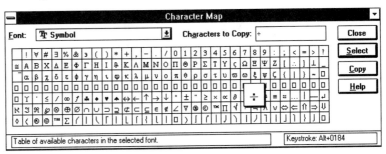

Double-click on the character you want to use. Then click the "Copy" button. Click in the Mathcad worksheet and press [**Ctrl**]**V** to paste the character into your worksheet. Note that you cannot use a name already used by Mathcad. For example, you cannot redefine the "+" operator.

- When you paste the character, it will appear in the default math font as shown on the right. A blue selection box encloses the character.

- To see the "÷", you'll need to change this into the Symbol font. Press the [↓] key to turn the blue selection box into an insertion point directly in front of the character.

- Press [**Ctrl**]**G** to display the character in the Symbol font.

You can now continue as if you were defining a function of two variables that happens to have an unusual looking "name".

- Type a left parenthesis followed by two names separated by a comma. Complete this argument list by typing a right parenthesis.

$$\div(\mathbf{x}, \mathbf{y})$$

- Press the colon (:) key. You see the definition symbol, " : =", followed by a placeholder.

$$\div(\mathbf{x}, \mathbf{y}) := \blacksquare$$

- Type the function definition in the placeholder.

$$\div(\mathbf{x}, \mathbf{y}) := \frac{\mathbf{x}}{\mathbf{y}}$$

At this point, you've defined a function which behaves in every way like the user-defined functions described in Chapter 6. You could, if you wanted to, type "÷(1, 2) =" in your worksheet and see the result "0.5" on the other side of the equal sign.

The difference between functions and operators lies not so much in the way they're defined but in the way they're displayed. This is discussed further in the next section.

Using a custom operator

Once you've defined a new operator, you can use it in your calculations just as you would use one of Mathcad's built-in operators. You can't, however, just type the name of your operator since Mathcad has no way of knowing whether you intend to use your new operator or whether you just want to define a variable having the same name.

The procedure for inserting a custom operator depends on whether the operator has one operand (like "−1" or "5!" for example) or two (like "1÷2"). In either case, you'll need to click on the button labelled "=?" just below the menu commands. This opens a palette that you'll need in the following procedures.

To insert an operator having two operands:

- Click on the button labelled "*xfy*" on the palette. You'll see three empty placeholders.

- In the middle placeholder, insert the name of the operator. You may find it more convenient to copy the name from the operator definition and paste it into the placeholder.

- In the remaining two placeholders, place the two operands.

  $1 \div 2$

- Press = to evaluate the expression.

  $1 \div 2 = 0.5$

Another way to display an operator having two operands is to use the other button showing the letters "x", "f" and "y" arranged like a water molecule. If you follow the preceding steps using this operator, you'll see the tree shaped display shown in the lower-left corner of Figure 12.

To insert an operator having only one operand, decide first whether you want the operator to appear before the operand, as in "−1", or after the operand as in "5!". The former is called a *prefix* operator; the latter is a *postfix* operator. The example below shows how to use a prefix operator. The steps for creating a postfix operator are almost identical.

In the following example, the symbol "¬" comes from the Symbol font. Look on the Character Map dialog box just below the "÷". Before you can reproduce the steps in this example, you'll first have to define an operator "¬(*x*)". To do so, follow the steps for defining ÷(*x*, *y*) in the previous section, substituting the symbol "¬" for "÷" and using only one argument instead of two.

- To make a *prefix* operator click on the button labelled "*fx*" on the symbol palette. Otherwise, click on the "*xf*" button. In either case, you'll see two empty placeholders.

- If you clicked the "*fx*" button, put the operator name in the first placeholder. Otherwise put it in the second placeholder. In either case, you may find it more convenient to copy the name from the operator definition and paste it into the placeholder.

- In the remaining placeholder, place the operand.

- Press = to evaluate the expression.

Be careful when you use operators this way. Since the placeholders look identical, there are no visual cues to tell you where the operands go and where the operator goes.

The most convenient way to use operators like this is create them once and then save them in a QuickSheet. To do this, choose **QuickSheets** from the **Help** menu and click on "Math Symbols" to see a selection of common math symbols. You can drag any of these to your worksheet to help you define a new operator. Once you've defined the new operator, click on "Personal QuickSheets" and drag its definition into the QuickSheet. When you need to use this operator again, just open your Personal QuickSheet and drag it back off.

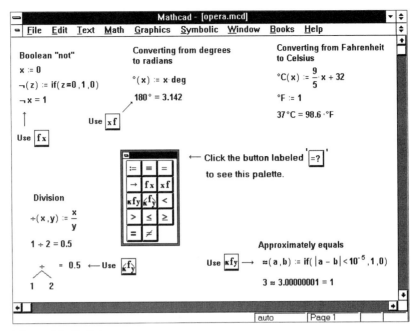

Figure 12: Defining your own operators.

Display of functions as operators

As noted earlier, there is really no fundamental difference between functions and operators. The steps given in the section "Defining a custom operator" exactly parallel the steps given on page 139 for defining a function.

Since you *define* an operator just as if it were a function, you might expect to be able to *display* that operator as if it were a function as well. Figure 13 shows that this is indeed true. Although notation like "÷(1, 2)" is very unconventional, nothing stops you from using it.

Conversely, you can *display* a function as if it were an operator. For example, many publishers prefer to omit parentheses around the arguments to certain functions ($\sin x$ rather than $\sin(x)$). You can do the same thing by treating the *sin* function as an operator with one operand and following the steps in the section "Using a custom operator". The lower half of Figure 13 shows an example of this.

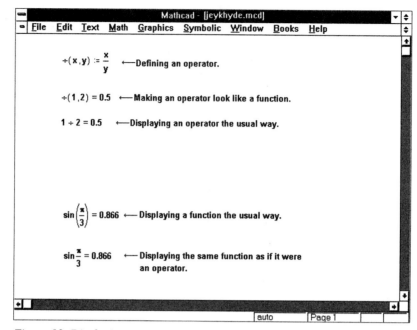

Figure 13: Displaying an operator as a function and a function as an operator.

Chapter 11 Operators

Chapter 12
Built-in Functions

This chapter lists and describes many of Mathcad's built-in functions. Functions associated with Mathcad's statistical and data analysis features are described in Chapter 13, "Statistical Functions." Functions used for working with vectors are described in Chapter 9, "Vectors and Matrices".

The following sections make up this chapter:

Inserting built-in functions

Using the **Choose Function** dialog box to see all available functions and get help on what they do.

Transcendental functions

Basic trigonometric, exponential, hyperbolic and Bessel functions.

Truncation and round-off functions

Functions which extract something from a number, including the real or imaginary part, the mantissa, or the modulo function.

Discrete transform functions

Functions for discrete complex Fourier transforms and wavelet transforms.

Sorting functions

Functions to sort elements of vectors and matrices.

Piecewise continuous functions

Using piecewise continuous functions to perform conditional branching and iteration.

This section describes how to use the Choose Function command to see a list of all functions available to you together with a brief description of each function. Mathcad's set of built-in functions can change depending on whether you've installed additional function packs or whether you've written your own built-in functions. These functions can come from four sources:

Built-in Mathcad functions

This is the core set of functions that come with Mathcad. These functions are all documented in other parts of this *User's Guide*. If you're not using Mathcad PLUS, you'll find that some functions described in this *User's Guide* are not available in your version of Mathcad.

Mathcad Function Packs.

A Function Pack consists of a collection of advanced functions geared to a particular area of application. Documentation for these functions comes with the Function Pack itself. The list of available Function Packs is constantly expanding and includes collections for image processing, numerical analysis and advanced statistical analysis. To find out more about Mathcad's library of Function Packs, call 617-577-1017. (From inside the USA, call 1-800-MATHCAD.)

Electronic Books

Some but not all Electronic Books come with additional functions. Documentation for any of these functions is in the Electronic Book itself.

Functions you write yourself

If you have Mathcad PLUS and a 32 bit C-compiler, you can write your own built-in functions. See Appendix F, "Creating a User DLL", for more details.

To see the list of built-in functions available with your copy of Mathcad, choose **Choose Function** from the **Math** menu. Although built-in function names are not font sensitive, they are case sensitive. You must type the names of built-in functions exactly as shown in the following tables: uppercase, lowercase, or mixed, as indicated. Alternatively, you can use the Choose Function dialog box to insert a function together with placeholders for its arguments. To do so:

- Click in a blank area of your document or on a placeholder.

- Choose **Choose Function** from the **Math** menu. Mathcad opens the Choose Function dialog box shown on the following page.

- Double-click on the function you want to insert from the left-hand scrolling list.

- Close the dialog box if you no longer need it by clicking the "Cancel" button.

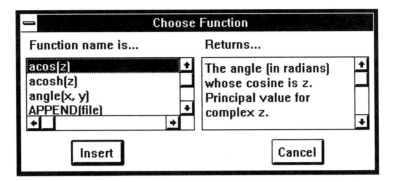

The left-hand scrolling list of the Choose Function dialog box shows all of Mathcad's built-in functions along with their arguments. The box on the right gives a description of the currently selected function.

To apply a function to an expression you have already entered, enclose the expression in a selection box and follow the steps given on the preceding page.

Transcendental functions

This section describes Mathcad's trigonometric, hyperbolic, and exponential functions together with all their inverses. It also describes Mathcad's built-in cylindrical Bessel functions.

Trigonometric functions and their inverses

Mathcad's trig functions and their inverses accept any scalar argument: real, complex or imaginary. They also return complex numbers wherever appropriate. Complex arguments and results are computed using the identities:

$$\sin(z) = \frac{e^{i \cdot z} - e^{-i \cdot z}}{2 \cdot i}$$

$$\cos(z) = \frac{e^{i \cdot z} + e^{-i \cdot z}}{2}$$

$$e^{i \cdot z} = \cos(z) + i \cdot \sin(z)$$

If you want to apply one of these functions to every element of a vector or matrix, use the vectorize operator as described on page 207.

Note that all of these trig functions expect their arguments in *radians*. To pass degrees, use the built-in unit *deg*. For example, to evaluate the sine of 45 degrees, type `sin(45*deg)`.

Keep in mind that because of round-off errors inherent in a computer, Mathcad may return a very large number where you would ordinarily expect a singularity. In general, you should be cautious whenever you encounter any such singularity.

sin(z)	Returns the sine of z. In a right triangle, this is the ratio of the length of the side *opposite* the angle over the length of the hypotenuse.
cos(z)	Returns the cosine of z. In a right triangle, this is the ratio of the length of the side *adjacent* to the angle over the length of the hypotenuse.
tan(z)	Returns (sin(z)/cos(z)), the tangent of z. In a right triangle, this is the ratio of the length of the side *opposite* the angle over the length of the side *adjacent* to the angle. z should not be an odd multiple of $\pi/2$.
csc(z)	Returns 1/sin(z), the cosecant of z . z should not be an even multiple of π.
sec(z)	Returns 1/cos(z), the secant of z. z should not be an odd multiple of $\pi/2$.
cot(z)	Returns 1/tan(z), the cotangent of z. z should not be an even multiple of π.

The inverse trigonometric functions below all return an angle in radians between 0 and 2·π. To convert this result into degrees, you can either divide by the built-in unit *deg* or type *deg* in the units placeholder as described on page 175.

Because of roundoff error inherent in computers, you may find that *atan* of a very large number returns $\pi/2$. As a general rule, it's best to avoid numerical computations near such singularities.

asin(z)	Returns the angle (in radians) whose sine is z.
acos(z)	Returns the angle (in radians) whose cosine is z.
atan(z)	Returns the angle (in radians) whose tangent is z.

Hyperbolic functions

The hyperbolic functions *sinh* and *cosh* are given by:

$$\sinh(z) = \frac{e^z - e^{-z}}{2}$$

$$\cosh(z) = \frac{e^z + e^{-z}}{2}$$

Both these functions will accept and return complex arguments. As the above identities indicate, when you use complex arguments, the hyperbolic functions behave very much like like trigonometric functions. In fact:

$$\sinh(i \cdot z) = i \cdot \sin(z)$$
$$\cosh(i \cdot z) = \cos(z)$$

$\sinh(z)$	Returns the hyperbolic sine of z.
$\cosh(z)$	Returns the hyperbolic cosine of z.
$\tanh(z)$	Returns $\sinh(z)/\cosh(z)$, the hyperbolic tangent of z.
$\operatorname{csch}(z)$	Returns $1/\sinh(z)$, the hyperbolic cosecant of z.
$\operatorname{sech}(z)$	Returns $1/\cosh(z)$, the hyperbolic secant of z.
$\coth(z)$	Returns $1(z)/\tanh(z)$, the hyperbolic cotangent of z.
$\operatorname{asinh}(z)$	Returns the number whose hyperbolic sine is z.
$\operatorname{acosh}(z)$	Returns the number whose hyperbolic cosine is z.
$\operatorname{atanh}(z)$	Returns the number whose hyperbolic tangent is z.

Log and exponential functions

Mathcad's exponential and logarithmic functions will accept and return complex arguments. Complex arguments to the exponential are given by:

$$e^{x + i \cdot y} = e^x \cdot (\cos(y) + i \cdot \sin(y))$$

In general, a complex argument to the natural log function returns:

$$\ln(x + i \cdot y) = \ln|x + i \cdot y| + \operatorname{atan}(y/x) \cdot i + 2 \cdot n \cdot \pi \cdot i$$

Mathcad's *ln* function returns the value corresponding to $n = 0$. Namely:

$$\ln(x + i \cdot y) = \ln|x + i \cdot y| + \operatorname{atan}(y/x) \cdot i$$

This is called the *principal branch* of the natural log function. Figure 1 illustrates some of the basic properties of log functions.

$\exp(z)$ Returns e raised to the power z.

$\ln(z)$ Returns the natural log of z. ($z \neq 0$).

$\log(z)$ Returns the base 10 log of z. ($z \neq 0$).

Figure 1 shows how you can use these functions to easily find the log to any base.

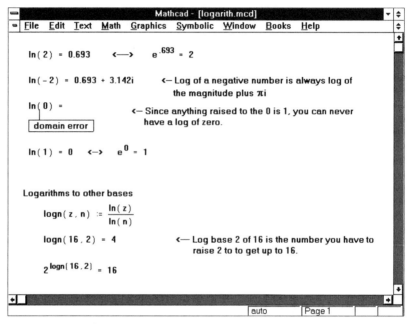

Figure 1: Using logarithmic functions.

Bessel functions

These functions typically arise as solutions to the wave equation subject to cylindrical boundary conditions.

Bessel functions of the first kind and second kind, $J_n(x)$ and $Y_n(x)$, are solutions to the differential equation:

$$x^2 \cdot \frac{d^2 y}{dx^2} + x \cdot \frac{dy}{dx} + (x^2 - n^2) \cdot y = 0$$

Modified Bessel functions of the first and second kind, $I_n(x)$ and $K_n(x)$, are solutions to the slightly different differential equation:

$$x^2 \cdot \frac{d^2 y}{dx^2} + x \cdot \frac{dy}{dx} - (x^2 + n^2) \cdot y = 0$$

J0(x)	Returns $J_0(x)$. x real.
J1(x)	Returns $J_1(x)$. x real.
Jn(m, x)	Returns $J_m(x)$. x real, $0 \leq m \leq 100$.
Y0(x)	Returns $Y_0(x)$. x real, $x > 0$.
Y1(x)	Returns $Y_1(x)$. x real, $x > 0$.
Yn(m, x)	Returns $Y_m(x)$. $x > 0$, $0 \leq m \leq 100$.
I0(x)	Returns $I_0(x)$. x real.
I1(x)	Returns $I_1(x)$. x real.
In(m, x)	Returns $I_m(x)$. x real, $0 \leq m \leq 100$.
K0(x)	Returns $K_0(x)$. x real, $x > 0$.
K1(x)	Returns $K_1(x)$. x real, $x > 0$.
Kn(m, x)	Returns $K_m(x)$. $x > 0$, $0 \leq m \leq 100$.

Special functions

The following functions arise in a wide variety of problems.

erf(x)	Returns the value of the error function at x: $$\mathrm{erf}(x) = \int_0^x \frac{2}{\sqrt{\pi}} e^{-t^2}\, dt$$ x must be real.
$\Gamma(z)$	Returns the value of the Euler gamma function at z. For real z, the values of this function coincide with the following integral: $$\Gamma(z) = \int_0^\infty t^{z-1} e^{-t}\, dt$$ For complex z, the values are the analytic continuation of the real function. Euler's gamma function is undefined for $z = 0, -1, -2, \ldots$

Euler's gamma function satisfies the recurrence relationship:

$$\Gamma(z + 1) = z\Gamma(z)$$

which means that when z is a positive integer:

$$\Gamma(z + 1) = z!.$$

The error function arises frequently in statistics. You can also use it to define the complementary error function as:

$$\text{erfc}(x) := 1 - \text{erf}(x)$$

Truncation and round-off functions

These functions all have in common the fact that they extract something from their arguments.

The functions *Re*, *Im*, and *arg* extract the corresponding part of a complex number. For more information on these functions, see Chapter 7, "Variables and Constants."

The functions *ceil* and *floor* will return the next integer above and below their arguments respectively. You can use these functions to create a function that returns just the mantissa of a number:

```
mantissa(x) := x - floor(x)
```

Figure 2 shows how you can use the *floor* and *ceil* functions to round off numbers.

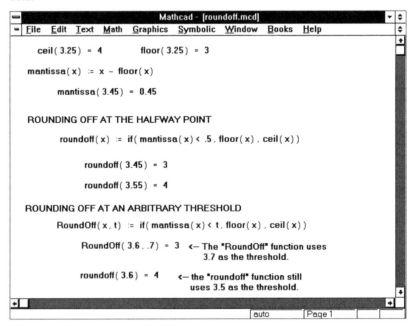

Figure 2: Creating a round-off function.

Re(z)	Real part of z.
Im(z)	Imaginary part of z.
arg(z)	Argument of z: the value of θ when z is written as $r \cdot e^{i \cdot \theta}$. Result is between −π and π.
floor(x)	Greatest integer ≤ x (x real).
ceil(x)	Least integer ≥ x (x real).
mod(x, y)	Remainder on dividing x by y. Result has same sign as x.
angle(x, y)	Angle (in radians) from positive x-axis to the point (x, y) in the x-y plane. Arguments must be real. Returns a value between zero and 2π.

Discrete transform functions

Mathcad contains functions for performing the FFT and its inverse. If you are using Mathcad PLUS, you also have the one-dimensional discrete wavelet transform and its inverse. All these functions require vectors as arguments. When you define a vector **v** for use with Fourier or wavelet transforms, be sure to start with v_0. If you do not define v_0, Mathcad automatically sets it to zero. This can distort the results of the transform functions.

Introduction to Discrete Fourier transforms

Mathcad comes with two types of Fourier transform pairs: *fft / ifft* and *cfft / icfft*. These functions are discrete: they apply to and return vectors and matrices only. You cannot use them with other functions.

Use the *fft* and *ifft* functions if:

- The data values in the time domain are real, and

- the data vector has 2^m elements.

Use the *cfft* and *icfft* functions in all other cases.

The first condition is required because the *fft/ifft* pair takes advantage of the fact that, for real data, the second half of the transform is just the conjugate of the first. Mathcad discards the second half of the result vector. This saves both time and memory. The *cfft/icfft* pair does not assume symmetry in the transform. For this reason, you *must* use this pair for complex valued data. Since the real numbers are just a subset of the complex numbers, you can use the *cfft/icfft* pair for real numbers as well.

The second condition is required because the *fft/ifft* Fourier transform pair uses a highly efficient fast Fourier transform algorithm. In order to do so, the vector you use with *fft* must have 2^m elements. The *cfft/icfft* Fourier transform pair uses an algorithm that permits vectors as well as matrices of arbitrary size. When you use this transform pair with a matrix, you get back a two-dimensional Fourier transform.

Note that if you used *fft* to get to the frequency domain, you *must* use *ifft* to get back to the time domain. Similarly, if you used *cfft* to get to the frequency domain, you *must* use *icfft* to get back to the time domain.

Different sources use different conventions concerning the initial factor of the Fourier transform and whether to conjugate the results of either the transform or the inverse transform. The functions *fft*, *ifft*, *cfft*, and *icfft* use $1/\sqrt{N}$ as a normalizing factor and a positive exponent in going from the time to the frequency domain. The functions *FFT*, *IFFT*, *CFFT*, and *ICFFT* use $1/N$ as a normalizing factor and a negative exponent in going from the time to the frequency domain. Be sure to use these functions in pairs. For example, if you used CFFT to go from the time domain to the frequency domain, you *must* use ICFFT to transform back to the time domain.

Fourier transforms on real data

With 2^m real-valued data points, you can use the *fft/ifft* Fourier transform pair. These functions take advantage of symmetry conditions present only when the data is real. This saves both time and memory.

---

fft(**v**)   This function returns the Fourier transform of a 2^m element vector of real data representing measurements at regular intervals in the time domain.

The vector **v** must have 2^m elements. The result is a vector of $1 + 2^{m-1}$ complex coefficients representing values in the frequency domain. If **v** contains other than 2^m elements, Mathcad returns the error message "*wrong size vector.*"

The elements of the vector returned by *fft* satisfy the following equation:

$$c_j = \frac{1}{\sqrt{n}} \sum_{k=0}^{n-1} v_k\, e^{\,2\pi i (j/n)k}$$

In this formula, n is the number of elements in **v** and i is the imaginary unit.

The elements in the vector returned by the *fft* function correspond to different frequencies. To recover the actual frequency, you must know the sampling frequency of the original signal. If **v** is an *n* element vector passed to the *fft* function, and the sampling frequency is f_s, the frequency corresponding to c_k is

$$f_k = \frac{k}{n} \cdot f_s$$

Note that this makes it impossible to detect frequencies above the sampling frequency. This is a limitation not of Mathcad, but of the underlying mathematics itself. In order to correctly recover a signal from the Fourier transform of its samples, you must sample the signal with a frequency of at least twice its bandwidth. A thorough discussion of this phenomenon is outside the scope of this manual but within that of any textbook on digital signal processing.

---

ifft(**v**)   This function returns the inverse Fourier transform of a vector of data representing values in the frequency domain. The inverse transform will be pure real.

The vector **v** must have $1 + 2^m$ elements for *m* integer. The result is a vector of 2^{m+1} complex coefficients representing values in the frequency domain. If **v** contains other than $1 + 2^m$ elements, Mathcad returns the error message "*wrong size vector.*"

The argument **v** is a vector similar to those generated by the *fft* function. To compute the result, Mathcad first creates a new vector **w** by taking the conjugates of the elements of **v** and appending them to the vector **v**. Then Mathcad computes a vector **d** whose elements satisfy this formula:

$$d_j = \frac{1}{\sqrt{n}} \sum_{k=0}^{n-1} w_k \, e^{-2\pi i (j/n)k}$$

This is the same formula as the *fft* formula, except for the minus sign in the *exp* function. The *fft* and *ifft* functions are exact inverses. For all real **v**, ifft(fft(**v**)) = **v**.

Fourier transforms on complex data

There are two reasons why you may not be able to use the *fft/ifft* transform pair discussed in the previous section:

- The data may be complex valued. This means that Mathcad can no longer exploit the symmetry present in the real valued case.

- The data vector might not have 2^m data points in it. This means Mathcad cannot take advantage of the highly efficient FFT algorithm used by the *fft/ifft* Fourier transform pair.

Complex Fourier transforms require the following functions:

---

cfft(**A**)   Returns the fast Fourier transform of a vector or matrix of complex data representing equally spaced measurements in the time domain. The array returned is the same size as the array you used as an argument.

icfft(**A**)   Returns the inverse Fourier transform of a vector or matrix of data representing values in the frequency domain. The result is an array representing values in the time domain. The *icfft* function is the inverse of the *cfft* function. Like *cfft*, this function returns an array of the same size as its argument.

Although the *cfft/icfft* Fourier transform pair will work on arrays of any size, they work significantly faster when the number of rows and columns contains many smaller factors. Vectors with length 2^m fall into this category. So do vectors having lengths like 100 or 120. On the other hand, a vector whose length is a large prime number will slow down the Fourier transform algorithm.

The *cfft* and *icfft* functions are exact inverses. That is, icfft(cfft(**v**)) = **v**. Figure 3 shows an example of Fourier transforms in Mathcad.

When you use the *cfft* with a matrix, the result is the two-dimensional Fourier transform of the input matrix.

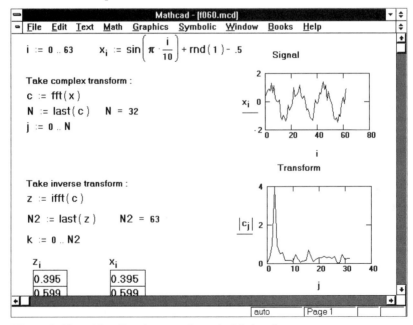

Figure 3: Use of fast Fourier transforms in Mathcad.

Alternate forms of the Fourier transform

The definitions for the Fourier transform discussed earlier are not the only ones used. For example, the following definitions for the discrete Fourier transform and its inverse appear in Ronald Bracewell's *The Fourier Transform and Its Applications* (McGraw-Hill, 1986):

$$F(\nu) = \frac{1}{n} \sum_{\tau=1}^{n} f(\tau) e^{-2\pi i (\nu/n)\tau}$$

$$f(\tau) = \sum_{\nu=1}^{n} F(\nu) e^{2\pi i (\tau/n)\nu}$$

These definitions are very common in the engineering literature. To use these definitions rather than those presented in the last section, use the functions *FFT*, *IFFT*, *CFFT*, and *ICFFT*. These differ from those discussed in the last section as follows:

- Instead of a factor of $1/\sqrt{n}$ in front of both forms, there is a factor of $1/n$ in front of the transform and no factor in front of the inverse.

- The minus sign appears in the exponent of the transform instead of in its inverse.

The functions *FFT*, *IFFT*, *CFFT*, and *ICFFT* are used in exactly the same way as the functions discussed in the previous section.

Wavelet transforms

Mathcad PLUS includes two wavelet transforms for performing the one-dimensional discrete wavelet transform and its inverse. The transform is performed using the Daubechies four-coefficient wavelet basis.

⊕ wave(**v**)   Returns the discrete wavelet transform of **v**, a 2^m element vector containing real data. The vector returned is the same size as **v**.

⊕ iwave(**v**)   Returns the inverse discrete wavelet transform of **v**, a 2^m element vector containing real data. The vector returned is the same size as **v**.

Sorting functions

Mathcad includes three functions shown in Figure 4 for sorting arrays and one for reversing the order of their elements:

---

sort(**v**)   Returns the elements of the vector **v** sorted in ascending order.

csort(**A**, n) Sorts the rows of the matrix **A** so as to place the elements in column n in ascending order. The result has the same size as **A**.

rsort(**A**, n) Sorts the columns of the matrix **A** so as to place the elements in row n in ascending order. The result has the same size as **A**.

reverse(**v**)   Reverses the order of the elements of the vector **v** or the rows of
reverse(**A**)   the matrix **A**.

The above sorting functions accept matrices and vectors with complex elements. However in sorting them, Mathcad ignores the imaginary part.

To sort a vector or matrix in descending order, first sort in ascending order, then use *reverse*. For example, reverse(sort(**v**)) returns the elements of **v** sorted in descending order.

Unless you change the value of ORIGIN, matrices are numbered starting with row zero and column zero. If you forget this, it's easy to make the error of sorting a matrix on the wrong row or column by specifying an incorrect n argument for *rsort* and *csort*. To sort on the first column of a matrix, for example, you must use csort(**A**, 0).

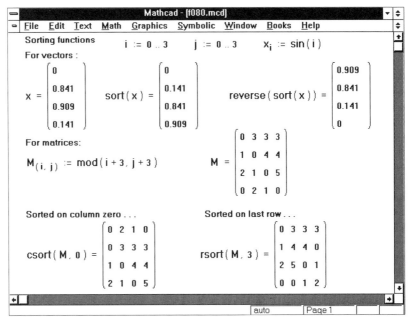

Figure 4: Sorting functions.

Piecewise continuous functions

Piecewise continuous functions are useful for branching and iteration. There are five Mathcad functions falling into this category. The *if* function is useful for choosing one of two values based on a condition. The Heaviside step function, $\Phi(x)$, and the Kronecker Delta function, $\delta(m,n)$, are special cases of the *if* function.

The *until* function is used to drive iteration. It is unique among Mathcad functions because it is designed to work only with range variables. This is the only Mathcad function which can actually halt iteration upon the occurrence of a condition.

If you're using Mathcad PLUS, you'll be able to use Mathcad's programming features to perform both conditional branching and looping more easily. See Chapter 14 for a description of Mathcad's programming features.

The last function is ε, the completely anti-symmetric tensor function. This returns a 0, 1 or -1 depending on the permutation of its arguments. Although this function is of limited applicability, it would be difficult to perform this function using any other combination of Mathcad functions.

The if function

Use *if* to define a function that behaves one way below a certain number and behaves completely differently above that number. That point of discontinuity is specified by its first argument, *cond*. The remaining two arguments let you specify the behavior of the function on either side of that discontinuity.

---

if(*cond, tval, fval*)   Returns *tval* if *cond* is nonzero (true)
                           Returns *fval* if *cond* is zero (false).

Although the argument *cond* can be any expression at all, it is usually more convenient to use a boolean expression from the table below. In the following table, *x* and *y* must be real scalars, while *w* and *z* can be complex scalars.

Condition	How to type	Description
$w = z$	[Ctrl]=	Boolean equals. Returns 1 if expressions are equal; otherwise 0.
$x > y$	>	Greater than.
$x < y$	<	Less than.
$x \geq y$	[Ctrl]0	Greater than or equal to.
$x \leq y$	[Ctrl]9	Less than or equal to.
$w \neq z$	[Ctrl]3	Not equal to.

Note that boolean expressions involving inequalities cannot be used with complex numbers. This is because it is meaningless to speak of one complex number being "larger" or "smaller" than another.

To save time, Mathcad only evaluates those arguments it has to. For example, if *cond* is false, there is no need to evaluate *tval* since it will not be returned anyway. Because of this, errors in the unevaluated argument can escape detection. For example, Mathcad will never detect the the fact that ln(0) is undefined in the expression below:

$$\text{if}(\,|x|\, <\, 0, \ln(0), \ln(x)\,)$$

Figure 5 shows several equations using the *if* function. You can combine boolean operators to create more complicated conditions. For example, the condition

$$(x < 1) \cdot (x > 0)$$

acts like an "and" gate, returning 1 only if *x* is between 0 and 1. Similarly, the expression

$$(x > 1) + (x < 0)$$

acts like an "or" gate, returning a 1 if either $x > 1$ or $x < 0$, but not if x is between 0 and 1.

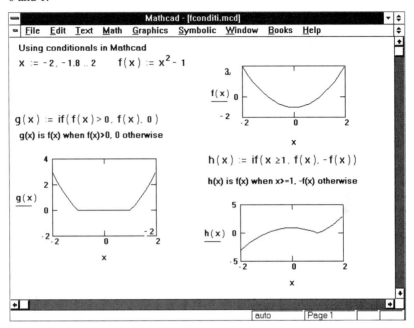

Figure 5: Conditionals in Mathcad.

The until function

Mathcad's *until* function allows you to halt an iteration when a particular condition is met. The *until* function has no effect when its first argument involves no range variables. When the first argument does involve a range variable, Mathcad will iterate until the first argument evaluates to a negative value. When this happens, Mathcad halts iteration.

---

until(x, z)   Returns z until the test expression x becomes negative. x should be an expression involving a range variable.

Do not use the *until* function in equations with more than one range variable (for example, multiple summations). Mathcad will halt all iteration on all range variables the first time that the first argument of *until* is negative. This usually does not produce the desired result.

The *until* function is useful in iterative processes with a specified convergence condition. For example, Figure 6 shows how to use the *until* function to test an iterative process for convergence. The iteration in the equation for x_i continues until x_i is within *err* of *a*. Figure 6 also shows how to use the *last* function to detect when iteration has halted and to compute the size of the resulting array.

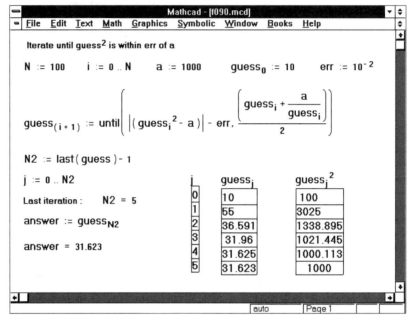

Figure 6: Using the until function to halt an iteration.

When you use the *until* function, be sure that the value of the test expression does in fact change somewhere in the iteration. Otherwise, you may find yourself in an infinite loop. If this does occur, press the [Esc] key to interrupt calculation.

Impulse and step functions

These two functions are special cases of the *if* function. The Heaviside step function is equivalent to:

$$\Phi(x) := if(x < 0, 0, 1)$$

For integer *m* and *n*, the Kronecker delta function is equivalent to

$$\delta(m,n) := if(m = n, 1, 0)$$

$\Phi(x)$ Heaviside step function. 1 if $x \geq 0$; otherwise, 0.

$\delta(m, n)$ Kronecker's delta function. Returns 1 if $m = n$; otherwise, 0. Both arguments must be integer.

You can use the Heaviside step function to define a pulse of width w by defining:

$$\texttt{pulse(x,w)} := \Phi(\texttt{x}) - \Phi(\texttt{x-w})$$

A lowpass and highpass filter having width $2 \cdot w$ could then be defined as:

$$\texttt{lowpass(x,w)} := \texttt{pulse(x+w, 2*w)}$$

$$\texttt{highpass(x,w)} := 1 - \texttt{pulse(x+w, 2*w)}$$

Figure 7 illustrates the use of the Heaviside step function for creating filters.

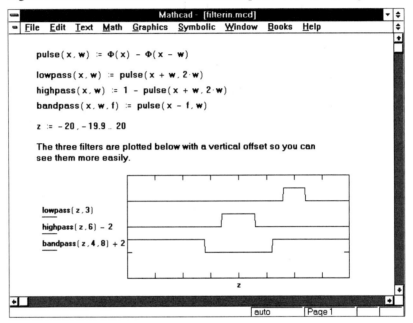

Figure 7: Using the step function for filtering.

Antisymmetric tensor function

The arguments to this function are three integers between 0 and 2 inclusive. It basically determines how many times you have to swap two numbers in order to get back to the sequence [0, 1, 2] from whatever sequence [i, j, k] you passed to it.

More generally, $\varepsilon(i, j, k) = 1$ if [i, j, k] is an even permutation of [0, 1, 2] (an even number of swaps), and $\varepsilon(i, j, k) = -1$ if [i, j, k] is an odd permutation of [0, 1, 2] (an odd number of swaps). This explains why $\varepsilon(0, 1, 2) = 1$.

For example, $\varepsilon(2, 0, 1) = 1$ because to get from [2, 0, 1] back to [0, 1, 2] you'll have to swap twice. On the other hand, $\varepsilon(0, 2, 1) = -1$ because to get from [0, 2, 1] back to [0, 1, 2] you only have to swap once. If two numbers are the same, for example $\varepsilon(0, 1, 1)$, you can never get back to [0, 1, 2], so the function just returns 0.

Piecewise continuous functions   283

Although this function is not used very often, it is truly indispensable when you need it. It is very difficult to perform this same feat using any other combination of Mathcad functions.

$\varepsilon(i, j, k)$ Completely antisymmetric tensor of rank 3. i, j, and k must be integers between 0 and 2 inclusive (or between ORIGIN and ORIGIN+2 inclusive if ORIGIN $\neq$ 0). Result is 0 if any two are the same, 1 for even permutations, -1 for odd permutations.

Chapter 13
Statistical functions

This chapter lists and describes many of Mathcad's built-in functions. These functions perform a wide variety of computational tasks, including statistical analysis, interpolation, and regression.

The following sections make up this chapter:

Population statistics

Functions for computing the mean, variance, standard deviation, and correlation of sample data.

Probability distributions

Functions for evaluating probability densities, cumulative probability distributions and their inverses for over a dozen common distribution functions.

Histograms

How to count the number of data values falling into specified intervals.

Random numbers

Generating random numbers having various distributions.

Interpolation and prediction functions

Linear and cubic spline interpolation. Functions for multivariate interpolation.

Regression functions

Functions for linear regression, polynomial regression, and regression using combinations of arbitrary functions.

Smoothing functions

Functions for smoothing time series with either a running median, a Gaussian kernel, or an adaptive linear least squares method.

Mathcad includes six functions for population statistics. In the following descriptions, m and n represent the number of rows and columns in the specified arrays. In the formulas below, the built-in variable ORIGIN is set to its default value of zero.

---

mean(**A**)   Returns the mean of the elements of an $m \times n$ array **A** using the formula:

$$\text{mean}(\mathbf{A}) = \frac{1}{mn} \sum_{i=0}^{m-1} \sum_{j=0}^{n-1} A_{i,j}$$

median(**A**)   Returns the median of the elements of an $m \times n$ array **A**. This is the value above and below which there are an equal number of values. If **A** has an even number of elements, this is the arithmetic mean of the two central values.

var(**A**)   Returns the variance of the elements of an $m \times n$ array **A** using the formula:

$$\text{var}(\mathbf{A}) = \frac{1}{mn} \sum_{i=0}^{m-1} \sum_{j=0}^{n-1} |A_{i,j} - \text{mean}(\mathbf{A})|^2$$

cvar(**A**, **B**)   Returns the covariance of the elements in the $m \times n$ arrays **A** and **B** using the formula:

$$\text{cvar}(\mathbf{A}, \mathbf{B}) = \frac{1}{mn} \sum_{i=0}^{m-1} \sum_{j=0}^{n-1} [A_{i,j} - \text{mean}(\mathbf{A})] \overline{[B_{i,j} - \text{mean}(\mathbf{B})]}$$

where the bar indicates complex conjugation.

stdev(**A**)   Returns the standard deviation (square root of the variance) of the elements of the $m \times n$ array **A**:

$$\text{stdev}(\mathbf{A}) = \sqrt{\text{var}(\mathbf{A})}$$

corr(**A**, **B**)   Returns a scalar: the correlation coefficient (Pearson's r) for the two $m \times n$ arrays **A** and **B**.

Mathcad includes several functions for working with several common probability densities. These functions fall into three classes:

- **Probability densities:** These give the likelihood that a random variable will take on a particular value.

- **Cumulative probability distributions:** These give the probability that a random variable will take on a value *less than or equal to* a specified value. These are obtained by simply integrating (or summing when appropriate) the corresponding probability density over an appropriate range.

- **Inverse cumulative probability distributions:** These functions take a probability as an argument and return a value such that the probability that a random variable will be *less than or equal to* that value is whatever probability you supplied as an argument.

Mathcad PLUS comes with all the functions listed in the next three sections. If you're not using Mathcad PLUS, you'll have all functions associated with the following probability distributions: normal, chi squared, Student's t, F, binomial, Poisson, and uniform.

Probability densities

Mathcad
PLUS

These functions return the likelihood that a random variable will take on a particular value. The probability density functions are the derivatives of the corresponding cumulative distribution functions discussed in the next section.

$\oplus$ dbeta(x, s_1, s_2)   Returns the probability density for the beta distribution:

$$\frac{\Gamma(s_1 + s_2)}{\Gamma(s_1) \cdot \Gamma(s_2)} \cdot x^{s_1 - 1} \cdot (1 - x)^{s_2 - 1}$$

in which (s_1, $s_2 > 0$) are the shape parameters. ($0 < x < 1$).

dbinom(k, n, p)   Returns $P(X = k)$ when the random variable X has the binomial distribution:

$$\frac{n!}{k! \, (n - k)!} \, p^k \, (1 - p)^{n - k}$$

in which n and k are integers satisfying $0 \le k \le n$. p satisfies $0 \le p \le 1$.

⊕ dcauchy(x, l, s)   Returns the probability density for the Cauchy distribution:

$$(\pi s (1 + ((x - l) / s)^2))^{-1}$$

in which l is a location parameter and $s > 0$ is a scale parameter.

dchisq(x, d)   Returns the probability density for the chi-squared distribution:

$$\frac{e^{-x/2}}{2\Gamma(d/2)} \left(\frac{x}{2}\right)^{(d/2 - 1)}$$

in which $d > 0$ is the degrees of freedom and $x > 0$.

⊕ dexp(x, r)   Returns the probability density for the exponential distribution:

$$re^{-rx}$$

in which $r > 0$ is the rate and $x > 0$.

dF(x, d_1, d_2)   Returns the probability density for the F distribution:

$$\frac{d_1^{0.5 d_1} d_2^{0.5 d_2} \Gamma((d_1 + d_2)/2)}{\Gamma(d_1/2)\Gamma(d_2/2)} \cdot \frac{x^{0.5(d_1 - 2)}}{(d_2 + d_1 x)^{0.5(d_1 + d_2)}}$$

in which $d_1, d_2 > 0$ are the degrees of freedom and $x > 0$.

⊕ dgamma(x, s)   Returns the probability density for the Gamma distribution:

$$\frac{x^{s - 1} e^{-x}}{\Gamma(s)}$$

in which $s > 0$ is the shape parameter and $x \geq 0$.

⊕ dgeom(k, p)   Returns $P(X = k)$ when the random variable X has the geometric distribution:

$$p (1 - p)^k$$

in which $0 < p \leq 1$ is the probability of success and k is a non-negative integer.

⊕ dlnorm(x, μ, σ)   Returns the probability density for the log normal distribution:

$$\frac{1}{\sqrt{2\pi}\sigma x} \exp\left[-\frac{1}{2\sigma^2}(\ln(x) - \mu)^2\right]$$

⊕ dlogis(x, l, s)   Returns the probability density for the logistic distribution:

$$\frac{\exp(-(x-l)/s)}{s(1+\exp(-(x-l)/s))^2}$$

in which l is the location parameter and $s > 0$ is the scale parameter.

⊕ dnbinom(k, n, p)   Returns $P(X=k)$ when the random variable X has the negative binomial distribution:

$$\binom{n+k-1}{k} p^n (1-p)^k$$

in which $0 < p \leq 1$ and n and k are integers, $n > 0$ and $k \geq 0$

dnorm(x, μ, σ)   Returns the probability density for the normal distribution:

$$\frac{1}{\sqrt{2\pi}\sigma}\exp\left[-\frac{1}{2\sigma^2}(x-\mu)^2\right]$$

in which μ and σ are the mean and standard deviation. $\sigma > 0$.

dpois(k, λ)   Returns $P(X=k)$ when the random variable X has the Poisson distribution:

$$\frac{\lambda^k}{k!}e^{-\lambda}$$

in which $\lambda > 0$ and k is a nonnegative integer.

dt(x, d)   Returns the probability density for the Student's t distribution:

$$\frac{\Gamma((d+1)/2)}{\Gamma(d/2)\sqrt{\pi d}}\left(1+\frac{x^2}{d}\right)^{-0.5(d+1)}$$

in which d is the degrees of freedom, $d > 0$ and x is real.

dunif(x, a, b)   Returns the probability density for the uniform distribution:

$$\frac{1}{b-a}$$

in which b and a are the endpoints of the interval with $a < b$ and $a \leq x \leq b$.

⊕ dweibull(x, s)   Returns the probability density for the Weibull distribution:

$$sx^{s-1}\exp(-x^s)$$

in which $s > 0$ is the shape parameter and $x > 0$.

Cumulative probability distributions

Mathcad
PLUS

These functions return the probability that a random variable is less than or equal to a specified value. The cumulative probability distribution is simply the probability density function integrated from $-\infty$ to the specified value. For integer random variables, the integral is replaced by a summation over the appropriate range.

The probability density functions corresponding to each of the following cumulative distributions are given in the section "Probability distributions" beginning on page 287.

Figure 1 at the end of this section illustrates the relationship between these three functions.

cnorm(x)	Returns the cumulative standard normal distribution function. Equivalent to pnorm(x, 0, 1).
$\oplus$ pbeta(x, s_1, s_2)	Returns the cumulative beta distribution with shape parameters s_1 and s_2. (s_1, $s_2 > 0$).
pbinom(k, n, p)	Returns the cumulative binomial distribution for k successes in n trials. n is a positive integer. p is the probability of success, $0 \le p \le 1$.
$\oplus$ pcauchy(x, l, s)	Returns the cumulative Cauchy distribution with scale parameter s and location parameter l. $s > 0$.
pchisq(x, d)	Returns the cumulative chi-squared distribution in which $d > 0$ is the degrees of freedom.
$\oplus$ pexp(x, r)	Returns the cumulative exponential distribution in which $r > 0$ is the rate.
pF(x, d_1, d_2)	Returns the cumulative F distribution in which $d_1, d_2 > 0$ are the degrees of freedom.
$\oplus$ pgamma(x, s)	Returns the cumulative Gamma distribution in which $s > 0$ is the shape parameter.
$\oplus$ pgeom(k, p)	Returns the cumulative geometric distribution. p is the probability of success. $0 < p \le 1$.
$\oplus$ plnorm(x, μ, σ)	Returns the cumulative log normal distribution. This is the distribution whose natural log is a normal distribution having mean μ and standard deviation $\sigma > 0$.
$\oplus$ plogis(x, l, s)	Returns the cumulative logistic distribution. l is the location parameter. $s > 0$ is the scale parameter.
$\oplus$ pnbinom(k, n, p)	Returns the cumulative negative binomial distribution in which $0 < p \le 1$. n must be a positive integer.

pnorm(x, μ, σ)	Returns the cumulative normal distribution with mean μ and standard deviation σ. σ > 0.
ppois(k, λ)	Returns the cumulative Poisson distribution. λ > 0.
pt(x, d)	Returns the cumulative Student's t distribution. d is the degrees of freedom. d > 0.
punif(x, a, b)	Returns the cumulative uniform distribution. b and a are the endpoints of the interval. a < b.
⊕ pweibull(x, s)	Returns the cumulative Weibull distribution. s > 0.

Inverse cumulative probability distributions

Mathcad
PLUS

These functions take a probability p as an argument and return the value of x such that $P(X \le x) = p$.

The probability density functions corresponding to each of the following inverse cumulative distributions are given in the section "Probability distributions" beginning on page 287.

⊕ qbeta(p, s_1, s_2)	Returns the inverse beta distribution with shape parameters s_1 and s_2. $(0 \le p \le 1)$ $(s_1, s_2 > 0)$.
qbinom(p, n, r)	Returns the number of successes in n trials of the Bernoulli process such that the probability of at most that number of successes is p. r is the probability of success on a single trial. $0 \le r \le 1$ and $0 \le p \le 1$. n must be an integer greater than zero.
⊕ qcauchy(p, l, s)	Returns the inverse Cauchy distribution with scale parameter s and location parameter l. $s > 0$. $0 < p < 1$.
qchisq(p, n)	Returns the inverse chi-squared distribution in which $d > 0$ is the degrees of freedom. $0 \le p < 1$.
⊕ qexp(p, r)	Returns the inverse exponential distribution in which $r > 0$ is the rate. $0 \le p < 1$.
qF(p, d_1, d_2)	Returns the inverse F distribution in which $d_1, d_2 > 0$ are the degrees of freedom. $0 \le p < 1$.
⊕ qgamma(p, s)	Returns the inverse Gamma distribution in which $s > 0$ is the shape parameter. $0 \le p < 1$.
⊕ qgeom(p, r)	Returns the inverse geometric distribution. r is the probability of success on a single trial. $0 < p < 1$ and $0 < r < 1$.

⊕ qlnorm(p, μ, σ)   Returns the inverse log normal distribution. The log normal distribution is a distribution whose natural log is the normal distribution having mean μ and standard deviation $\sigma > 0$. $0 \le p < 1$.

⊕ qlogis(p, l, s)   Returns the inverse logistic distribution. l is the location parameter. $s > 0$ is the scale parameter. $0 < p < 1$.

⊕ qnbinom(p, n, r)   Returns the inverse negative binomial distribution with size n and probability of success r. $0 < r \le 1$ and $0 \le p \le 1$.

qnorm(p, μ, σ)   Returns the inverse normal distribution with mean μ and standard deviation σ. $0 < p < 1$ and $\sigma > 0$.

qpois(p, λ)   Returns the inverse Poisson distribution. $\lambda > 0$ and $0 \le p \le 1$.

qt(p, d)   Returns the inverse Student's t distribution. d is the degrees of freedom. $d > 0$ and $0 < p < 1$.

qunif(p, a, b)   Returns the inverse uniform distribution. b and a are the endpoints of the interval. $a < b$ and $0 \le p \le 1$.

⊕ qweibull(p, s)   Returns the inverse Weibull distribution. $s > 0$ and $0 < p < 1$.

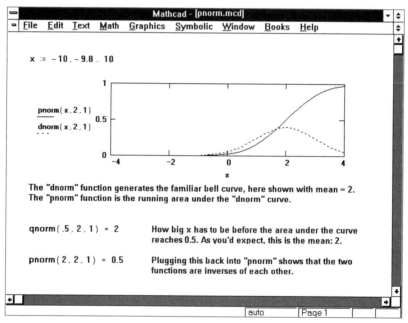

Figure 1: Relationship between probability densities, cumulative distributions and their inverses.

Mathcad includes one function, *hist*, for computing frequency distributions for histograms:

---

hist(**int**, **A**)   Returns a vector representing the frequencies with which values in **A** fall in the intervals represented by the **int** vector. The elements in both **int** and **A** must be real. In addition, the elements of **int** must be in ascending order. The resulting vector is one element shorter than **int**.

Mathcad interprets **int** as a set of points defining a sequence of intervals in a histogram. The values in **int** must should be in ascending order. The result of this function is a vector **f**, in which f_i is the number of values in **A** satisfying the condition:

$$int_i \leq value < int_{i+1}$$

Mathcad ignores data points less than the first value in **int** or greater than the last value in **int**. Figure 2 shows how to use histograms in Mathcad.

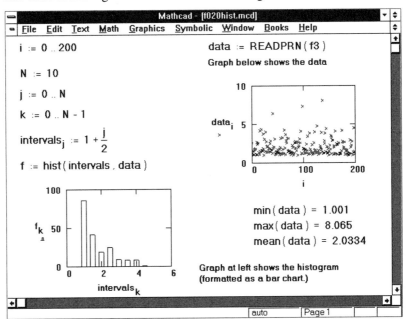

Figure 2: A histogram.

Mathcad comes with a number of functions for generating random numbers having a variety of probability distributions. The functional forms of the distributions associated with the following functions are given in the section "Probability distributions" beginning on page 287.

Mathcad PLUS comes with all the functions listed in this section. If you're not using Mathcad PLUS, you'll have all random number generating functions associated with the following probability distributions: normal, chi-squared, Student's t, F, binomial, Poisson, and uniform.

⊕ rbeta(m, s_1, s_2)   Returns a vector of m random numbers having the beta distribution. $s_1, s_2 > 0$ are the shape parameters.

rbinom(m, n, p)   Returns a vector of m random numbers having the binomial distribution. $0 \leq p \leq 1$. n is an integer satisfying $n > 0$.

⊕ rcauchy(m, l, s)   Returns a vector of m random numbers having the Cauchy distribution. $s > 0$ is the scale parameter. l is the location parameter.

rchisq(m, d)   Returns a vector of m random numbers having the chi-squared distribution. $d > 0$ is the degrees of freedom.

⊕ rexp(m, r)   Returns a vector of m random numbers having the exponential distribution. $r > 0$ is the rate.

rF(m, d_1, d_2)   Returns a vector of m random numbers having the F distribution. $d_1, d_2 > 0$ are the degrees of freedom.

⊕ rgamma(m, s)   Returns a vector of m random numbers having the gamma distribution. $s > 0$ is the shape parameter.

⊕ rgeom(m, p)   Returns a vector of m random numbers having the geometric distribution. $0 < p \leq 1$.

⊕ rlnorm(m, μ, σ)   Returns a vector of m random numbers having the log normal distribution. This is the distribution whose log is the normal distribution having mean μ and standard deviation $\sigma > 0$.

⊕ rlogis(m, l, s)   Returns a vector of m random numbers having the logistic distribution in which l is the location parameter and $s > 0$ is the scale parameter.

⊕ rnbinom(m, n, p)   Returns a vector of m random numbers having the negative binomial distribution. $0 < p \leq 1$. n is an integer satisfying $n > 0$.

rnorm(m, μ, σ)   Returns a vector of m random numbers having the normal distribution. $\sigma > 0$.

---

rpois(*m*, λ)	Returns a vector of *m* random numbers having the Poisson distribution. $\lambda > 0$.
rt(*m*, *d*)	Returns a vector of *m* random numbers having the Student's *t* distribution. $d > 0$.
runif(*m*, *a*, *b*)	Returns a vector of *m* random numbers having the uniform distribution in which *b* and *a* are the endpoints of the interval and $a < b$.
rnd(*x*)	Returns a uniformly distributed random number between 0 and *x*. Equivalent to runif(1, 0, *x*).
⊕ rweibull(*m*, *s*)	Returns a vector of *m* random numbers having the Weibull distribution in which $s > 0$ is the shape parameter.

Each time you recalculate an equation containing one of these functions, Mathcad generates new random numbers. To force Mathcad to generate new random numbers, click on the equation containing the function and press [**F9**]. Figure 3 shows an example of how to use Mathcad's random number generator. Figure 4 shows how to generate a large vector of random numbers having a specified distribution.

These functions have a "seed value" associated with them. Each time you reset the seed, Mathcad generates new random numbers based on that seed. A given seed value will always generate the same sequence of random numbers. Pressing [**F9**] advances Mathcad along this random number sequence. Changing the seed value however, advances Mathcad along an altogether different random number sequence.

To change the seed value, choose **Randomize** from the **Math** menu and change the value of "seed" in the dialog box. Be sure to supply an integer.

To reset Mathcad's random number generator without changing the seed value, choose **Randomize** from the **Math** menu and click "OK" to accept the current seed. Then click on the equation containing the random number generating function and press [**F9**]. Since the randomizer has been reset, Mathcad generates the same random numbers it would generate if you restarted Mathcad.

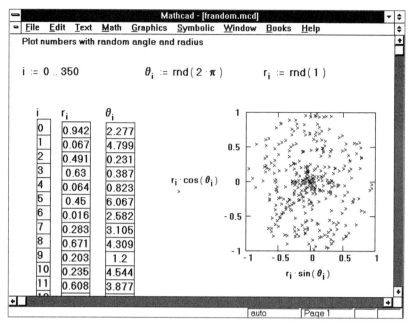

Figure 3: Uniformly distributed random numbers. Since the random number generator generates different numbers every time, it's unlikely that you'll be able to reproduce this example exactly as you see it here.

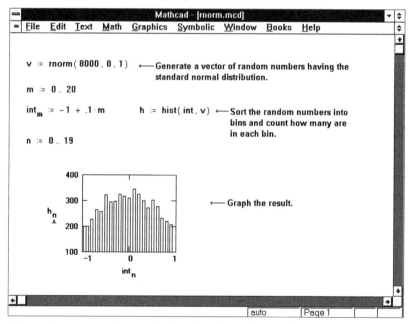

Figure 4: A vector of normally distributed random numbers. Since the random numbers are different every time, it's unlikely that you'll be able to reproduce this example exactly as you see it here.

Chapter 13 Statistical functions

If you want to check a test case several times with the same random numbers, reset the random number generator between calculations as described above.

To see a new set of random numbers, change the seed value as described above. This causes Mathcad to generate a different set of random numbers from what you see when you start Mathcad. Each time you want to reset Mathcad to regenerate these random numbers, reset the seed as described above. To see a different set of random numbers, change the seed value.

Interpolation and prediction functions

Interpolation involves using existing data points to predict values between these data points. Mathcad allows you to either connect the data points with straight lines (linear interpolation) or to connect them with sections of a cubic polynomial (cubic spline interpolation).

Unlike the regression functions discussed in the next section, these interpolation functions return a curve which must pass through the points you specify. Because of this, the resulting function is very sensitive to spurious data points. If your data is noisy, you should consider using the regression functions instead.

Linear prediction involves using existing data values to predict values beyond the existing ones. Mathcad provides a function which allows you to predict future data points based on past data points.

Whenever you use arrays in any of the functions described in this section, be sure that every element in the array contains a data value. Since every element in a array must have a value, Mathcad assigns 0 to any elements you have not explicitly assigned.

Linear interpolation

In linear interpolation, Mathcad connects the existing datapoints with straight lines. This is accomplished by the *linterp* function described below.

---

linterp($\mathbf{vx}$, $\mathbf{vy}$, x) Uses the data vectors $\mathbf{vx}$ and $\mathbf{vy}$ to return a linearly interpolated y value corresponding to the third argument x. The arguments $\mathbf{vx}$ and $\mathbf{vy}$ must be vectors of the same length. The vector $\mathbf{vx}$ must contain real values in ascending order.

To find the interpolated value for a particular x, Mathcad finds the two points between which the value falls and returns the corresponding y value on the straight line between the two points.

For *x* values before the first point in **vx**, Mathcad extrapolates the straight line between the first two data points. For *x* values beyond the last point in **vx**, Mathcad extrapolates the straight line between the last two data points.

For best results, the value of *x* should be between the largest and smallest values in the vector **vx**. The *linterp* function is intended for interpolation, not extrapolation. Consequently, computed values for *x* outside this range are unlikely to be useful. Figure 5 shows some examples of linear interpolation.

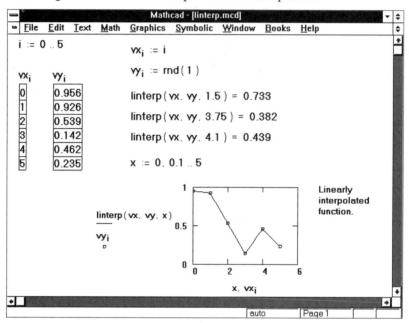

Figure 5: Examples of linear interpolation. Since the random number generator gives different numbers every time, you may not be able to recreate this example exactly as you see it.

Cubic spline interpolation

Cubic spline interpolation lets you pass a curve through a set of points in such a way that the first and second derivatives of the curve are continuous across each point. This curve is assembled by taking three adjacent points and constructing a cubic polynomial passing through those points. These cubic polynomials are then strung together to form the completed curve.

To fit a cubic spline curve through a set of points:

- Create the vectors **vx** and **vy** containing the *x* and *y* coordinates through which you want the cubic spline to pass. The elements of **vx** should be in ascending order. (Although we use the names **vx**, **vy** and **vs**, there is nothing special about these variable names; you can use whatever names you prefer in your own work.)

Chapter 13 Statistical functions

- Generate the vector **vs** := cspline(**vx,vy**) The vector **vs** is a vector of intermediate results designed to be used with *interp*.

- To evaluate the cubic spline at an arbitrary point, say *x0*, evaluate interp(**vs, vx, vy**, *x0*) where **vs**, **vx** and **vy** are the vectors described earlier.

Note that you could have accomplished the same task by evaluating:

$$\text{interp}(\text{cspline}(\mathbf{vx}, \mathbf{vy}), \mathbf{vx}, \mathbf{vy}, x0)$$

As a practical matter though, you'll probably be evaluating *interp* for many different points. Since the call to *cspline* can be time-consuming, and since the result won't change from one point to the next, it makes sense to do it once and just keep re-using the result as described above.

Figure 6 shows how to compute the spline curve for the example in Figure 5.

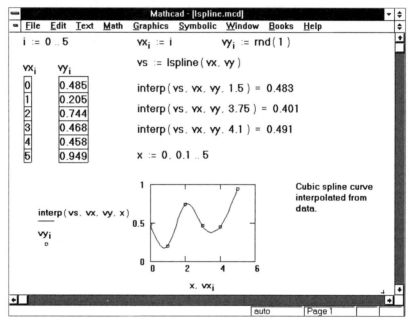

Figure 6: Spline curve for the points stored in x and y. Since the random number generator gives different numbers every time, you may not be able to recreate this example exactly as you see it.

Here is a description of the steps involved in the example in Figure 6:

The equation with the *cspline* function computes the array **vs** containing, among other things, the second derivatives for the spline curve used to fit the points in **vx** and **vy**.

Once the **vs** array is computed, the *interp* function computes the interpolated values of the curve.

Note that the **vs** array needs to be computed only once, even for multiple interpolations. Since the spline calculations that lead to **vs** are time-consuming, it is more efficient to store these intermediate results as a vector than it is to recalculate them as needed.

In addition to *cspline*, Mathcad comes with two other cubic spline functions. The three spline functions are:

---

cspline(**vx**, **vy**)   These all return a vector of intermediate results which we'll
pspline(**vx**, **vy**)   call **vs**. This vector, **vs**, is used in the *interp* function described
lspline(**vx**, **vy**)   below. The arguments **vx** and **vy** must be real vectors of the
same length. The values in **vx** must be real and in ascending
order.

These three functions differ only in the boundary conditions:

- The *lspline* function generates a spline curve that approaches a straight line at the endpoints.

- The *pspline* function generates a spline curve that approaches a parabola at the endpoints.

- The *cspline* function generates a spline curve that can be fully cubic at the endpoints.

---

interp(**vs**, **vx**, **vy**, x)   Returns the interpolated y value corresponding to the
argument x. The vector **vs** is a vector of intermediate
results obtained by evaluating *lspline*, *pspline*, or
cspline using the data vectors **vx** and **vy**.

To find the interpolated value for a particular x, Mathcad finds the two points between which it falls. It then returns the y value on the cubic section enclosed by these two points. For x values before the first point in **vx**, Mathcad extrapolates the cubic section connecting the first two points of **vx**. Similarly, for x values beyond the last point in **vx**, Mathcad extrapolates the cubic section connecting the last two points of **vx**.

For best results, do not use the *interp* function on values of x far from the fitted points. Splines are intended for interpolation, not extrapolation. Consequently, computed values for such x values are unlikely to be useful.

Interpolating a vector of points

You can use the vectorize operator to return a whole vector of interpolated values corresponding to a vector of data points. This works with both *interp* and *linterp*.

Figure 7 shows how to perform this operation. To apply the vectorize operator to the function, click on the function name and press [↑] until the selection box encloses the function. Then press [Ctrl]- (hold down the [Ctrl] key and press the minus sign).

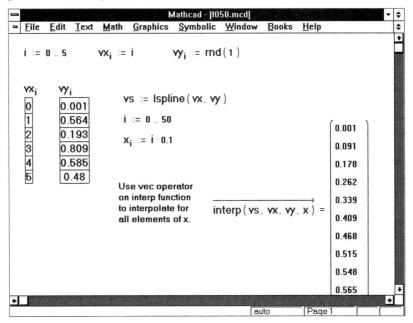

Figure 7: Interpolating a vector of points. Note that since these are random numbers, it's unlikely you'll be able to reproduce this example exactly as you see here.

Mutivariate cubic spline interpolation

Mathcad handles two dimensional cubic spline interpolation in much the same way as the one-dimensional case discussed earlier. Instead of passing a curve through a set of points in such a way that the first and second derivatives of the curve are continuous across each point, Mathcad passes a surface through a grid of points. This surface corresponds to a cubic polynomial in x and y in which the first and second partial derivatives are continuous in the corresponding direction across each grid point.

The first step in two-dimensional spline interpolation is exactly the same as that in the one-dimensional case: specify the points through which the surface is to pass. The procedure, however, is more complicated because you now have to specify a grid of points:

- Create the $n \times 2$ matrix **Mxy** whose elements, $Mxy_{i, 0}$ and $Mxy_{i, 1}$ specify the x and y coordinates along the *diagonal* of a rectangular grid. This matrix plays the exactly the same role as **vx** in the one-dimensional case described earlier. Since these points describe a diagonal, the elements in each column of **Mxy** be in ascending order ($Mxy_{i,k} < Mxy_{j,k}$ whenever $i < j$).

- Create the $n \times n$ matrix **Mz** whose ij^{th} element is the z coordinate corresponding to the point $x = Mxy_{i,0}$ and $y = Mxy_{j,1}$. This plays exactly the same role as **vy** in the one-dimensional case described earlier.

- Generate the vector **vs** := cspline(**Mxy**, **Mz**) The vector **vs** is a vector of intermediate results designed to be used with *interp*.

- To evaluate the cubic spline at an arbitrary point, say $(x0, y0)$ evaluate

$$\text{interp}\left(\textbf{vs}, \textbf{Mxy}, \textbf{Mz}, \begin{bmatrix} x0 \\ y0 \end{bmatrix}\right)$$

where **vs**, **Mxy** and **Mz** are the arrays described earlier. The result is the value of the interpolating surface corresponding to the arbitrary point $(x0, y0)$.

Note that you could have accomplished exactly the same task by evaluating:

$$\text{interp}\left(\text{cspline}(\textbf{Mxy}, \textbf{Mz}), \textbf{Mxy}, \textbf{Mz}, \begin{bmatrix} x0 \\ y0 \end{bmatrix}\right)$$

As a practical matter though, you'll probably be evaluating *interp* for many different points. Since the call to *cspline* can be time-consuming, and since the result won't change from one point to the next, it makes sense call it once and just keep re-using the result as described above.

In addition to *cspline*, Mathcad comes with two other cubic spline functions. The three spline functions are:

cspline(**Mxy**, **Mz**) pspline(**Mxy**, **Mz**) lspline(**Mxy**, **Mz**)	These all return a vector of intermediate results which we'll call **vs**. This vector, **vs**, is used in the *interp* function described below. **Mxy** is an $n \times 2$ matrix whose elements $Mxy_{i,0}$ and $Mxy_{i,1}$ specify points on the diagonal of an $n \times n$ grid. The ij^{th} element of the $n \times n$ matrix **Mz** specifies the value of the interpolating surface at $(Mxy_{i,0}, Mxy_{j,1})$.

These three functions differ only in the boundary conditions:

- The *lspline* function generates a spline curve that approaches a plane along the edges.

- The *pspline* function generates a spline curve that approaches a second degree polynomial in *x* and *y* along the edges.

- The *cspline* function generates a spline curve that that approaches a third degree polynomial in *x* and *y* along the edges.

---

interp(**vs**, **Mxy**, **Mz**, **v**)   Returns the interpolated *z* value corresponding to the point $x = v_0$ and $y = v_1$. The vector **vs** comes from evaluating *lspline*, *pspline*, or *cspline* using the data matrices **Mxy** and **Mz**.

For best results, do not use the *interp* function on values of *x* and *y* far from the grid points. Splines are intended for interpolation, not extrapolation. Consequently, computed values for such *x* and *y* values are unlikely to be useful.

Linear prediction

Mathcad
PLUS

The functions described so far in this section allow you to find data points lying between existing data points. However, you may need to find data points that lie beyond your existing ones. Mathcad provides the function *predict* which uses some of your existing data to predict data points lying beyond the existing ones. This function uses a linear prediction algorithm which is useful when your data is smooth and oscillatory, though not necessarily periodic. Linear prediction can be seen as a kind of extrapolation method but should not be confused with linear or polynomial extrapolation.

⊕ predict(**v**, *m*, *n*)   Returns *n* predicted values based on *m* consecutive values from the data vector **v**. Elements in **v** should represent samples taken at equal intervals.

The *predict* function uses the last *m* of the original data values to compute prediction coefficients. Once it has these coefficients, it uses the last *m* points to predict the coordinates of the $(m + 1)^{th}$ point, in effect creating a moving window *m* points wide.

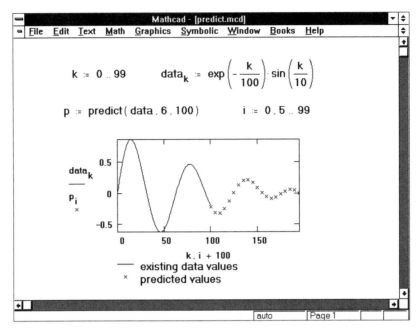

Figure 8: Using predict to find future data values.

Regression functions

Mathcad includes a number of functions for performing regression. Typically, these functions generate a curve or surface of a specified type which in some sense minimizes the error between itself and the data you supply. The functions differ primarily in the type of curve or surface they use to fit the data.

Unlike the interpolation functions discussed in the previous section, these functions do not require that the fitted curve or surface pass through the data points you supply. The regression functions in this section are therefore far less sensitive to spurious data than the interpolation functions.

Unlike the smoothing functions in the next section, the end result of a regression is an actual function, one that can be evaluated at points in between the points you supply.

Whenever you use arrays in any of the functions described in this section, be sure that every element in the array contains a data value. Since every element in a array must have a value, Mathcad assigns 0 to any elements you have not explicitly assigned.

Linear regression

These functions return the slope and intercept of the line that best fits your data in a least square sense. If you place your x values in the vector **vx** and your sampled y values in **vy**, that line is given by:

$$y = \text{slope}(\mathbf{vx}, \mathbf{vy}) \cdot x + \text{intercept}(\mathbf{vx}, \mathbf{vy})$$

Figure 9 shows how you can use these functions to fit a line through a set of data points.

slope(**vx**, **vy**)	Returns a scalar: the slope of the least-squares regression line for the data points in **vx** and **vy**.
intercept(**vx**, **vy**)	Returns a scalar: the y-intercept of the least-squares regression line for the data points in **vx** and **vy**.

These functions are useful not only when your data is inherently linear but when it is exponential as well. More specifically, if your x and y are related by:

$$y = A e^{kx}$$

You can apply these functions to the log of your data values and make use of the fact that:

$$\log(y) = \log(A) + kx$$

In which case:

$$A = \exp(\text{intercept}(\mathbf{vx}, \mathbf{vy})) \text{ and } k = \text{slope}(\mathbf{vx}, \mathbf{vy})$$

The resulting fit weighs the errors differently from a least-squares exponential fit but is usually a good approximation.

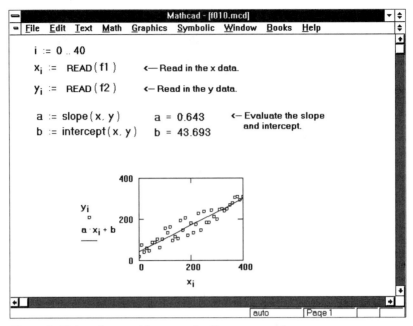

Figure 9: Using slope and intercept for linear regression.

Polynomial regression

These functions are useful when you have set of measured y values corresponding to x values and you want to fit a polynomial through those y values.

Use *regress* when you want to use a single polynomial to fit all your data values. The *regress* function lets you fit a polynomial of any order. However as a practical matter, you would rarely need to go beyond $n = 4$.

Since *regress* tries to accommodate all your data points using a single polynomial, it will not work well when your data does not behave like a single polynomial. For example, suppose you expect your y_i to be linear from x_1 to x_{10} and to behave like a cubic equation from x_{11} to x_{20}. If you use *regress* with $n = 3$ (a cubic), you may get a good fit for the second half but a terrible fit for the the first half.

The *loess* function alleviates these kinds of problems by performing a more localized regression. Instead of generating a single polynomial the way *regress* does, *loess* generates a different second order polynomial depending on where you are on the curve. It does this by examining the data in a small neighborhood of the point you're interested in. The argument *span* controls the size of this neighborhood. As *span* gets larger, *loess* becomes equivalent to *regress* with $n = 2$. A good default value is *span* = 0.75.

Figure 10 shows how *span* affects the fit generated by the *loess* function. Note how a smaller value of *span* makes the fitted curve track fluctuations in data more effectively. A larger value of *span* tends to smear out fluctuations in data and generate a smoother fit.

Chapter 13 Statistical functions

regress(**vx**, **vy**, *n*)	A vector required by the *interp* function to find the nth order polynomial that best fits data vectors **vx** and **vy**. **vx** is an *m* element vector containing *x* coordinates. **vy** is an *m* element vector containing the *y* coordinates corresponding to the *m* points specified in **vx**.
⊕ loess(**vx**, **vy**, *span*)	A vector required by the *interp* function to find the set of second order polynomials that best fit particular neighborhoods of data points specified in vectors **vx** and **vy**. **vx** is an *m* element vector containing *x* coordinates. **vy** is an *m* element vector containing the *y* coordinates corresponding to the *m* points specified in **vx**. The argument *span*, (*span* > 0), specifies how large a neighborhood *loess* will consider in performing this local regression.
interp(**vs**, **vx**, **vy**, *x*)	Returns the interpolated *y* value corresponding to the *x*. The vector **vs** comes from evaluating *loess* or *regress* using the data matrices **vx** and **vy**.

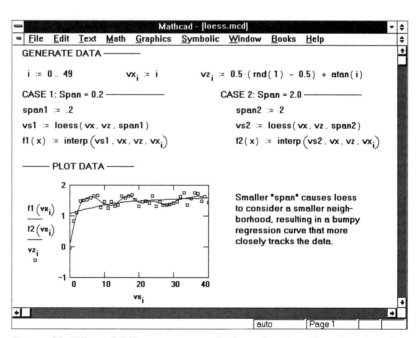

Figure 10: Effect of different spans on the loess function. Note that since these are random numbers, it's unlikely you'll be able to reproduce this example exactly as you see here.

Multivariate polynomial regression

Mathcad
PLUS

The *loess* and *regress* functions discussed in the previous section are also useful when you have set of measured z values corresponding to x and y values and you want to fit a polynomial surface through those z values.

The properties of these functions are described in the previous section. When using these functions to fit z values corresponding to two independent variables x and y, the meanings of the arguments must be generalized. Specifically:

- The argument **vx** which was an m-element vector of x values becomes an m-row and 2 column array, **Mxy**. Each row of **Mxy** contains an x in the first column and a corresponding y value in the second column.

- The argument x for the *interp* function becomes a 2-element vector **v** whose elements are the x and y values at which you want to evaluate the polynomial surface representing the best fit to the data points in **Mxy** and **vz**.

---

regress(**Mxy**, **vz**, k)	A vector required by the *interp* function to find the kth order polynomial that best fits data arrays **Mxy** and **vz**. **Mxy** is an $m \times 2$ matrix containing x-y coordinates. **vz** is an m element vector containing the z coordinates corresponding to the m points specified in **Mxy**.
⊕ loess(**Mxy**, **vz**, *span*)	A vector required by the *interp* function to find the set of second order polynomials that best fit particular neighborhoods of data points specified in arrays **Mxy** and **vz**. **Mxy** is an $m \times 2$ matrix containing x-y coordinates. **vz** is an m element vector containing the z coordinates corresponding to the m points specified in **Mxy**. The argument *span* (*span* > 0 specifies how large a neighborhood *loess* will consider in performing this local regression.)
interp(**vs**, **Mxy**, **vz**, **v**)	Returns the interpolated z value corresponding to the point $x = v_0$ and $y = v_1$. The vector **vs** comes from evaluating *loess* or *regress* using the data matrices **Mxy** and **vz**.

You can add independent variables by simply adding columns to the **Mxy** array. You would then add a corresponding number of rows to the vector **v** that you pass to the *interp* function. The *regress* function can have as many independent variables as you want. However, *regress* will calculate more slowly and require more memory when the number of independent variables and the degree are greater than four. The *loess* function is restricted to at most four independent variables.

Keep in mind that for *regress*, the number of data values, m must satisfy

$$m > \binom{n+k-1}{k} \cdot \frac{n+k}{n}$$

where n is the number of independent variables (hence the number of columns in **Mxy**), k is the degree of the desired polynomial, and m is the number of data values (hence the number of rows in **vz**). For example, if you have five explanatory variables and a fourth degree polynomial, you will need more than 126 observations.

Generalized regression

Mathcad
PLUS

Unfortunately, not all data sets can be modeled by lines or polynomials. There are times when you need to model your data with a linear combination of arbitrary functions, none of which represent terms of a polynomial. For example, in a Fourier series you try to approximate data using a linear combination of complex exponentials. Or you may believe your data can be modeled by a weighted combination of Legendre polynomials, but you just don't know what weights to assign.

The *linfit* function is designed to solve these kinds of problems. If you believe your data could be modeled by a linear combination of arbitrary functions:

$$y = a_0 {\cdot} f_0(x) + a_1 {\cdot} f_1(x) + \ldots + a_n {\cdot} f_n(x)$$

you should use *linfit* to evaluate the a_i. Figure 11 shows an example in which a linear combination of three functions: x, x^2, and $(x+1)^{-1}$ is used to model some data.

There are times however when the flexibility of *linfit* is still not enough. Your data may have to be modeled not by a linear combination of data but by some function whose parameters must be chosen. For example, if your data can be modeled by the sum:

$$f(x) = a_1 {\cdot} \sin(2x) + a_2 {\cdot} \tanh(3x)$$

and all you need to do is solve for the unknown weights a_1 and a_2, then you have a *linfit* type of problem.

By contrast, if instead your data is to be modeled by the sum:

$$f(x) = 2 {\cdot} \sin(a_1 x) + 3 {\cdot} \tanh(a_2 x)$$

and you now have to solve for the unknown parameters a_1 and a_2, you would have a *genfit* problem.

Anything you can do with *linfit* you can also do, albeit less conveniently, with *genfit*. The difference between these two functions is the difference between solving a system of linear equations and solving a system of nonlinear equations. The former is easily done using the methods of linear algebra. The latter is far more difficult and generally must be solved by iteration. This explains why *genfit* needs a vector of guess values as an argument and *linfit* does not.

Figure 12 shows an example in which *genfit* is used to find the exponent that best fits a set of data.

---

linfit(**vx**, **vy**, **F**) Returns a vector containing the coefficients used to create a linear combination of the functions in **F** which best approximates the data in vectors **vx** and **vy**. **F** is a function which returns a vector consisting of the functions to be linearly combined.

⊕ genfit(**vx**, **vy**, **vg**, **F**) A vector containing the parameters that make a function f of x and n parameters $u_0, u_1, ..., u_{n-1}$ best approximate the data in **vx** and **vy**. **F** is a function that returns an $n + 1$ element vector containing f and its partial derivatives with respect to its n parameters. **vg** is an n-element vector of guess values for the n parameters.

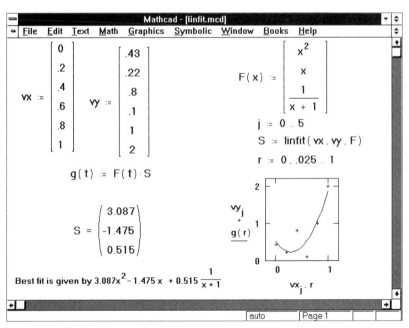

Figure 11: Using linfit to find coefficients for a linear combination of functions that best fits the data.

Chapter 13 Statistical functions

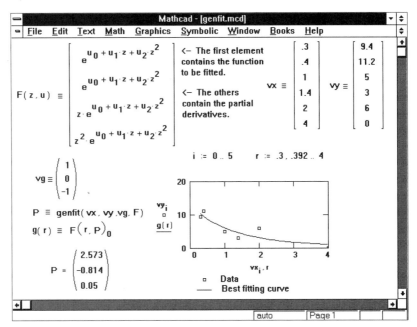

$$F(z,u) \equiv \begin{bmatrix} e^{u_0 + u_1 \cdot z + u_2 \cdot z^2} \\ e^{u_0 + u_1 \cdot z + u_2 \cdot z^2} \\ z \cdot e^{u_0 + u_1 \cdot z + u_2 \cdot z^2} \\ z^2 \cdot e^{u_0 + u_1 \cdot z + u_2 \cdot z^2} \end{bmatrix}$$

<- The first element contains the function to be fitted.

<- The others contain the partial derivatives.

$$vx \equiv \begin{bmatrix} .3 \\ .4 \\ 1 \\ 1.4 \\ 2 \\ 4 \end{bmatrix} \quad vy \equiv \begin{bmatrix} 9.4 \\ 11.2 \\ 5 \\ 3 \\ 6 \\ 0 \end{bmatrix}$$

$$vg \equiv \begin{pmatrix} 1 \\ 0 \\ -1 \end{pmatrix}$$

$$i := 0 .. 5 \qquad r := .3, .392 .. 4$$

$$P \equiv genfit(vx, vy, vg, F)$$

$$g(r) \equiv F(r, P)_0$$

$$P = \begin{pmatrix} 2.573 \\ -0.814 \\ 0.05 \end{pmatrix}$$

□ Data
── Best fitting curve

Figure 12: Using genfit for finding the parameters of a function so that it best fits the data.

Smoothing functions

Mathcad PLUS

Smoothing involves taking a set of y (and possibly x) values and returning a new set of y values that is smoother than the original set. Unlike the regression and interpolation functions discussed earlier, smoothing results in a new set of y values, not a function that can be evaluated between the data points you specify. Thus, if you are interested in y values *between* the y values you specify, you should use a regression or interpolation function.

Whenever you use vectors in any of the functions described in this section, be sure that every element in the vector contains a data value. Since every element in a vector must have a value, Mathcad assigns 0 to any elements you have not explicitly assigned.

The *medsmooth* function is the most robust of the three since it is least likely to be affected by spurious data points. This function uses a running median smoother, computes the residuals, smoothes the residuals the same way, and adds these two smoothed vectors together. The details are as follows:

■ Evaluation of medsmooth(vy, n) begins with the running median of the input vector vy. We'll call this vy'. The ith element is given by:
$vy'_i = \text{median}(vy_{i-\frac{n-1}{2}}, \ldots vy_i, \ldots vy_{i+\frac{n-1}{2}})$.

■ It then evaluates the residuals: $vr = vy - vy'$.

- The residual vector, **vr**, is smoothed using the same procedure described in step 1. This creates a smoothed residual vector, **vr** ′.

- The *medsmooth* function returns the sum of these two smoothed vectors: medsmooth(**vy**, n) = **vy**′ + **vr** ′.

Note that *medsmooth* will leave the first and last $(n − 1)/2$ points unchanged. In practice, the length of the smoothing window, n, should be small compared to the length of the data set.

The *ksmooth* function uses a Gaussian kernel to compute local weighted averages of the input vector **vy**. This smoother is most useful when your data lies along a band of relatively constant width. If your data lies scattered along a band whose width fluctuates considerably, you should use an adaptive smoother like *supsmooth*.

For each vy_i in the n-element vector **vy**, the *ksmooth* function returns a new vy'_i given by:

$$vy'_i = \frac{\sum_{j=1}^{n} K\left(\frac{vx_i - vx_j}{b}\right) vy_j}{\sum_{j=1}^{n} K\left(\frac{vx_i - vx_j}{b}\right)}$$

where:

$$K(t) = \frac{1}{\sqrt{2\pi} \cdot (0.37)} \cdot \exp\left(-\frac{t^2}{2 \cdot (0.37)^2}\right)$$

and b is a bandwidth which you supply to the *ksmooth* function. The bandwidth is usually set to a few times the spacing between data points on the x axis depending on how big a window you want to use when smoothing.

The *supsmooth* function uses a symmetric k nearest neighbor linear least square fitting procedure to make a series of line segments through your data. Unlike *ksmooth* which uses a fixed bandwidth for all your data, *supsmooth* will adaptively choose different bandwidths for different portions of your data.

medsmooth($\mathbf{vy}$, n)	Returns an m-element vector created by smoothing $\mathbf{vy}$ with running medians. $\mathbf{vy}$ is an m-element vector of real numbers. n is the width of the window over which smoothing occurs. n must be an odd number less than the number of elements in $\mathbf{vy}$.
⊕ ksmooth($\mathbf{vx}$,$\mathbf{vy}$, b)	Returns an n-element vector created by using a Gaussian kernel to return weighted averages of $\mathbf{vy}$. $\mathbf{vy}$ and $\mathbf{vx}$ are n-element vectors of real numbers. The bandwidth b controls the smoothing window and should be set to a few times the spacing between your x data points.
⊕ supsmooth($\mathbf{vx}$,$\mathbf{vy}$)	Returns an n-element vector created by the piecewise use of a symmetric k-nearest neighbor linear least square fitting procedure in which k is adaptively chosen. $\mathbf{vy}$ and $\mathbf{vx}$ are n-element vectors of real numbers. The elements of $\mathbf{vx}$ must be in increasing order.

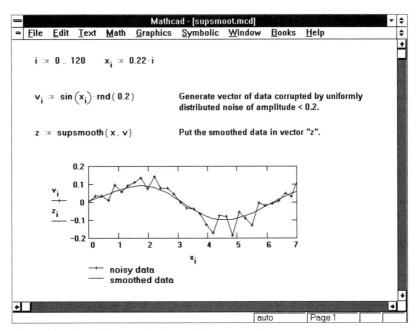

Figure 13: Smoothing noisy data with supsmooth.

Chapter 14
Programming

If you're using Mathcad PLUS, you'll be able to write programs. A Mathcad program is an expression which is itself made up of other expressions. A Mathcad program has many attributes associated with programming languages including conditional branching, looping constructs, local scoping of variables, the ability to use other programs as subroutines, and the ability to call itself recursively.

Mathcad programs make it easy to do tasks that are either impossible or very inconvenient to do in any other way.

This chapter contains the following sections:

Defining a program

How to create simple programs. Local assignment statements.

Conditional statements

Using a condition to suppress execution of a statement.

Looping

Using "while" loops and "for" loops to control iteration.

Programs within programs

Using subroutines and recursion in a Mathcad program.

Programming examples

A sampling of programs illustrating useful techniques and displaying some of the power of Mathcad's approach to programming.

A Mathcad program is a special kind of Mathcad expression. Like any expression, a program returns a value when followed by an equals sign. Just as you can define a variable or function in terms of an expression, you can also define it in terms of a program.

The main difference between a program and an expression is the way you tell Mathcad how to compute an answer. When you use an expression, you have to describe how to compute the answer in one statement. But when you use a program, you can use as many statements as you want to describe how to compute the answer. In effect, you can think of a program as being a "compound expression."

The following example shows how to make a simple program to define the function:

$$f(x, w) = \log\left(\frac{x}{w}\right)$$

Although the example chosen is so simple as to render programming unecessary, it does illustrate how to separate the statements making up the program and how to use the local assignment operator, "←".

- Type the left side of the function definition, followed by a "`:=`". Make sure the placeholder is selected.

  $$f(\mathbf{x},\mathbf{w}) := \blacksquare$$

- Open the programming palette by clicking on the programming button in the palette controls. Then click on the "Add line" button. Alternatively, press]. You'll see a vertical bar with two placeholders. These placeholders will hold the statements making up your program. You can continue adding placeholders for statements as you need them by repeatedly clicking the "Add Line" button.

  $$f(\mathbf{x},\mathbf{w}) := \begin{vmatrix} \blacksquare \\ \blacksquare \end{vmatrix}$$

- Press [Tab] to move to the top placeholder. In the top placeholder, type z, and click on the "←" button on the programming palette. Alternatively, press { to insert a "←".

  $$f(\mathbf{x},\mathbf{w}) := \begin{vmatrix} z \leftarrow \blacksquare \\ \blacksquare \end{vmatrix}$$

- In the placeholder to the right of the "←", type **x/w**.

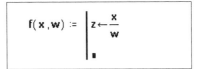

$$f(x,w) := \begin{vmatrix} z \leftarrow \dfrac{x}{w} \\ \blacksquare \end{vmatrix}$$

- The remaining placeholder is the actual value to be returned by the program. Type **log(z)**.

$$f(x,w) := \begin{vmatrix} z \leftarrow \dfrac{x}{w} \\ \log(z) \end{vmatrix}$$

You can now use this function just as you would any other function. Figure 1 shows this function along with an equivalent function defined on one line instead of two. Note that z is undefined everywhere outside the program. The definition of z inside the program is local to the program. It has no effect anywhere else.

A program can have any number of statements. To add an additional statement, click the "Add Line" button on the toolbar again. Mathcad inserts a placeholder below whatever statement you've selected. To delete the placeholder, enclose it in a selection box and press [**Del**].

Figure 2 shows a more complex example involving the quadratic formula. Although you can define the quadratic formula with a single statement as shown in the top half of the figure, you may find it simpler to define it with a series of simple statements as shown in the bottom half. This lets you avoid having to edit very complicated expressions.

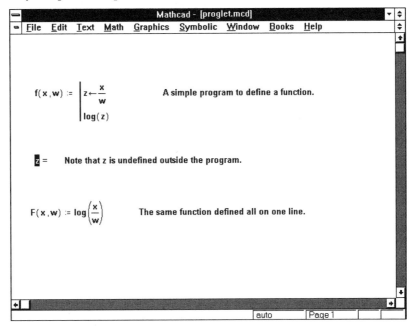

Figure 1: A function defined both in terms of a program and in terms of an expression.

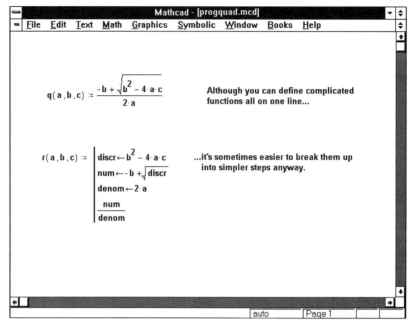

Figure 2: A more complex function defined in terms of both an expression and a program.

A Mathcad program, therefore, is an expression made up of a sequence of statements, each one of which is an expression in itself. Like any expression, a Mathcad program must have a value. This value is simply the value of the expression forming the last statement executed by the program. It could be a single number as shown in Figures 1 and 2, or it could be an array of numbers as shown in Figure 6. It could even be a mixture of the two as described in the section "Nested arrays" in Chapter 9.

The remaining sections describe how to use conditional statements and how to use various looping structures to control program flow.

In general, Mathcad evaluates each statement in your program from the top down. There may be times, however, when you want Mathcad to evaluate a statement only when a particular condition is met. You can do this by including an "if" statement in your program. For example, suppose you want to define a function that forms a semi-circle around the origin but is otherwise constant. To do this:

- Type the left side of the function definition, followed by a ":=". Make sure the placeholder is selected.

$$f(x) := \blacksquare$$

- Click the "Add Line" button on the programming palette. Alternatively, press]. You'll see a vertical bar with two placeholders. These placeholders will hold the statements making up your program.

$$f(x) := \left| \begin{array}{l} \blacksquare \\ \blacksquare \end{array} \right.$$

- In the top placeholder, click the "if" button on the programming palette. Alternatively, press }.

$$f(x) := \left| \begin{array}{l} \blacksquare \ \text{if} \ \blacksquare \\ \blacksquare \end{array} \right.$$

- In the right placeholder, type a boolean expression: an expression that's either true or false. In the left placeholder, type the value you want the expression to take whenever the expression in the right placeholder is true.

$$f(x) := \left| \begin{array}{l} 0 \ \text{if} \ |x| > 2 \\ \blacksquare \end{array} \right.$$

- Select the remaining placeholder and click the "otherwise" button on the programming palette.

$$f(x) := \left| \begin{array}{l} 0 \ \text{if} \ |x| > 2 \\ \blacksquare \ \text{otherwise} \end{array} \right.$$

- In the remaining placeholder, type the value you want the program to return if the condition in the first statement is not met.

$$f(x) := \left| \begin{array}{l} 0 \ \text{if} \ |x| > 2 \\ \sqrt{4 - x^2} \ \text{otherwise} \end{array} \right.$$

Figure 3 shows a plot of this function. Note that since this function only has two branches, it's not hard to define it using the *if* function as shown in Figure 3. However, as the number of branches exceeds two, the *if* function rapidly becomes unwieldy. An example is shown in Figure 4.

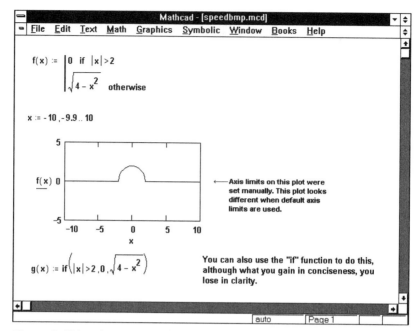

Figure 3: Using the "if" statement to define a piecewise continuous function.

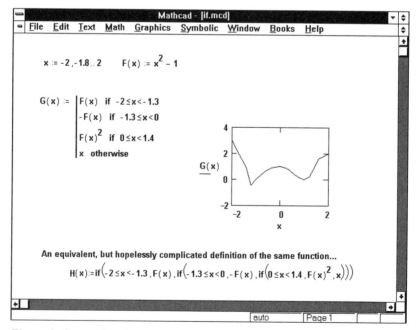

Figure 4: Comparing the "if" statement in a program with the built-in "if" function.

One of the greatest strengths of programmability is the ability to execute a sequence of statements over and over again in a loop. Mathcad provides two such loops. The choice of which loop to use depends on how you plan to tell the loop to stop executing.

- If you know exactly how many times a loop is to execute, you can use a *for* loop.

- If you want the loop to stop upon the occurrence of a condition, but you don't know *when* that condition will occur, use a *while* loop.

"while" loops

A *while* loop is driven by the truth of some condition. Because of this, you don't need to know in advance how many times the loop is to execute. It is important, however, to have a statement somewhere, either within the loop or elsewhere in the program, that eventually makes the condition false. Otherwise, the loop will execute indefinitely. If you *do* find yourself in an endless loop, you can stop it by pressing [**Esc**].

To create a *while* loop:

- Click the button labelled "while" on the programming palette.

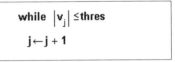

- In the top placeholder, type a condition. This would typically be a boolean expression like the one shown.

- In the remaining placeholder, type the expression you want evaluated repeatedly. If necessary, you can add additional placeholders by clicking the "Add Line" button on the programming palette.

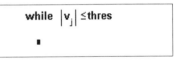

Figure 5 shows a larger program incorporating the above loop. Upon encountering a *while* loop, Mathcad checks the condition. If the condition is true, Mathcad executes the body of the loop and checks the condition again. If the condition is false, Mathcad exits the loop.

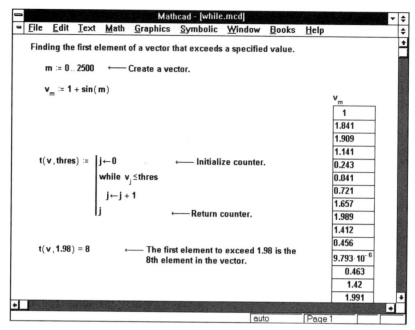

Figure 5: Using a "while" loop to find the first occurrence of a particular number in a matrix.

The "break" statement

It is often convenient to break out of a loop or stop program execution upon the occurrence of some condition. For example, there is a possibility of a runaway iteration in the program in Figure 5. If every element in **v** is less than *thresh*, the condition will never become false and iteration will continue past the end of the vector, resulting in an "*index out of bounds*" error message. To prevent this from being a problem, you can use a *break* statement as shown in Figure 6.

The program in Figure 6 will return 0 if no elements larger than *thresh* were found. Otherwise it returns the index and value of the first element exceeding *thresh*.

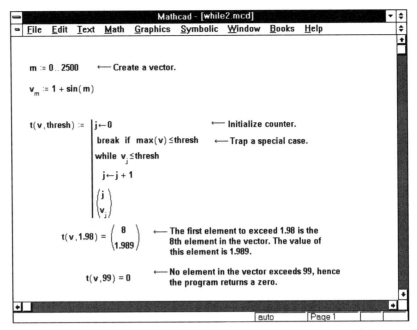

Figure 6: Example in Figure 5 modified to return both the index and the actual array value. Note the use of "break" to prevent an error arising when thresh is too large.

To insert the *break* statement, click on the "break" button in the programming palette. Note that in Figure 6, you would click the "break" button first, then click "if".

"for" loops

A *for* loop is a loop that terminates after a predetermined number of iterations. Iteration is controlled by an iteration variable defined at the top of the loop.

To create a *for* loop:

- Click the button labelled "for" on the programming palette.

```
for ▮ ∈ ▪
    ▪
```

- In the placeholder to the left of the ∈, type the name of the iteration variable.

```
for i ∈ ▪
    ▪
```

- In the placeholder to the right of the "∈", enter the range of values the iteration variable should take. You specify this range the same way you would for a range variable. See Chapter 10, "Range variables," for more details.

```
for i ∈ 1 .. n
    ▪
```

- In the remaining placeholder, type the expression you want to evaluate repeatedly. This expresssion generally involves the iteration variable. If necessary, you can add additional placeholders by clicking the "Add Line" button on the programming palette.

```
for i ∈ 1 .. n
    s ← s + i
```

The upper half of Figure 7 shows this *for* loop being used to add a sequence of integers. The undefined variable in Figure 7 shows that the definition of an iteration variable is local to the program. It has no effect anywhere outside the program.

The lower half shows an example in which the iteration variable is defined not in terms of a range but in terms of the elements of a vector. Although the expression to the right of the "∈" is usually a range, it can also be a vector, a list of scalars, ranges and vectors separated by commas.

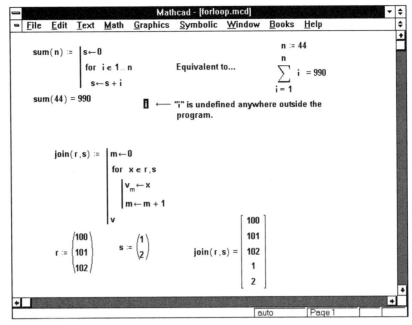

Figure 7: Using a "for" loop with two different kinds of iteration variables.

Programs within programs

The examples in previous sections have been chosen more for their simplicity than their power. This section shows some examples of more complicated programs capable of performing tasks that would be difficult if not impossible without the availability of these programming features.

Much of the flexibility inherent in programming arises from the ability to embed programming structures inside one another. In Mathcad, you can do this in three ways:

- You can make one of the statements in a program be another program.

- You can define a program elsewhere and call it from within another program as if it were a subroutine.

- You can define a function recursively.

The remainder of this section illustrates these techniques by example.

Subroutines

Recall that a program is just an expression made up of statements, each one of which contains an expression. Since a program statement must be an expression, and since a program is itself an expression, it follows that a program statement can be another program.

Figure 8 shows two examples of programs containing a statement which is itself a program. The example on the right-hand side of Figure 8 shows how to nest programs even more deeply. In principle, there is no limit to how deeply nested a program can be. As a practical matter, however, programs containing deeply nested programs can become too complicated to understand at a glance.

One way many programmers avoid overly complicated programs is to bury the complexity in a "subroutine." Figure 9 shows how you can do something similar in Mathcad. By defining *intsimp* elsewhere and using it within *adapt*, the program used to define *adapt* becomes considerably simpler. Imagine how complicated the definition for *adapt* would be if both occurrences of *intsimp* within it had to be replaced by the lengthy definition for *intsimp* at the top of the figure.

The function *adapt* carries out an adaptive quadrature or integration routine by using *intsimp* to approximate the area in each subinterval. If you look at the last line, you'll notice that *adapt* actually calls itself. In other words, it's defined recursively. The following section discusses recursive function definitions in more detail.

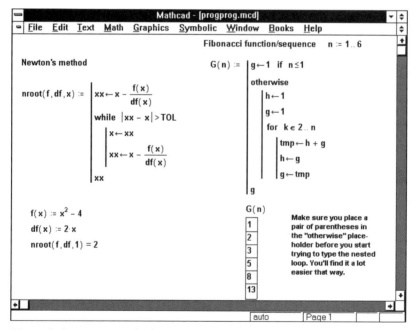

Figure 8: Programs in which statements are themselves programs.

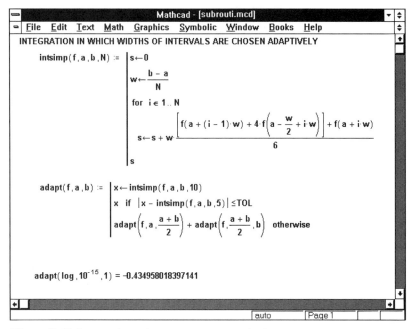

Figure 9: Using a subroutine to manage complexity.

Recursion

Recursion is a powerful programming technique that involves defining a function in terms of itself as shown in Figure 10. Recursive function definitions should always have at least two parts:

■ An initial condition to prevent the recursion from going forever, and

■ A definition of the function in terms of a previous value of the function.

The idea is similar to that underlying mathematical induction: if you can get $f(n + 1)$ from $f(n)$, and you know $f(0)$, then you know all there is to know about f.

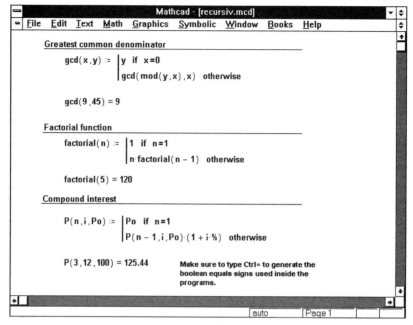

Figure 10: Defining a function recursively.

Keep in mind however, that although recursive function definitions, despite their elegance and conciseness, are not always the most computationally efficient definitions. You may find that an equivalent definition using one of the iterative loops described earlier will evaluate more quickly.

Programming examples

With only seven buttons on the programming palette, Mathcad's programming environment is easy to use. Nevertheless, this simplicity conceals a surprising amount of programming power. When combined with Mathcad's rich numerical functionality and used in conjunction with the abstract data structures provided by Mathcad's nested arrays, these seven operators enable you to write sophisticated programs in Mathcad.

The following figures illustrate just a few of the possibilities. As you experiment with programming in Mathcad, you'll discover many new applications. For further programming examples, see the corresponding QuickSheets by choosing **QuickSheets** from the **Help** menu.

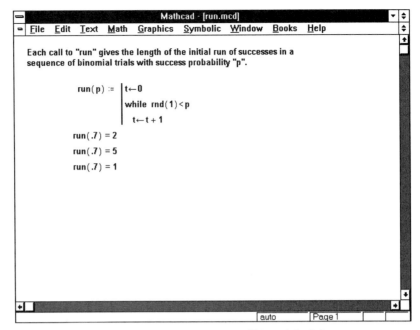

Figure 11: Program to generate a sequence of binomial trials.

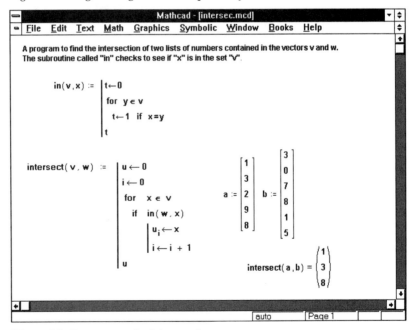

Figure 12: Program to find the numbers common to two vectors.

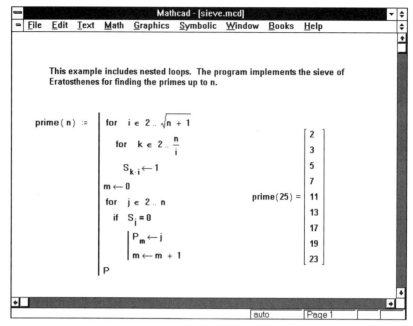

Figure 13: Using the sieve of Eratosthenes to find prime numbers.

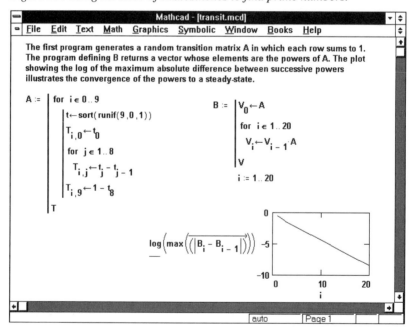

Figure 14: Powers of a random transition matrix.

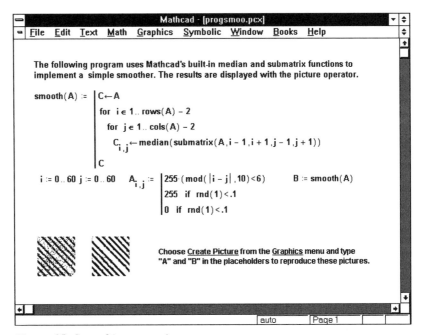

The following program uses Mathcad's built-in median and submatrix functions to implement a simple smoother. The results are displayed with the picture operator.

$$\text{smooth}(A) := \begin{vmatrix} C \leftarrow A \\ \text{for } i \in 1 .. \text{rows}(A) - 2 \\ \quad \text{for } j \in 1 .. \text{cols}(A) - 2 \\ \qquad C_{i,j} \leftarrow \text{median}(\text{submatrix}(A, i-1, i+1, j-1, j+1)) \\ C \end{vmatrix}$$

$$i := 0 .. 60 \quad j := 0 .. 60 \quad A_{i,j} := \begin{vmatrix} 255 \cdot (\text{mod}(|i-j|, 10) < 6) \\ 255 \text{ if } \text{rnd}(1) < .1 \\ 0 \text{ if } \text{rnd}(1) < .1 \end{vmatrix} \qquad B := \text{smooth}(A)$$

Choose <u>Create Picture</u> from the <u>Graphics</u> menu and type "A" and "B" in the placeholders to reproduce these pictures.

Figure 15: Smoothing a matrix.

Chapter 15
Solving Equations

This chapter describes how to solve equations ranging from a single equation in one unknown to systems of up to fifty equations in fifty unknowns.

The following sections make up this chapter:

Solving one equation

How to use Mathcad's root functions to numerically solve one equation in one unknown.

Systems of equations

How to use "solve blocks" to solve systems of n equations in n unknowns.

Using the solver effectively

Examples of how to efficiently solve systems of equations for various values of a parameter.

To solve a single equation in a single unknown, use the *root* function. This function takes an expression and one of the variables from the expression. It then varies that variable until the expression is equal to zero. Once this is done, the function returns the value that makes the expression equal zero.

---

root(*f*(*z*), *z*) Returns the value of *z* at which the expression or function *f*(*z*) is equal to 0. Both arguments to this function must be scalar. The function returns a scalar.

The first argument is either a function defined elsewhere in the worksheet, or an expression. It must return a scalar value.

The second argument is a variable name that appears in the expression. It is this variable that Mathcad will vary to make the expression go to zero. You should assign a number to this variable before using the *root* function. Mathcad uses this as a starting value in its search for a solution.

For example, to define *a* as the solution to the equation $e^x = x^3$, follow these steps:

- Define a guess value for *x*. Type **x:3**. Your choice of guess value determines which root Mathcad returns.

$$x := 3$$

- Set the whole expression equal to zero. In other words, rewrite $x^3 = e^x$ as $x^3 - e^x = 0$. It is this expression that you give the *root* function.

- Type
  a:root(x^3[Space]-e^x[Space],x)
  This defines the variable *a* to be a root of the desired equation.

$$a := \text{root}\left(x^3 - e^x, x\right)$$

- Type **a=** to see the root.

$$a = 1.857$$

When you use the root function, keep these suggestions in mind:

- Make sure that the variable is defined with a guess value before you use the *root* function.

- For expressions with several roots, for example $x^2 - 1 = 0$, your guess value determines which root Mathcad will return. Figure 1 shows an example in which the *root* function returns several different values, each of which depends on the initial guess value.

- Mathcad will solve for complex roots as well as real roots. To find a complex root, you must start with a complex value for the initial guess.

- Solving an equation of the form $f(x) = g(x)$ is equivalent to using the *root* function as follows:

$$\text{root}(f(x) - g(x), x)$$

The root function can solve only one equation in one unknown. To solve several equations simultaneously, use the technique described in the next section, "Systems of Equations." To solve an equation symbolically, or to find an exact numerical answer in terms of elementary functions, choose **Solve for Variable** from the **Symbolic** menu. See Chapter 17, "Symbolic Calculation."

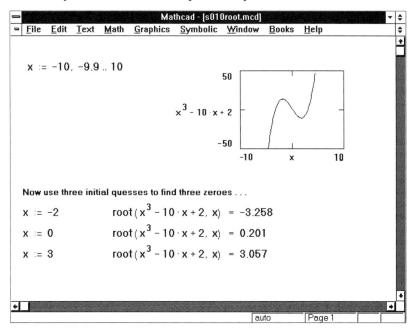

Figure 1: Using a plot and the root function to find roots of an expression.

What to do when the root function does not converge

Mathcad evaluates the *root* function using the *secant method*. The guess value you supply for x becomes the starting point for successive approximations to the root value. When the magnitude of $f(x)$ evaluated at the proposed root is less than the value of the predefined variable TOL, the *root* function returns a result.

If after many approximations Mathcad still cannot find an acceptable answer, it marks the *root* function with the error "*not converging*." This error can be caused by any of the following:

- The expression has no roots.

- The roots of the expression are far from the initial guess.

- The expression has local maxima or minima between the initial guess and the roots.

- The expression has discontinuities between the initial guess and the roots.

- The expression has a complex root but the initial guess was real (or vice versa).

To find the cause of the error, try plotting the expression. This will help determine whether or not the expression crosses the *x*-axis and if so, approximately where it does so. In general, the closer your initial guess is to where the expression crosses the *x*-axis, the more quickly the *root* function will converge on an acceptable result.

Hints on using the root function

Here are some hints on getting the most out of the *root* function:

- To change the accuracy of the *root* function, change the value of the built-in variable TOL. If you increase TOL, the *root* function will converge more quickly, but the answer will be less accurate. If you decrease TOL, the *root* function will converge more slowly, but the answer will be more accurate. To change TOL at a specified point in the worksheet, include a definition like *TOL* := 0.01. To change TOL for the whole worksheet, choose **Built-In Variables** from the **Math** menu and replace the number in the text box beside "TOL." After you click "OK," choose **Calculate Worksheet** from the **Math** menu to update the entire worksheet using the new value of TOL

- If an expression has multiple roots, try different guess values to find them. Plotting the function is a good way to determine how many roots there are, where they are, and what initial guesses are likely to find them. Figure 1 shows an example of this. If two roots are close together, you may have to reduce TOL to distinguish between them.

- If *f*(*x*) has a small slope near its root, then root(*f*(*x*), *x*) may converge to a value *r* that is relatively far from the actual root. In such cases, even though |*f*(*r*)| < TOL, *r* may be far from the point where *f*(*r*) = 0. To find a more accurate root, decrease the value of TOL. Or, try finding root(*g*(*x*), *x*), where

$$g(x) = \frac{f(x)}{\frac{d}{dx}f(x)}$$

- For an expression *f*(*x*) with a known root *a*, solving for additional roots of *f*(*x*) is equivalent to solving for roots of *h*(*x*) = *f*(*x*)/(*x*−*a*). Dividing out known roots like this is useful for resolving two roots that may be close together. It's often easier to solve for roots of *h*(*x*) as defined here than it is to try to find other roots for *f*(*x*) with different guesses.

Solving an equation repeatedly

Suppose you want to solve an equation many times while varying one of the parameters in the equation. For example, suppose you want to solve the equation $e^x = a \cdot x^2$ for several different values of the parameter a. The simplest way to do this is to define a function:

$$f(a, x) := \text{root}(e^x - a \cdot x^2, x)$$

To solve the equation for a particular value of a, supply both a and a guess value, x, as arguments to this function. Then evaluate the function by typing $f(a,x)=$.

Figure 2 shows an example of how such a function can be used to find several solutions to the *root* function. Note that since the guess value, x, is passed into the function itself, there is no need to define it elsewhere in the worksheet.

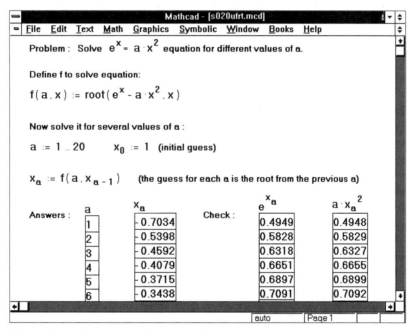

Figure 2: Defining a user function with the root function.

Finding the roots of a polynomial

To find the roots of an expression having the form:

$$v_n x^n + \ldots + v_2 x^2 + v_1 x + v_0,$$

you can use the *polyroots* function rather than the *root* function. Unlike *root*, *polyroots* does not require a guess value. Moreover, *polyroots* returns all roots at once, whether real or complex. Figures 3 and 4 show examples.

---

polyroots(**v**) Returns the roots of an nth degree polynomial whose coefficients are in **v**, a vector of length $n + 1$. Returns a vector of length n.

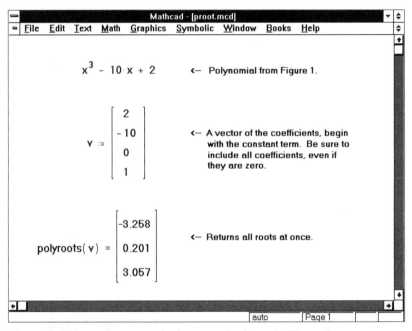

Figure 3: Using polyroots to do the example shown in Figure 1.

The *polyroots* function will always return numerical values for the roots of a polynomial. To find the roots symbolically, use **Solve for Variable** from the **Symbolic** menu. See Chapter 17, "Symbolic Calculation."

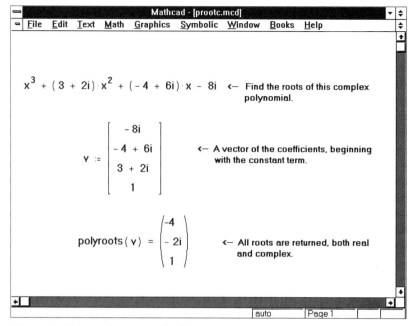

Figure 4: Using polyroots to find the roots of a polynomial.

Systems of equations

Mathcad lets you solve a system of up to fifty simultaneous equations in fifty unknowns. The first part of this section sketches the procedure. The remainder contains several examples as well as a discussion of some common errors. The method given here will always return numbers for the unknown variables. To see the unknowns in terms of the other variables and constants, use the symbolic solve blocks discussed on page 404.

There are four steps to solving a system of simultaneous equations. These are:

- Provide an initial guess for all the unknowns you intend to solve for. Mathcad solves equations by making a series of guesses which ultimately converge on the right answer. The initial guesses you provide give Mathcad a place to start searching for solutions.

- Type the word *Given*. This tells Mathcad that what follows is a system of equations. You can type *Given* in any combination of upper and lower case letters, and in any font. Just be sure you don't type it while in a text region or paragraph.

- Now type the equations and inequalities in any order below the word *Given*. Make sure you use the symbol "=" to separate the left and right sides of an equation. Press [Ctrl]= to type "=." You can separate the left and right sides of an inequality with any of the symbols $<, >, \leq$ and $\geq$.

- Type any equation that involves the *Find* function. Like *Given*, you can use any combination of upper and lowercase letters. You can also use any font, size or style.

Find(*z1, z2, z3, . . .*)   Returns the solution to a system of equations. Number of arguments matches the number of unknowns.

The *Find* function returns values as follows:

- If *Find* has one argument, it returns the value of that variable that solves the equation between it and the *Given*.

- If *Find* has more than one argument, it returns a vector of answers. For example, Find(*z1, z2*) returns a vector containing the values of *z1* and *z2* that solve the system of equations.

The word *Given*, the equations and inequalities that follow, and whatever expression involves the *Find* function, form a "solve block."

Figure 5 shows a worksheet that contains a solve block for one equation in one unknown. Since there is only one equation, only one equation appears between the word *Given* and the expression involving *Find.* Since there is only one unknown, the *Find* function has only one argument. For one equation in one unknown, you can also use the *root* function shown below.

$$a := \text{root}(x^2 + 10 - e^x, x)$$

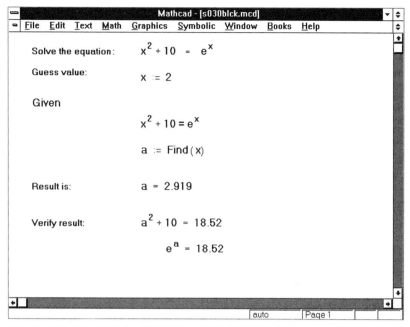

Figure 5: A solve block with one equation in one unknown.

Mathcad is very specific about the types of expressions that can appear between the *Given* and the *Find.* The table below lists all the expressions that can be placed in a solve block. These expressions are often called "constraints." In the table below, x and y represent real-valued scalar expressions, z and w represent arbitrary scalar expressions.

Condition	Keystroke	Description
$z = w$	[Ctrl]=	Constrained to be equal.
$x > y$	>	Greater than.
$x < y$	<	Less than.
$x \geq y$	[Ctrl]0	Greater than or equal to.
$x \leq y$	[Ctrl]9	Less than or equal to.

Note that Mathcad does not allow the following inside a solve block:

- Constraints with "$\neq$" in solve blocks.

- Range variables or expressions involving range variables of any kind.

- Inequalities of the form $a < b < c$.

If you want to include the outcome of a solve block in an iterative calculation, see the section "Using the solver effectively" later in this chapter.

Solve blocks cannot be nested inside each other. Each solve block can have only one *Given* and one *Find.* You can however, define a function like $f(x) := \text{Find}(x)$ at the end of one solve block and use this same function in another solve block. This too is discussed in the section "Using the solver effectively" later in this chapter.

As a rule, you should not use assignment statements (statements like **x := 1**) inside a solve block. Mathcad marks assignment statements inside solve blocks with the error message "*invalid.*"

Figure 6 shows a solve block with several kinds of constraints. There are two equations and two unknowns. As a result, the *Find* function contains two arguments, *x* and *y*, and returns a vector with two components.

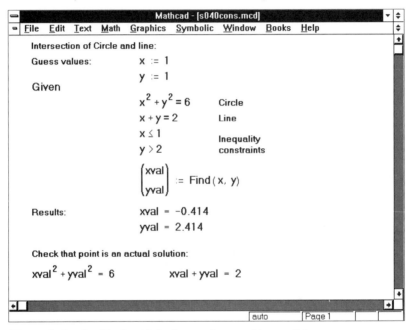

Figure 6: A solve block with both equations and inequalities.

What to do with your solution

The *Find* function that terminates a solve block behaves like any other function. There are three things you can do with it:

- You can display it with an equation like Find(*variable*) =. An example is shown in the top half of Figure 7. If you have several variables, you can display a vector of results with an equation like:Find(*var1, var2, . . .*) =. An example of how this would look for a system of two equations in two unknowns is shown in Figure 8.

- You can define a variable in terms of it by ending the solve block with an equation like $a := \mathrm{Find}(x)$. This is useful when you want to use the solution of a system of equations elsewhere in the worksheet. Once you make this definition, a has the solved value of the variable. An example of this is shown in the lower half of Figure 7. If the *Find* returns a vector of values, you can enter an equation like $variable := \mathrm{Find}(var1, var2, \ldots)$. If you do this, *variable* will end up being a vector instead of a scalar. You can also define variables as shown in Figure 6.

- Finally, you can define another function in terms of it by ending the solve block with an equation like $f(a, b, c, \ldots) := \mathrm{Find}(x, y, z, \ldots)$. This construction is useful for solving system of equations repeatedly for different values of some parameters $a, b, c, \ldots$ that appear within the system of equations itself. This method is described in the section "Using the solver effectively," later in this chapter.

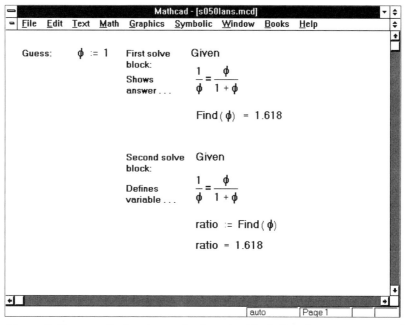

Figure 7: You can display the result of a solve block directly, or you can put the result in a variable name for later use.

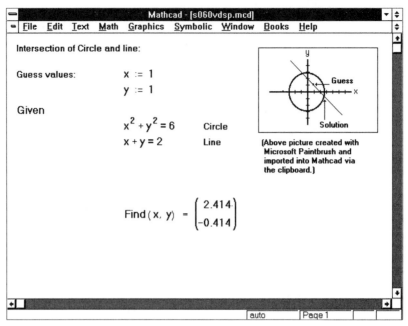

Figure 8: When there are two or more unknowns, the Find function no longer returns a scalar. Instead, it returns a vector with as many elements as there are unknowns.

Mathcad can return only one solution for a solve block. There may, however, be multiple solutions to a set of equations. To find a different solution, try different starting values or enter an additional inequality constraint that the current solution does not satisfy. Figure 9 shows how different starting values can yield a solution different from that shown in Figure 8. Figure 10 shows how to add an inequality to force Mathcad to find a different solution.

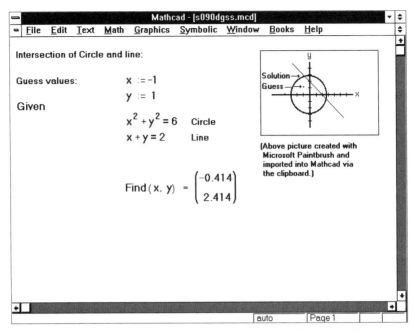

Figure 9: A different guess leads to a solution different from that shown in Figure 8.

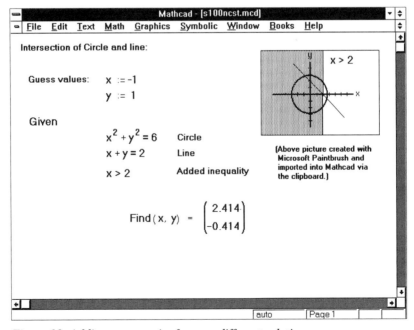

Figure 10: Adding a constraint forces a different solution.

What to do when the solver does not reach a solution

If the solver cannot make any further improvements to the solution but the constraints are *not* all satisfied, then the solver stops and marks the *Find* with the error "*did not find solution.*"

If you are having difficulty finding a solution, it often helps to plot the curve or curves in question. Plotting can provide graphical insight into where the solution might be. This will help you choose appropriate initial guesses for the variables.

Figure 11 shows a problem for which Mathcad could not find a solution.

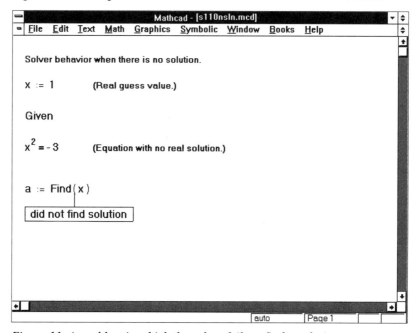

Figure 11: A problem in which the solver fails to find a solution.

The solver returns the error message "*did not find solution*" when the difference between successive approximations to the solution is greater than TOL *and*:

- The solver reaches a point where it cannot reduce the error any further.

- The solver reaches a point from which there is no preferred direction. Because of this, the solver has no basis on which to make further iterations.

- The solver reaches the limit of its accuracy. Roundoff errors make it unlikely that further computation would increase accuracy of the solution. This often happens if you set TOL to a value below 10^{-15}.

The following problems may cause this sort of failure:

- There may actually be no solution.

- You may have given real guesses for an equation with no real solution. If the solution for a variable is complex, the solver will not find it unless the starting value for that variable is also complex. Figure 11 shows an example.

- The solver may have become trapped in a local minimum for the error values. The solving method that Mathcad uses will sometimes reach a point from which it cannot minimize the errors any further. To find the actual solution, try using different starting values or add an inequality to keep Mathcad from being trapped in the local minimum.

- The solver may have become trapped on a point that is not a local minimum, but from which it cannot determine where to go next. The strategies for avoiding this problem are the same as those for avoiding a local minimum: change the initial guesses or add an inequality to avoid the undesirable stopping point.

- It may not be possible to solve the constraints to within the desired tolerance. If the value of TOL is relatively small, Mathcad may have reached something very close to a solution but still be unable to solve all the constraints to an error less than TOL. Try defining TOL with a larger value somewhere above the solve block. Increasing the tolerance changes what Mathcad considers close enough to call a solution.

What to do when there are too few constraints

If there are fewer constraints than variables, Mathcad cannot run the solver at all. Mathcad marks the *Find* with the error "*too few constraints.*"

A problem like that shown in Figure 12 is *underdetermined*. The constraints do not give enough information to find a solution. Because there are five arguments in the *Find* function, Mathcad thinks that you want to solve two equations with five unknowns. In general, such a problem has an infinite number of solutions.

To use the solver in Mathcad, you must provide at least as many equations as there are variables to solve for. If you specify the value of some of the variables, you may be able to solve for the remaining variables. Figure 13 shows how to fix the problem in Figure 12. Because the *Find* function contains only the arguments z and w, Mathcad knows that you want x, y, and v to be held constant at 10, 50 and 0 respectively. A solve block with two equations becomes legitimate because there are now only two unknowns, z and w.

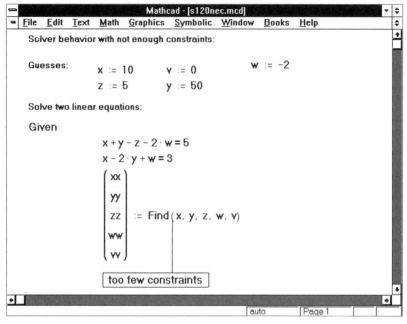

Figure 12: Five arguments in the Find make the solver think you want to solve two equations in five unknowns.

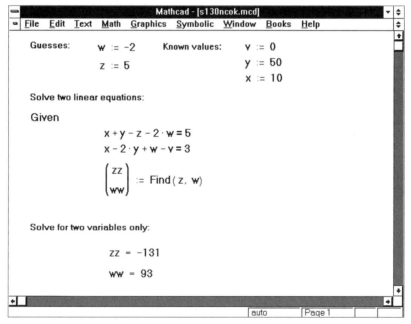

Figure 13: The problem can be solved with fewer variables as arguments to Find.

Chapter 15 Solving Equations

This section provides some ideas on how to effectively exploit Mathcad's ability to solve systems of simultaneous equations.

Repeatedly solving an equation

The techniques given thus far, while they are effective for solving a particular system of equations, are limited by two things:

- Every time you use a *Find*, you must have the rest of the solve block to go with it. If you don't, you get the error *"no matching Given."*

- If you want to change some of the parameters or constants in your system of equations to see how these affect the solution, you have to go all the way back to the solve block to change them.

Both these drawbacks are overcome by Mathcad's ability to define a function in terms of a solve block.

If you define a function with *Find* somewhere on the right hand side, this function will solve the system of equations each time you use it. This overcomes the first problem.

If this function has as its arguments the same parameters that you want to vary in the solve block, you can simply change the parameters by changing the numbers you place in the function's argument list. This overcomes the second problem.

Figure 14 shows a concrete example. The friction factor, f, of a pipe depends on the pipe's diameter D, its roughness ε, and the Reynolds number R. It's quite conceivable that you would want to experiment with different size pipes (D) made of different types of concrete (ε).

The equation in Figure 14 shows the relationship between these parameters. The equation is too complicated to define a function of R, D and ε simply by solving for f in terms of R, D and ε.

You can, however, define a function in terms of a solve block. Whenever you ask Mathcad to evaluate the function *FricFac*(ε, D, R), Mathcad takes the ε, D, and R that you supply, replaces the corresponding variables in the solve block, solves for f, and returns the value.

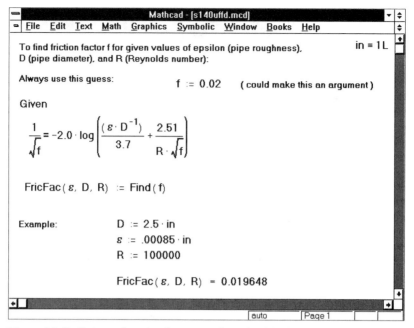

Figure 14: Defining a function in terms of a solve block.

Suppose that you've settled on a pipe size and material (*D* and ε), and you now want to try several different values of the Reynolds numbers. Although the *FricFac* function in Figure 14 was defined in terms of a solve block, it still is a function like any other. As such, you can use it with range variables.

Figure 15 shows how to solve for and plot the friction factor for many different values of the Reynolds number. Note that when you use range variables in conjunction with a solve block this way, you are actually solving the system of equations once for each value of the range variable. As a result, this type of calculation has the potential to be quite time consuming.

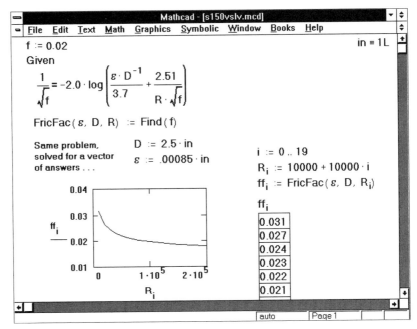

File   Edit   Text   Math   Graphics   Symbolic   Window   Books   Help

$f := 0.02$ $in \equiv 1L$

Given

$$\frac{1}{\sqrt{f}} = -2.0 \cdot \log\left(\frac{\varepsilon \cdot D^{-1}}{3.7} + \frac{2.51}{R \cdot \sqrt{f}}\right)$$

$FricFac(\varepsilon, D, R) := Find(f)$

Same problem, $D := 2.5 \cdot in$ $i := 0 .. 19$
solved for a vector $\varepsilon := .00085 \cdot in$ $R_i := 10000 + 10000 \cdot i$
of answers . . . $ff_i := FricFac(\varepsilon, D, R_i)$

ff_i

ff_i
0.031
0.027
0.024
0.023
0.022
0.021

Figure 15: A vector of solutions.

The previous example involves only one equation in one unknown. It is possible to solve a system of equations iteratively as well, however special care must be taken when you display the result to avoid receiving a *"non-scalar value"* error message.

The example in Figure 16 is a variation of that shown in Figure 10. Suppose you are looking for the intersection of a line and a circle of varying radius, R. In keeping with the example of Figure 15, you could define a function in terms of a solve block. In this case, the appropriate function is $F(R) := Find(x, y)$. This function returns a vector whose elements are the x and y coordinates of the intersection.

The key difference is that this function returns a vector of two values for each value of R. Therefore when you ask it to display the answers by typing **F(R) =**, you are asking it to display not just a table of numbers, but a table in which each element is a vector of two numbers. Since Mathcad has no way to display this on your screen it returns the error message *"non-scalar value."*

The solution is to display a table of the components $F(R)_0$ and $F(R)_1$ separately. By typing **F(R)[0=**, you get a table of all the x values of the intersection points. Similarly, by typing **F(R)[1=**, you get a table of all the y values of the intersection points.

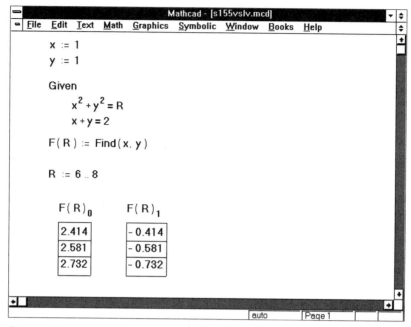

Figure 16: How to display three solutions, each of which is a two element vector.

Solving the same problem for different variables

You will occasionally run into a problem in which you want to change the roles of knowns and unknowns in an equation. For example, consider the equation that relates interest rate, loan amount, term of loan, and payments. If you know three of these four quantities, you can solve for the missing one.

The worksheet in Figure 17 shows that for a 12% loan on a 30-year mortgage and a payment of $1000 per month, the largest possible loan is $97,218.33.

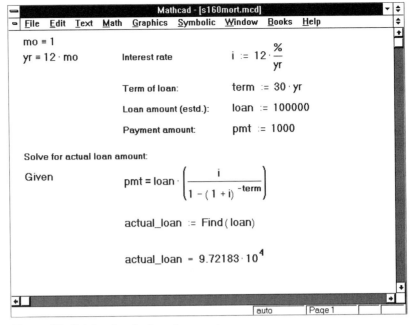

Figure 17: Solving for the loan in a mortgage.

With a few simple changes, the same worksheet can be used to solve for the interest rate. Suppose now that the amount of the loan is known to be $120,000. How far would interest rates have to drop to before the payments dropped to $1000 per month? Figure 18 shows the answer.

If you compare Figures 17 and 18, you'll see that they are very much the same. The main difference lies in the argument of the *Find* function. To change what is fixed and what is variable in an equation, simply change the arguments of the *Find* function.

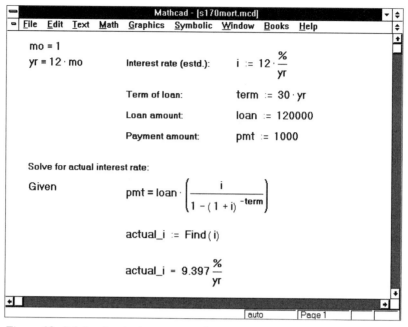

mo = 1
yr = 12 · mo

Interest rate (estd.): $i := 12 \cdot \dfrac{\%}{yr}$

Term of loan: term := 30 · yr

Loan amount: loan := 120000

Payment amount: pmt := 1000

Solve for actual interest rate:

Given

$$pmt = loan \cdot \left(\frac{i}{1 - (1+i)^{-term}} \right)$$

$$actual\_i := Find(i)$$

$$actual\_i = 9.397 \frac{\%}{yr}$$

auto   Page 1

Figure 18: Solving for the interest rate in a mortgage.

Approximate solutions

Mathcad supplies a function very similar to *Find* called *Minerr*. This function uses exactly the same algorithm as *Find*. The difference is that if the solver cannot make any further improvements to the solution, *Minerr* returns a value anyway. The *Find* function on the other hand, will return the error message "*did not find solution*" instead. You use *Minerr* exactly the way you would use *Find*.

Minerr($z1, z2, z3, \ldots$)   Returns the solution to a system of equations. Number of arguments matches the number of unknowns.

Minerr usually returns an answer that minimizes the errors in the constraints. However, *Minerr* cannot verify that its answers represent an absolute minimum for the errors in the constraints. If you use *Minerr* in a solve block, you should always include additional checks on the reasonableness of the results. The built-in variable *ERR* gives the size of the error vector for the approximate solution. There is no built-in variable for determining the size of the error for individual solutions to the unknowns.

Minerr is particularly useful for solving certain non-linear least squares problems. Figure 19 shows an example in which *Minerr* is used to obtain the unknown parameters in a Weibull distribution. The function *genfit* is also useful for solving non-linear least squares problems. See Chapter 265 for more information on *genfit*.

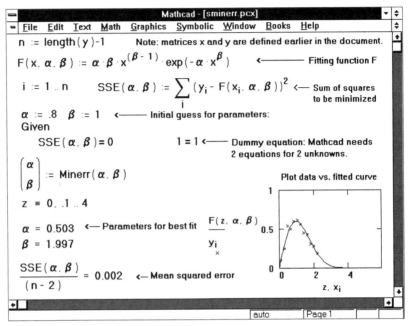

Figure 19: Using the minerr function to do non-linear least squares fitting.

Using the symbolic solver

You can usually find numerical roots quickly and accurately with Mathcad's *root* function. But there are some circumstances in which you might want to use Mathcad's symbolic solver find exact or approximate roots:

- If the equation you're solving has a parameter, a symbolic solution may allow you to express the answer directly in terms of the parameter. Then instead of solving the equation over again for each new value of the parameter, you can just substitute its value into your symbolic solution.

- If you need all the complex roots of a polynomial of degree 4 or less, the symbolic solver will give them to you in a single vector, either exactly or numerically. The symbolic solver will also find complete solutions for *some* polynomials of higher degree.

Chapter 15 Solving Equations

Chapter 16
Solving Differential Equations

This chapter describes how to solve both ordinary and partial differential equations having real valued solutions. Mathcad comes with a variety of functions for solving differential equations. Some of these exploit properties of the differential equation to improve speed and accuracy. Others are useful when you intend to plot the solution rather than simply evaluate it at an endpoint.

The following sections make up this chapter:

Solving ordinary differential equations

Using the *rkfixed* function to solve an nth order ordinary differential equation with initial conditions. This section is a prerequisite for all other sections in this chapter.

Systems of differential equations

How to adapt the *rkfixed* function to solve systems of differential equations with initial conditions.

Specialized differential equation solvers

A description of additional differential equation solving functions and when you may want to use them.

Boundary value problems

How to solve boundary value problems involving multivariate functions.

Solving ordinary differential equations

In a differential equation, you solve for an unknown function rather than just a number. For ordinary differential equations, the unknown function is a function of one variable. Partial differential equations are differential equations in which the unknown is a function of two or more variables.

Mathcad has a variety of functions for returning the solution to an ordinary differential equation. Each of these functions solves differential equations numerically. You'll always get back a matrix containing the values of the function evaluated over a set of points. These functions differ in the particular algorithm each uses for solving differential equations. Despite these differences however, each of these functions requires you to specify at least three things:

- The initial conditions.

- A range of points over which you want the solution to be evaluated.

- The differential equation itself, written in the particular form discussed in this chapter.

This section shows how to solve a single ordinary differential equation using the function *rkfixed*. It begins with an example of how to solve a simple first order differential equation and then proceeds to show how to solve higher order differential equations.

First order differential equations

A first order differential equation is one in which the highest order derivative of the unknown function is the first derivative. Figure 1 shows an example of how to solve the relatively simple differential equation:

$$\frac{dy}{dx} + 3 \cdot y = 0$$

subject to the initial condition:

$$y(0) = 4$$

The function *rkfixed* in Figure 1 uses the Fourth order Runge-Kutta method to return a two column matrix in which:

- The left hand column contains the points at which the solution to the differential equation is evaluated.

- The right hand column contains the corresponding values of the solution.

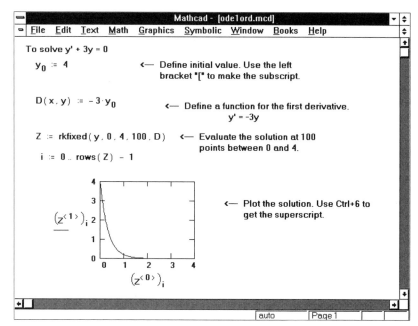

To solve $y' + 3y = 0$

$y_0 := 4$ $\longleftarrow$ Define initial value. Use the left
                bracket "[" to make the subscript.

$D(x, y) := -3 \cdot y_0$ $\longleftarrow$ Define a function for the first derivative.
                          $y' = -3y$

$Z := \text{rkfixed}(y, 0, 4, 100, D)$ $\longleftarrow$ Evaluate the solution at 100
                                       points between 0 and 4.

$i := 0 .. \text{rows}(Z) - 1$

$\longleftarrow$ Plot the solution. Use Ctrl+6 to
                get the superscript.

Figure 1: Solving a first order differential equation.

The arguments to the *rkfixed* function are:

---

rkfixed(**y**, *x1*, *x2*, *npoints*, **D**)

> **y** = A vector of n initial values where n is the order of the differential equation or the size of the system of equations you're solving. For a first order differential equation like that in Figure 1, the vector degenerates to one point, $y_0 = y(x1)$.

> *x1, x2* = The endpoints of the interval on which the solution to the differential equations will be evaluated. The initial values in **y** are the values at *x1*.

> *npoints* = The number of points beyond the initial point at which the solution is to be approximated. This controls the number of rows (1 + *npoints*) in the matrix returned by *rkfixed*.

> **D**(*x*, **y**) = An n-element vector-valued function containing the first derivatives of the unknown functions.

The most difficult part of solving a differential equation is solving for the first derivative so you can define the function $\mathbf{D}(x, \mathbf{y})$. In Figure 1 it was easy to solve for $y'(x)$. Sometimes, however, particularly with non-linear differential equations, it can be difficult. In such cases, you can sometimes solve for $y'(x)$ symbolically and paste it into the definition for $\mathbf{D}(x, \mathbf{y})$. To do so, use the Solve for Variable command from the Symbolic menu as discussed on page 401.

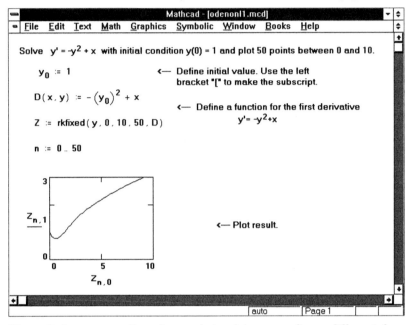

Figure 2: A more complicated example involving a non-linear differential equation.

Second order differential equations

Once you know how to solve a first order differential equation, you're most of the way to knowing how to solve higher order differential equations. We start with a second order equation. The key differences are:

- The vector of initial values **y** now has two elements: the value of the function and its first derivative at the starting value, $x1$.

- The function $\mathbf{D}(t, \mathbf{y})$ is now a vector with two elements:

$$\mathbf{D}(t, \mathbf{y}) = \begin{pmatrix} y'(t) \\ y''(t) \end{pmatrix}$$

- The solution matrix contains three columns: the left-hand one for the t values; the middle one for $y(t)$; and the right-hand one for $y'(t)$.

The example in Figure 3 shows how to solve the second order differential equation:

$$y'' = -y' + 2 \cdot y$$
$$y(0) = 1 \qquad y'(0) = 3$$

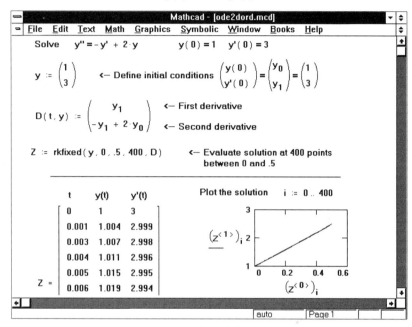

Figure 3: Solving a second order differential equation.

Higher order equations

The procedure for solving higher order differential equations is an extension of that used for second order differential equations. The main difference is that:

- The vector of initial values **y** now has n elements for specifying initial conditions of $y, y', y'' \ldots y^{(n-1)}$.

- The function **D** is now a vector with n elements:

$$\mathbf{D}(t,\mathbf{y}) = \begin{pmatrix} y'(t) \\ y''(t) \\ \cdot \\ \cdot \\ \cdot \\ y^{(n)}(t) \end{pmatrix}$$

- The solution matrix contains n columns: the left-hand one for the t values and the remaining columns for values of $y(t), y'(t), y''(t) \ldots y^{(n-1)}(t)$.

The example in Figure 4 shows how to solve the fourth order differential equation:

$$y'''' - 2k^2 y'' + k^4 y = 0$$

subject to the initial conditions:

$$y(0) = 0 \quad y'(0) = 1 \quad y''(0) = 2 \quad y'''(0) = 3$$

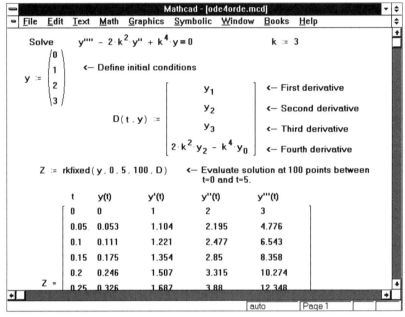

Figure 4: Solving a higher order differential equation.

Systems of differential equations

The procedure for solving a coupled system of differential equations follows closely that for solving a higher order differential equation. In fact, you can think of solving a higher order differential equation as just a special case of solving a system of differential equations.

Systems of first order differential equations

To solve a system of first order differential equations:

■ Define a vector containing the initial values of each unknown function.

■ Define a vector-valued function containing the first derivatives of each of the unknown functions.

■ Decide which points you want to evaluate the solutions at.

■ Pass all this information into *rkfixed*.

The *rkfixed* function will return a matrix whose first column contains the points at which the solutions are evaluated and whose remaining columns contain the solution functions evaluated at the corresponding point. Figure 5 shows an example solving the equations:

$$x'_0(t) = \mu \cdot x_0(t) - x_1(t) - (x_0(t)^2 + x_1(t)^2) \cdot x_0(t)$$

$$x'_1(t) = \mu \cdot x_1(t) + x_0(t) - (x_0(t)^2 + x_1(t)^2) \cdot x_1(t)$$

with initial conditions:

$$x_0(0) = 0 \text{ and } x_1(0) = 1$$

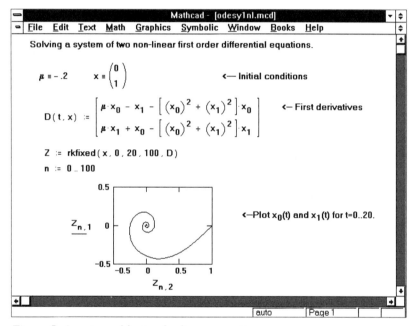

Figure 5: A system of first order linear equations.

Systems of higher order differential equations

The procedure for solving a system of nth-order differential equations is similar to the procedure for solving a system of first order differential equations. The main differences are:

■ The vector of initial conditions must contain initial values for the $n - 1$ derivatives of each unknown function in addition to initial values for the functions themselves.

■ The vector-valued function must contain expressions for the $n - 1$ derivatives of each unknown function in addition to the nth-derivative.

The example in Figure 6 shows how to go about solving the system of second order differential equations:

$$u''(t) = 2v(t)$$
$$v''(t) = 4v(t) - 2u(t)$$

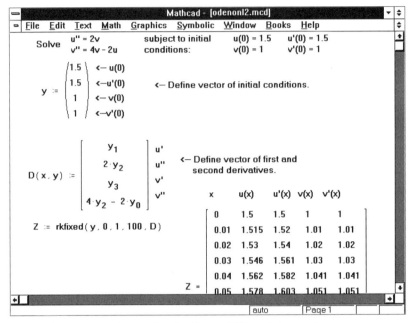

Figure 6: A system of second order linear differential equations.

The function *rkfixed* returns a matrix in which:

- The first column contains the values at which the solutions and their derivatives are to be evaluated.

- The remaining columns contain the solutions and their derivatives evaluated at the corresponding point in the first column. The order in which the solution and its derivatives appear matches the order in which you put them into the vector of initial conditions that you passed into *rkfixed*.

Specialized differential equation solvers

The *rkfixed* function discussed thus far is a good general purpose differential equation solver. Although it is not always the fastest method, the Runge-Kutta technique used by this function nearly always succeeds. However there are cases in which you may want to use one of Mathcad's more specialized differential equation solvers. These cases fall into three broad categories:

- Your system of differential equations may have certain properties which are best exploited by functions other than *rkfixed*. The system may be stiff (*Stiffb*, *Stiffr*); the functions could be smooth (*Bulstoer*) or slowly varying (*Rkadapt*),

- You may have a boundary value rather than an initial value problem (*sbval* and *bvalfit*),

- You may be interested in evaluating the solution only at one point (*bulstoer*, *rkadapt*, *stiffb* and *stiffr*).

You may also want to try several methods on the same differential equation to see which one works the best. Sometimes there are subtle differences between differential equations that make one method better than another.

The following sections describe the use of the various differential equation solvers and the circumstances in which they are likely to be useful.

Smooth systems

When you know the solution is smooth, use the *Bulstoer* function instead of *rkfixed*. The *Bulstoer* function uses the Bulirsch-Stoer method rather than the Runge-Kutta method used by *rkfixed*. Under these circumstances, the solution will be slightly more accurate than that returned by *rkfixed*.

The argument list and the matrix returned by *Bulstoer* is identical to that for *rkfixed*.

Bulstoer(**y**, *x1*, *x2*, *npoints*, **D**)

    y = A vector of *n* initial values.

    x1, *x2* = The endpoints of the interval on which the solution to the differential equations will be evaluated. The initial values in **y** are the values at *x1*.

    npoints = The number of points beyond the initial point at which the solution is to be approximated. This controls the number of rows (1 + *npoints*) in the matrix returned by *Bulstoer*.

    D(*x*, **y**) = An *n*-element vector-valued function containing the first derivatives of the unknown functions.

Slowly varying solutions

Given a fixed number of points, you can approximate a function more accurately if you evaluate it frequently wherever it's changing fast and infrequently wherever it's changing more slowly. If you know that the solution has this property, you may be better off using *Rkadapt*. Unlike *rkfixed* which evaluates a solution at equally spaced intervals, *Rkadapt* examines how fast the solution is changing and adapts its step-size accordingly. This "adaptive stepsize control" enables *Rkadapt* to focus on those parts of the integration domain where the function is rapidly changing rather than wasting time integrating a function where it isn't changing all that rapidly.

Note that although *Rkadapt* will use nonuniform step sizes internally when it solves the differential equation, it will nevertheless return the solution at equally spaced points.

Rkadapt takes the same arguments as *rkfixed*. The matrix returned by *Rkadapt* is identical in form to that returned by *rkfixed*.

Rkadapt(**y**, *x1*, *x2*, *npoints*, **D**)

> **y** = A vector of *n* initial values.

> *x1, x2* = The endpoints of the interval on which the solution to the differential equations will be evaluated. The initial values in **y** are the values at *x1*.

> *npoints* = The number of points beyond the initial point at which the solution is to be approximated. This controls the number of rows (1 + *npoints*) in the matrix returned by *Rkadapt*.

> **D**(*x*, **y**) = An *n*-element vector-valued function containing the first derivatives of the unknown functions.

Stiff systems

A system of differential equations expressed in the form:

$$\mathbf{y} = \mathbf{A} \cdot \mathbf{x}$$

is a stiff system if the matrix **A** is nearly singular. Under these conditions, the solution returned by *rkfixed* may oscillate or be unstable. When solving a stiff system, you should use one of the two differential equation solvers specifically designed for stiff systems: *Stiffb* and *Stiffr*. These use the Bulirsch-Stoer method and the Rosenbrock method for stiff systems respectively.

The form of the matrix returned by these functions is identical to that returned by *rkfixed*. However, *Stiffb* and *Stiffr* require an extra argument in the following section:

Stiffb(**y**, *x1*, *x2*, *npoints*, **D**, **J**)
Stiffr(**y**, *x1*, *x2*, *npoints*, **D**, **J**)

y = A vector of *n* initial values.

x1, *x2* = The endpoints of the interval on which the solution to the differential equations will be evaluated. The initial values in **y** are the values at *x1*.

npoints = The number of points beyond the initial point at which the solution is to be approximated. This controls the number of rows (1 + *npoints*) in the matrix returned by *Stiffb* or *Stiffr*.

D(*x*, **y**) = An *n*-element vector-valued function containing the first derivatives of the unknown functions.

J(*x*, **y**) = A function which returns the $n \times (n + 1)$ matrix whose first column contains the derivatives $\partial\mathbf{D}/\partial x$ and whose remaining rows and columns form the Jacobian matrix $(\partial\mathbf{D}/\partial y_k)$ for the system of differential equations. For example, if:

$$\mathbf{D}(x,\mathbf{y}) = \begin{pmatrix} x \cdot y_1 \\ -2 \cdot y_1 \cdot y_0 \end{pmatrix} \quad \text{then} \quad \mathbf{J}(x,\mathbf{y}) = \begin{pmatrix} y_1 & 0 & x \\ 0 & -2 \cdot y_1 & -2 \cdot y_0 \end{pmatrix}$$

Evaluating only the final value

The differential equation functions discussed so far presuppose that you're interested in seeing the solution $y(x)$ over a number of uniformly spaced x values in the integration interval bounded by $x1$ and $x2$. There may be times, however, when all you want is the value of the solution at the endpoint, $y(x2)$. Although the functions discussed so far will certainly give you $y(x2)$, they also do a lot of unecessary work returning intermediate values of $y(x)$ in which you have no interest.

If you're only interested in the value of $y(x2)$, use the functions listed below. Each function corresponds to one of those already discussed. The properties of each of these functions are identical to those of the corresponding function in the previous sections.

---

bulstoer(**y**, $x1$, $x2$, acc, **D**, $kmax$, $save$)
rkadapt(**y**, $x1$, $x2$, acc, **D**, $kmax$, $save$)
stiffb(**y**, $x1$, $x2$, acc, **D**, **J**, $kmax$, $save$)
stiffr(**y**, $x1$, $x2$, acc, **D**, **J**, $kmax$, $save$)

$\qquad$ **y** = A vector of n initial values.

$\quad$ $x1$, $x2$ = The endpoints of the interval on which the solution to the differential equations will be evaluated. The initial values in **y** are the values at $x1$.

$\qquad$ acc = Controls the accuracy of the solution. A small value of acc forces the algorithm to take smaller steps along the trajectory, thereby increasing the accuracy of the solution. Values of acc around 0.001 will generally yield accurate solutions.

$\quad$ **D**$(x, \mathbf{y})$ = An n-element vector-valued function containing the first derivatives of the unknown functions.

$\quad$ **J**$(x, \mathbf{y})$ = A function which returns the $n \times (n + 1)$ matrix whose first column contains the derivatives $\partial \mathbf{D}/\partial x$ and whose remaining rows and columns form the Jacobian matrix $(\partial \mathbf{D}/\partial y_k)$ for the system of differential equations. See page 368

$\quad$ $kmax$ = The maximum number of intermediate points at which the solution will be approximated. The value of $kmax$ places an upper bound on the number of rows of the matrix returned by these functions.

$\quad$ $save$ = The smallest allowable spacing between the values at which the solutions are to be approximated. This places a lower bound on the difference between any two numbers in the first column of the matrix returned by the function.

Boundary value problems

So far, all the functions discussed in this chapter assume that you know the value taken by the solutions and their derivatives at the beginning of the interval of integration. In other words, these functions are useful for solving initial value problems.

In many cases, however, you may know the value taken by the solution at the endpoints of the interval of integration. A good example is a stretched string constrained at both ends. Problems such as this are referred to as boundary value problems. The first section discusses two-point boundary value problems: one dimensional systems of differential equations in which the solution is a function of a single variable and the value of the solution is known at two points. The section following this discusses the more general case involving partial differential equations.

Two-point boundary value problems

The functions described so far involve finding the solution to an nth order differential equation when you know the value of the solution and its first $n-1$ derivatives at the beginning of the interval of integration. This section discusses what happens if you don't have all this information about the solution at the beginning of the interval of integration but you do know something about the solution elsewhere in the interval. In particular:

- You have an nth order differential equation.

- You know some but not all of the values of the solution and its first $n-1$ derivatives at the beginning of the interval of integration, $x1$.

- You know some but not all of the values of the solution and its first $n-1$ derivatives at the end of the interval of integration, $x2$.

- Between what you know about the solution at $x1$ and what you know about it at $x2$, you have n known values.

When this is the case, you should use *sbval* to evaluate the missing initial values at $x1$. Once you have these missing initial values, you will have an initial value problem rather than a two-point boundary value problem. You can then proceed to solve this using any of the functions discussed earlier in this chapter.

The example in Figure 7 shows how to use *sbval*. Note that *sbval* does not actually return a solution to a differential equation. It merely computes the initial values the solution must have in order for the solution to match the final values you specify. You must then take the initial values returned by *sbval* and solve the resulting initial value problem as discussed earlier in this chapter.

The *sbval* function returns a vector containing those initial values left unspecified at $x1$. The arguments to *sbval* are:

sbval(**v**, *x1*, *x2*, **D**, **load**, **score**)

v = Vector of guesses for initial values left unspecified at *x1*.

x1, *x2* = The endpoints of the interval on which the solution to the differential equations will be evaluated.

D(*x*, **y**) = An *n*-element vector-valued function containing the first derivatives of the unknown functions.

load(*x1*, **v**) = A vector-valued function whose *n* elements correspond to the values of the *n* unknown functions at *x1*. Some of these values will be constants specified by your initial conditions. Others will be unknown at the outset but will be found by *sbval*. If a value is unknown you should use the corresponding guess value from **v**.

score(*x2*, **y**) = A vector-valued function having the same number of elements as **v**. Each element is the difference between an initial condition at *x2*, as originally specified, and the corresponding estimate from the solution. The *score* vector measures how closely the proposed solution matches the initial conditions at *x2*. A value of 0 for any element indicates a perfect match between the corresponding initial condition and that returned by *sbval*.

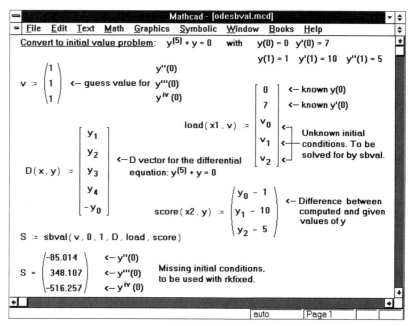

Figure 7: Using sbval to obtain initial values corresponding to given final values of a solution to a differential equation.

It's also possible that you don't have all the information you need to use *sbval* but you do know something about the solution and its first $n-1$ derivatives at some intermediate value, *xf*. This is the exactly the situation contemplated by *bvalfit*.

This function solves a two-point boundary value problem of this type by shooting from the endpoints and matching the trajectories of the solution and its derivatives at the intermediate point.

---

bvalfit(**v1**, **v2**, *x1*, *x2*, *xf*, **D**, **load1**, **load2**, **score**)

v1, **v2** = Vector **v1** contains guesses for initial values left unspecified at *x1*. Vector **v2** contains guesses for initial values left unspecified at *x2*.

x1, *x2* = The endpoints of the interval on which the solution to the differential equations will be evaluated.

xf = A point between *x1* and *x2* at which the trajectories of the solutions beginning at *x1* and those beginning at *x2* are constrained to be equal.

D(*x*, **y**) = An *n*-element vector-valued function containing the first derivatives of the unknown functions.

load1(*x1*, **v1**) = A vector-valued function whose *n* elements correspond to the values of the *n* unknown functions at *x1*. Some of these values will be constants specified by your initial conditions. If a value is unknown you should use the corresponding guess value from **v1**.

load2(*x2*, **v2**) = Analogous to *load1* but for values taken by the *n* unknown functions at *x2*.

score(*xf*, **y**) = An *n* element vector valued function used to specify how you want the solutions to match at *xf*. You'll usually want to define score(*xf*, **y**) := **y** to make the solutions to all unknown functions match up at *xf*.

This method becomes especially useful when derivative has a discontinuity somewhere in the integration interval as the example in Figure 8 illustrates.

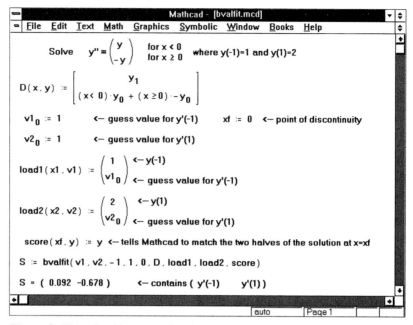

File   Edit   Text   Math   Graphics   Symbolic   Window   Books   Help

Solve $\quad y'' = \begin{pmatrix} y \\ -y \end{pmatrix} \quad \begin{matrix} \text{for } x < 0 \\ \text{for } x \geq 0 \end{matrix} \quad$ where y(-1)=1 and y(1)=2

$$D(x, y) := \begin{bmatrix} y_1 \\ (x<0) \cdot y_0 + (x \geq 0) \cdot -y_0 \end{bmatrix}$$

$v1_0 := 1 \qquad \leftarrow$ guess value for y'(-1) $\qquad$ xf := 0 $\quad \leftarrow$ point of discontinuity

$v2_0 := 1 \qquad \leftarrow$ guess value for y'(1)

$\text{load1}(x1, v1) := \begin{pmatrix} 1 \\ v1_0 \end{pmatrix} \begin{matrix} \leftarrow y(-1) \\ \leftarrow \text{guess value for y'(-1)} \end{matrix}$

$\text{load2}(x2, v2) := \begin{pmatrix} 2 \\ v2_0 \end{pmatrix} \begin{matrix} \leftarrow y(1) \\ \leftarrow \text{guess value for y'(1)} \end{matrix}$

$\text{score}(xf, y) := y \quad \leftarrow$ tells Mathcad to match the two halves of the solution at x=xf

$S := \text{bvalfit}(v1, v2, -1, 1, 0, D, \text{load1}, \text{load2}, \text{score})$

$S = (\ 0.092 \quad -0.678\ ) \qquad \leftarrow$ contains (y'(-1) $\quad$ y'(1))

auto   Page 1

Figure 8: Using bvalfit to match solutions in the middle of the integration interval.

Partial differential equations

A second type of boundary value problem arises when you are solving a partial differential equation. Rather than fixing the value of a solution at two points as was done in the previous section, we now fix the solution at a whole continuum of points representing some boundary.

Two partial differential equations that arise often in the analysis of physical systems are Poisson's equation:

$$\frac{\partial^2 u}{\partial x^2} + \frac{\partial^2 u}{\partial y^2} = \rho(x, y)$$

and its homogeneous form, Laplace's equation.

Mathcad has two functions for solving these equations over a square boundary. You should use the *relax* function if you know the value taken by the unknown function $u(x, y)$ on all four sides of a square region.

If $u(x, y)$ is zero on all four sides of the square, you can use *multigrid* function instead. This function will often solve the problem faster than *relax*. Note that if the boundary condition is the same on all four sides, you can simply transform the equation to an equivalent one in which the value is zero on all four sides.

The *relax* function returns a square matrix in which:

■ An element's location in the matrix corresponds to its location within the square region, and

- Its value approximates the value of the solution at that point.

This function uses the relaxation method to converge to the solution. Poisson's equation on a square domain is represented by:

$$a_{j,k}u_{j+1,k} + b_{j,k}u_{j-1,k} + c_{j,k}u_{j,k+1} + d_{j,k}u_{j,k-1} + e_{j,k}u_{j,k} = f_{j,k}$$

The arguments taken by these functions are shown below:

---

relax(**a**, **b**, **c**, **d**, **e**, **f**, **u**, *rjac*)

a, **b**, **c**, **d**, **e** = Square matrices all of the same size containing coefficients of the above equation.

f = Square matrix containing the source term at each point in the region in which the solution is sought.

u = Square matrix containing boundary values along the edges of the region and initial guesses for the solution inside the region.

rjac = Spectral radius of the Jacobi iteration. This number between 0 and 1 controls the convergence of the relaxation algorithm. Its optimal value depends on the details of your problem.

If the boundary condition is zero on all four sides of the square integration domain, use the *multigrid* function instead. An example is shown in Figure 9. The same problem solved with the *relax* function instead is shown in Figure 10.

---

multigrid(**M**, *ncycle*)

M = $1 + 2^n$ row square matrix whose elements correspond to the source term at the corresponding point in the square domain.

ncycle = The number of cycles at each level of the *multigrid* iteration. A value of 2 will generally give a good approximation of the solution.

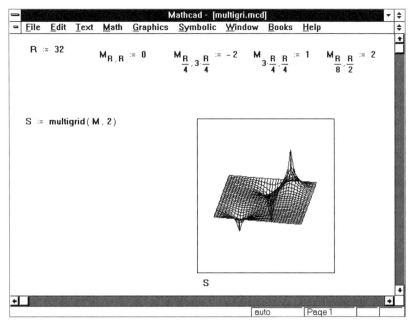

Figure 9: Using multigrid to solve a Poisson's equation in a square domain.

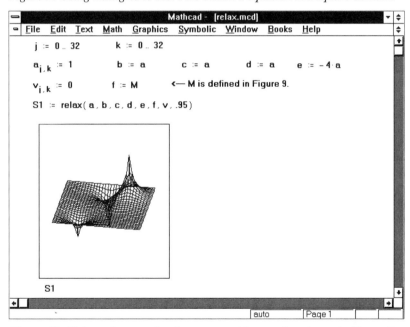

Figure 10: Using relax to solve the same problem as that shown in Figure 9.

Chapter 17
Symbolic Calculation

This chapter describes symbolic processing in Mathcad. The chapter includes the following sections:

What is symbolic math?

An overview of Mathcad's symbolic math features.

Live symbolic evaluation

Using the symbolic equal sign to perform a variety of symbolic transformations.

Symbolic algebra

Using menu commands to manipulate expressions algebraically.

Symbolic calculus

Evaluating indefinite integrals, derivatives and limits symbolically.

Solving equations symbolically

Algebraic solution of equations or systems of equations.

Symbolic matrix manipulation

Finding the symbolic transpose, inverse, and determinant of a matrix.

Symbolic transforms

Fourier, Laplace and z-transforms.

Displaying symbolic results

Controlling the display of symbolic results.

Symbolic optimization

Symbolically simplifying complex equations before numerically evaluating them.

Using functions and variables

Differences in how the symbolic and numerical processors work with variables and functions.

Limits to symbolic processing

Difficulties you may encounter in symbolic processing and what to do about them.

What is symbolic math?

Up until now, you've seen Mathcad engaging in *numerical* mathematics. This means that whenever you evaluate an expression, Mathcad returns one or more *numbers* as shown at the top of Figure 1. Although these numbers are quite useful, they provide little insight into the underlying relationship between the components in an expression.

When Mathcad engages in *symbolic* mathematics, however, the result of evaluating an expression is generally another expression as shown in the bottom of Figure 1. The form of this second expression is to a great extent under your control. You can factor the original expression, integrate it, expand it into a series, and so on. The way you control the form of that second expression is the subject of this chapter.

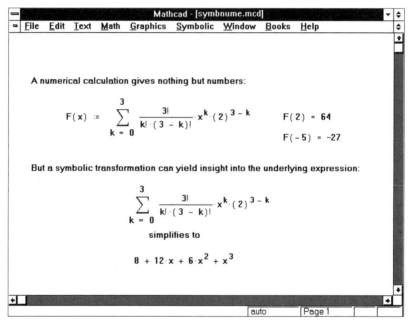

Figure 1: A numerical and symbolic evaluation of the same expression.

There are three ways to perform a symbolic transformation on an expression.

- If you're using Mathcad PLUS you can use the symbolic equal sign as described in the section "Live symbolic evaluation." This method feels very much as if you're engaging in numerical math.

- If you need more control over the symbolic transformation, you can use the individual commands described in the section "Using the Symbolic menu"

- If you're using Mathcad PLUS, you can make the numerical and symbolic processors work together; the latter simplifying an expression behind the scenes so that the former can work with it more efficiently. This is discussed in the section "Symbolic optimization."

Chapter 17 Symbolic Calculation

Symbolic processing also raises some subtle issues concerning the use of functions and variables. These are described in the section "Using functions and variables."

Finally, there are some fundamental limits inherent in computer based symbolic processing generally. These arise because nobody really knows how the human brain does symbolic processing. As a result, nobody really knows how to teach a computer to do it. These limits are discussed in the last section "Limitations of symbolic processing."

Live symbolic evaluation

Mathcad
PLUS

The symbolic equal sign provides a way to extend Mathcad's live document interface beyond the numerical evaluation of expressions. You can think of it as being analogous to the equal sign "=". Unlike the equal sign, which always gives a number on the right hand side, the symbolic equal sign is capable of giving expressions.

To use the symbolic equal sign you must be running Mathcad PLUS. If you are, you can simplify an expression as follows:

- Make sure the **Automatic Mode** command on the **Math** menu has a checkmark beside it. If it doesn't choose it from the menu.

- Make sure the **Live Symbolics** command on the **Math** menu has a checkmark beside it. If it doesn't choose it from the menu. Note that this command is gray until the **Automatic Mode** command from the **Math** menu is checked.

- Enter the expression you want to simplify.

- Press [Ctrl]. (the control key followed by a period). Mathcad displays an arrow, "→".

- Click outside the expression. Mathcad displays a simplified version of the original expression. If an expression cannot be simplified further, Mathcad simply repeats it to the right of the arrow.

The symbolic equal sign is a live operator just like any Mathcad operator. When you make a change anywhere above or to the left of it, Mathcad updates the result. The symbolic equal sign "knows" about previously defined functions and variables and uses them wherever appropriate. You can force the symbolic equal sign to ignore prior definitions of functions and variables by using the **assume** keyword as shown in Figure 4.

Figure 2 shows some examples of how to use this operator. Note that the "→" only applies to an entire expression. You cannot, for example, use the "→" to transform only part of an expression. Nor can you apply the "→" to the result of a previous "→".

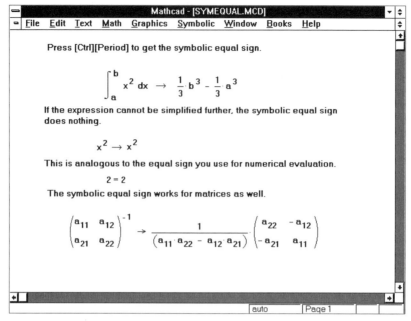

The Mathcad window shown contains:

Mathcad - [SYMEQUAL.MCD]

File Edit Text Math Graphics Symbolic Window Books Help

Press [Ctrl][Period] to get the symbolic equal sign.

$$\int_a^b x^2 \, dx \;\rightarrow\; \frac{1}{3} \cdot b^3 - \frac{1}{3} \cdot a^3$$

If the expression cannot be simplified further, the symbolic equal sign does nothing.

$$x^2 \rightarrow x^2$$

This is analogous to the equal sign you use for numerical evaluation.

$$2 = 2$$

The symbolic equal sign works for matrices as well.

$$\begin{pmatrix} a_{11} & a_{12} \\ a_{21} & a_{22} \end{pmatrix}^{-1} \;\rightarrow\; \frac{1}{\left(a_{11} \cdot a_{22} - a_{12} \cdot a_{21}\right)} \cdot \begin{pmatrix} a_{22} & -a_{12} \\ -a_{21} & a_{11} \end{pmatrix}$$

auto   Page 1

Figure 2: Using the symbolic equal sign.

Customizing the symbolic equal sign

The "→" takes the left-hand side and places a simplified version of it on the right-hand side. By default, it simplifies the left-hand side just as if you had chosen **Evaluate⇒Evaluate Symbolically** from the **Symbolic** menu (see page 387).

Of course, exactly what "simplify" means is a matter of opinion. As a result, you can, to a limited extent, control how the "→" transforms the expression by putting one of the following keywords before the expression containing it. For more comprehensive control over symbolic transformations, you must use the **Symbolic** menu.

Keyword	Function
simplify	Simplifies the expression, performing arithmetic, canceling common factors and using basic trigonometric and inverse function identities.
expand	Expands all powers and products of sums in the selected expression.
series	Expands an expression in one or more variables around a specified point. By default, the expansion is a polynomial of order six.
factor	Factors the selected expression into a product, if the entire expression can be written as a product.

assume	Tells Mathcad to treat the variable which follows as an undefined variable even though it may have had a number assigned to it. Also used to specify constraints to be used in the evaluation of the expression.
complex	Tells Mathcad to carry out symbolic evaluation in the complex domain. Result will usually be in the form $a + i \cdot b$.
float	Tells Mathcad to display a floating point value whenever possible.
literally	Prevents the symbolic processor from attempting to optimize whatever equation immediately follows.

Keywords are case sensitive and must therefore be typed exactly as shown. They are not, however, font sensitive.

Figure 3 shows some examples of how to use these keywords. Note that a keyword acts only on the very next occurrence of a "$\rightarrow$".

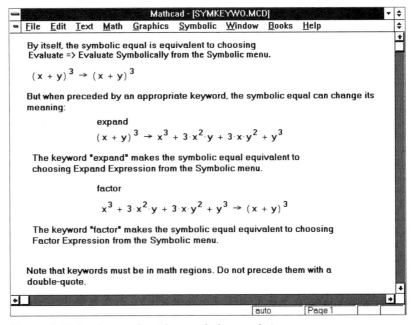

Figure 3: Using keywords with a symbolic equal sign.

When you use the symbolic equal sign to evaluate an expression, Mathcad checks all the variables and functions making up that expression to see if they've been defined earlier in the worksheet. If Mathcad does find a definition, it uses it. Any other variables and functions are evaluated symbolically.

There are three exceptions to this, all of which are illustrated in Figure 4. In evaluating an expression made up of previously defined variables and functions, Mathcad *ignores* prior definitions:

- when the variable is defined as a number containing a decimal point,

- when the keyword **assume** precedes the definition, or

- when the variable has been defined as a range variable.

You can also use the keyword **assume** to assume constraints on the variables in the expression. The last example in Figure 4 illustrates how an integral can be made to converge by assuming a variable is positive. Note that in order to specify more than one condition, you simply separate the conditions with a comma as shown in the last example in Figure 4.

The keyword **assume** must precede any other keywords applied to an expression. This is because a keyword will apply only to the expression immediately following it. An example is shown in the middle of Figure 4.

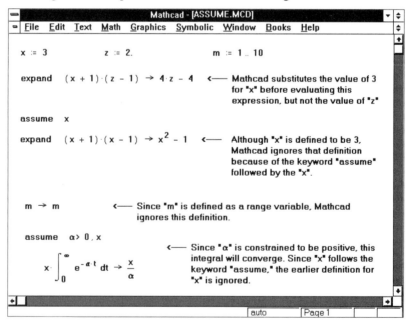

Figure 4: The keyword **assume** *controls whether or not Mathcad substitutes values for variable and function names into an expression.*

The keywords **complex** and **float** provide some additional control over the form in which Mathcad displays a symbolic result.

The keyword **complex** before an expression causes Mathcad to return a result in the form $a + i \cdot b$. This generally yields an unnecessarily complicated expression when all parameters are real. However when one or more parameters are complex, the ability to see this more general representation becomes useful. Figure 5 compares some transformations with and without the **complex** keyword.

The **float** keyword will make the next symbolic result display as a floating point number whenever possible. You can control the precision of this number by following **float** with an appropriate integer as shown in Figure 6. In Figure 6, Mathcad can display the term $\pi/2$ in floating point. The **float** keyword has no effect on X, however. Since X is not defined, Mathcad cannot display it as anything but X.

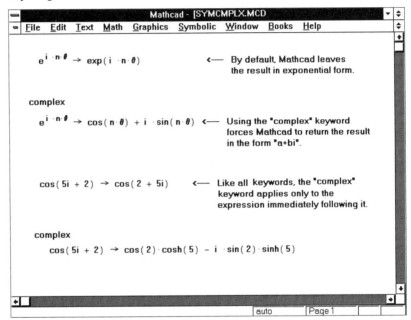

Figure 5: The keyword **complex** *controls whether or not Mathcad tries to return a result in the form* $a + b \cdot i$.

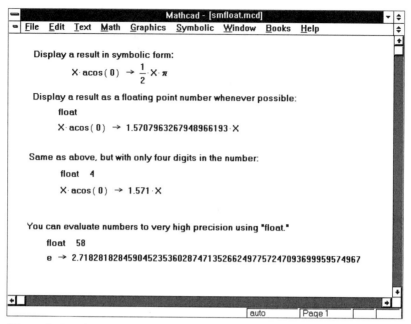

Mathcad - [smfloat.mcd]

File Edit Text Math Graphics Symbolic Window Books Help

Display a result in symbolic form:

$$X \cdot acos(0) \rightarrow \frac{1}{2} \cdot X \cdot \pi$$

Display a result as a floating point number whenever possible:

float

$$X \cdot acos(0) \rightarrow 1.5707963267948966193 \cdot X$$

Same as above, but with only four digits in the number:

float 4

$$X \cdot acos(0) \rightarrow 1.571 \cdot X$$

You can evaluate numbers to very high precision using "float."

float 58

$$e \rightarrow 2.7182818284590452353602874713526624977572470936999959574967$$

auto   Page 1

Figure 6: Use the **float** *keyword to display results in terms of numbers whenever possible.*

The **series** keyword is used to expand an expression around a particular combination of variables. By default, Mathcad expands a series around zero and includes all terms whose exponents sum to less than six. You can, however, specify the points around which to expand a series as shown in Figure 7. This is particularly useful when an expression has a singularity at 0. You can also specify the order of the expansion as shown in the last example in Figure 7.

Occasionally, a series will contain coefficients displayed in rather lengthy symbolic form. You may want to use the **float** keyword in conjunction with **series** as shown in Figure 7. In the expansion shown, you would get an expression involving exp(1) in the absence of the **float** keyword.

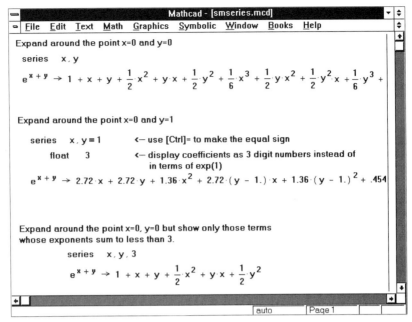

Figure 7: Use the **series** keyword to expand an expression around a particular point.

Using the Symbolic menu

Although the symbolic equal sign discussed in the last section is convenient to use, its repertoire of symbolic transformations is limited. The commands on the Symbolic menu provide considerably more control over the kinds of symbolic transformation you can do.

The basic steps for using the **Symbolic** menu are the same for all the menu commands:

- Enclose whatever you want to transform in a selection box.

- Choose the appropriate command from the **Symbolic** menu.

- Mathcad will place the transformed expression into your document.

There is an important difference between symbolic evaluation using the **Symbolic** menu and using the symbolic equal sign as described in the previous section. Results to the right of a symbolic equal sign are re-evaluated whenever you make a change to your worksheet. A result obtained through the **Symbolic** menu, on the other hand, will not update automatically.

For example, suppose that after selecting an expression you choose **Factor Expression** from the **Symbolic** menu. Mathcad inserts the factored result. If you now edit the original expression, the symbolic answer won't change. To get a new answer, you must select the expression you just changed and choose **Factor Expression** from the menu again. Mathcad inserts a new result and pushes down the old result.

The following sections describe the various **Symbolic** menu commands in detail.

Symbolic algebra

Certain commands from the **Symbolic** menu allow you to manipulate expressions algebraically. You can simplify, expand, and factor expressions. You can also collect like terms of an expression, find the coefficients of a polynomial, expand an expression into a series, or change all occurrences of a variable to whatever is on the clipboard.

Symbolic evaluation

In general, to evaluate an expression symbolically follow these steps:

- Enter the expression.

- Surround it with the blue selection box.

- Press [**Shift**][**F9**].

If you're using Mathcad PLUS, you'll have two other ways to evaluate an expression:

- You can choose **Evaluate⇒Complex Evaluation** to express results in complex form whenever possible.

- You can choose **Evaluate⇒Floating Point Evaluation** to express a result as a number whenever possible.

When evaluating expressions containing complex numbers, you may want to choose **Evaluate⇒Complex Evaluation** from the **Symbolic** menu. This will force Mathcad to express results in the form $a + b \cdot i$. Figure 8 shows an example.

Ordinarily, the symbolic processor returns results by rearranging variables. Thus, when Mathcad evaluates an expression involving π or e, it will usually return another expression involving π or $\exp(x)$. To force Mathcad to return a number instead, choose **Evaluate⇒Floating Point Evaluation** from the **Symbolic** menu. This brings up a dialog box in which you can specify the number of digits to the right of the decimal point. By default, this number is set to 20.

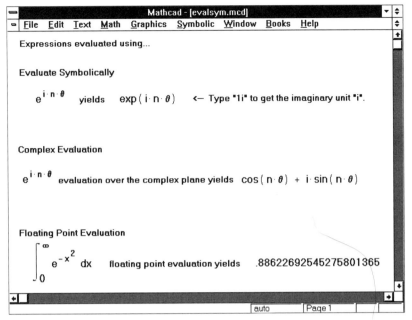

Figure 8: Evaluating expressions symbolically using additional commands from the Mathcad PLUS **Evaluate** *pull-right menu.*

The symbolic processor treats numbers containing a decimal point differently from numbers without a decimal point. The general rule is as follows:

- When you send numbers with decimal points to the symbolic processor, any numerical results you get back will be decimal approximations to the exact answer.

- When you send numbers without decimal points to the symbolic processor, any numerical results you get back will be expressed without decimal points whenever possible.

Figure 9 shows some examples of how the decimal point affects the answers you get from the symbolic processor. In this example, note how $\sqrt{17}$ comes back unchanged since there is no rational square root of 17. But $\sqrt{17.0}$ comes back as a decimal approximation to the irrational number $\sqrt{17}$.

When a symbolic operation gives an approximate decimal answer, this answer is always displayed with 20 significant digits. This display is not affected by Mathcad's local or global numerical formats.

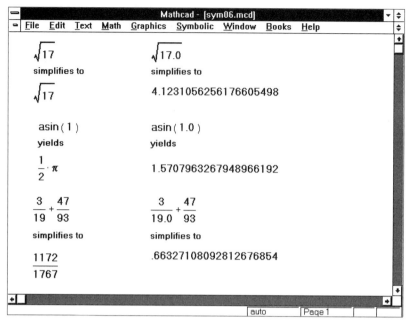

Figure 9: Numerical answers in symbolic calculations.

Simplifying an expression

The **Simplify** command carries out basic algebraic and trigonometric simplification of the selected expression. **Simplify** performs arithmetic, cancels common factors, uses basic trigonometric and inverse function identities, and simplifies square roots and powers.

You can simplify parts of expressions (for example, the denominator of a fraction, or one term of a sum) as well as entire expressions. You can also simplify expressions involving arrays such as sums or products of matrices. To do so, enclose the expression you want to select in the selection box before choosing **Simplify**.

Mathcad may sometimes be able to simplify parts of an expression even when it cannot simplify the entire expression. If selecting the entire expression and choosing **Simplify** doesn't give the answer you want, try selecting and simplifying subexpressions. If Mathcad can't simplify an expression any further, you'll just get the original expression back as the answer. Figure 10 illustrates some results of applying the **Simplify** command.

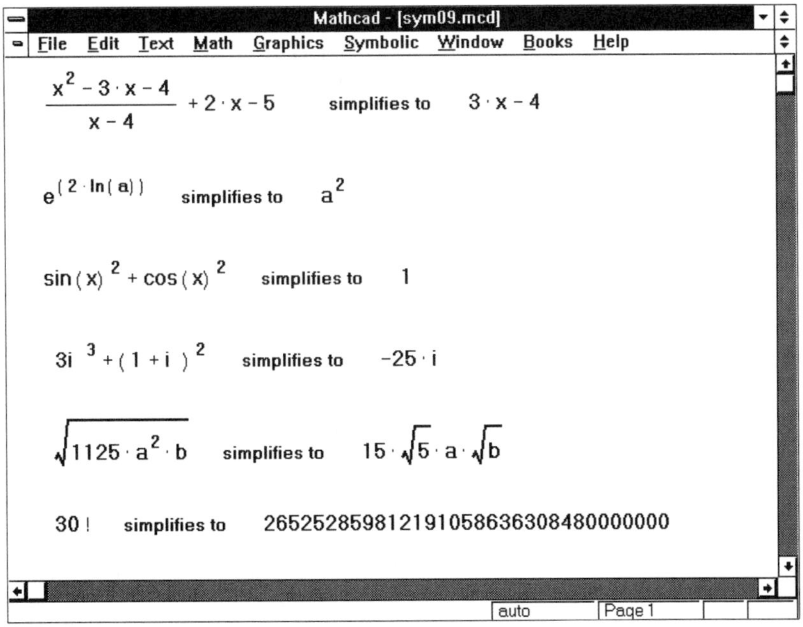
Mathcad - [sym09.mcd]
File Edit Text Math Graphics Symbolic Window Books Help
(x^2 - 3·x - 4)/(x - 4) + 2·x - 5 simplifies to 3·x - 4
e^(2·ln(a)) simplifies to a^2
sin(x)^2 + cos(x)^2 simplifies to 1
3i^3 + (1 + i)^2 simplifies to -25·i
√(1125·a^2·b) simplifies to 15·√5·a·√b
30! simplifies to 265252859812191058636308480000000
auto
Page 1

Figure 10: Some results of simplifying.

In general, when you simplify an expression, the simplified result will have the same numerical behavior as the original expression. However, when the expression includes functions with more than one branch, such as square root or the inverse trigonometric functions, the symbolic answer may differ from a numerical answer. For example, simplifying asin(sin(θ)) yields θ, but this equation holds true numerically in Mathcad only when θ is a number between $-\pi/2$ and $\pi/2$.

Expanding an expression

The **Expand Expression** command from the **Symbolic** menu expands all powers and products of sums in the selected expression. If the expression is a fraction, the numerator will be expanded and the expression will be written as a sum of fractions. Sines, cosines and tangents of sums of variables, or integer multiples of variables will be expanded as far as possible into expressions involving only sines and cosines of single variables. See Figure 12 for some examples.

Expanding an expression to a series

This section describes how to use the **Expand to Series** command from the **Symbolic** menu to expand an expression to a series.

To use the **Expand to Series** command:

- Select a variable in the function or expression for which you want to find a series expansion.
- Choose **Expand to Series**. A dialog box will prompt you for the order of the series. This determines the number of terms, and hence the error in the series.

Mathcad will then generate the corresponding series. The order is the order of the error term in the expansion. For example, if you select the x in $\sin(x)$ and ask for a series of order 6, you will get an expansion of the sine function in powers of x in which the highest power is x^5. The error is thus $O(x^6)$. The answers you get from **Series** show this error term using the O notation. Before you use the series for further calculations you will need to delete this error term.

The **Expand to Series** command is limited to series in a single variable; any other variables in the expression will be treated as constants. Mathcad will find Taylor series (series in nonnegative powers of the variable) for functions that are analytic at 0, and Laurent series for functions that have a pole of finite order at 0. To develop a series with a center other than 0, you can translate. For example, to get a series for the log function around 1:

- Apply **Expand to Series** to $\ln(x + 1)$.

- Use **Substitute for Variable** to substitute $x - 1$ for x.

Figure 11 shows some examples of series generated with this menu command. For an alternative method for generating series expansions, see the section on the **series** keyword in the section "Live symbolic evaluation" earlier in this chapter.

In using the approximations you get from the **Expand to Series** command, keep in mind that the Taylor series for a function may converge only in some small interval around the center. Furthermore, functions like *sin* or *exp* have series with infinitely many terms, while the polynomials returned by **Expand to Series** have only a few terms (how many depends on the order you select). Thus, when you approximate a function by the polynomial returned by **Expand to Series**, the approximation will be reasonably accurate close to the center, but may be quite inaccurate for values far from the center.

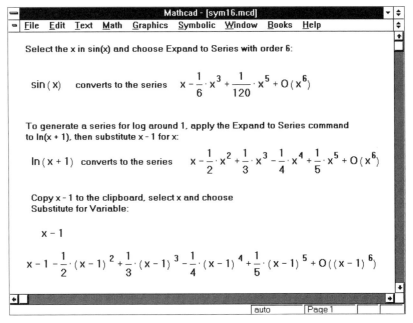

Figure 11: Generating a series.

Factoring an expression

The **Factor Expression** command from the **Symbolic** menu factors the selected expression. If this expression is a single integer, Mathcad will factor it into powers of primes. Otherwise, Mathcad will attempt to convert the expression into a product. This command will combine a sum of fractions into a single fraction and will often simplify a complex fraction with more than one fraction bar.

Note that Mathcad factors *only what is selected* when you use this command. For example, if you select the entire expression

$$a \cdot b + a \cdot c + x$$

and choose **Factor Expression**, Mathcad will return this expression unchanged as its answer, because the *whole* expression selected is not factorable. But if you select just the first two terms, Mathcad will return

$$a \cdot (b + c) + x$$

When you're simplifying by factoring, you may be able to simplify your expression quite a bit by selecting and factoring subexpressions even if the expression taken as a whole can't be factored. Choose **Factor Expression** to combine a sum of fractions into a single fraction or to simplify a complex fraction. See the examples in Figure 12.

Note that since the selection box follows the structure of the expression, you may need to insert parentheses before you can select a particular subexpression. For example, to select $a{\cdot}c + x$ in the expression above, you would insert a left parenthesis before the second a and a right parenthesis after the x.

Collecting like terms

The **Collect on Subexpression** menu command collects terms containing like powers of the subexpression you've selected. The result is a polynomial in the subexpression. The subexpression you select must be a single variable or a built-in function together with its argument. See Figure 12 for an example.

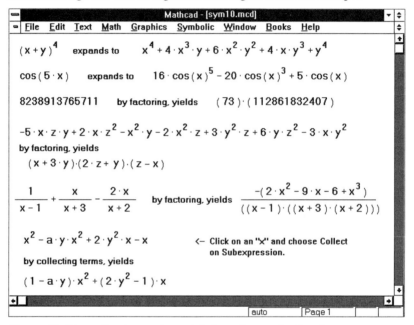

Figure 12: Expanding to a polynomial, factoring, and collecting terms.

Partial fraction decomposition

To convert an expression to a partial fraction:

- Select a variable in the denominator of the expression.

- Choose **Convert to Partial Fraction** from the **Symbolic** menu.

The symbolic processor will try to factor the denominator of the expression into linear or quadratic factors having integer coefficients. If it succeeds, it will expand the expression into a sum of fractions with these factors as denominators. All constants in the selected expression must be integers or fractions; Mathcad will not expand an expression that contains decimal points. See Figure 13 for some examples.

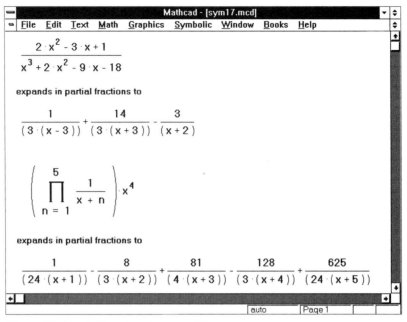

Figure 13: Partial fraction decomposition.

Finding coefficients of a polynomial

Mathcad
PLUS

Many expressions can be rewritten as polynomials, either in a particular variable or with respect to a subexpression. If you're using Mathcad PLUS you can use Mathcad's symbolic processor to do this:

- Select the variable in which you want your expression to be regarded as a polynomial.

- Choose **Polynomial Coefficients** from the **Symbolic** menu.

Mathcad returns a vector containing the coefficients of the equivalent polynomial. The first element of the vector is the constant term. The first expression in Figure 14 shows an example.

You can also enclose a function in a selection box if you want the symbolic processor to regard your expression as a polynomial with respect to a function. The second expression in Figure 14 shows an example of a polynomial in the function $\sin(x)$.

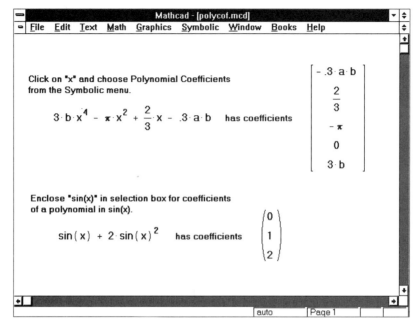

Figure 14: Finding the coefficients of some polynomials.

Substituting an expression for a variable

This command substitutes a selected expression for each occurrence of a variable. To use this command:

- Select the expression that will replace the variable.

- Copy it to the clipboard by choosing **Copy** from the **Edit** menu.

- Select an occurrence of the variable you want to replace and choose **Substitute for Variable** from the **Symbolic** menu.

Mathcad will substitute the expression on the clipboard for the selected variable. If the variable occurs more than once in the expression you are transforming, each occurrence Mathcad replaces each occurrence. Figure 15 shows some examples.

Note that **Substitute for Variable** will not substitute a vector or a matrix for a variable. To substitute a scalar expression for a variable that occurs in a matrix, put the expression in the clipboard with **Copy**. Then for each matrix element that contains the variable, click on the element and choose **Substitute for Variable**.

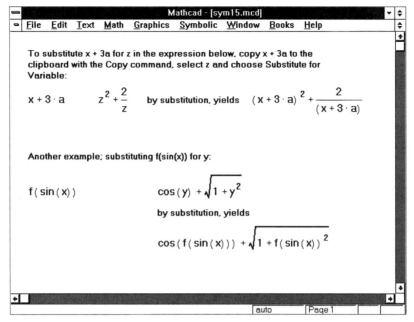

Figure 15: Substituting an expression for a variable.

Evaluating a summation

To evaluate a sum symbolically, you can use Mathcad's summation operator:

- Create the summation operator by typing [**Ctrl**][**Shift**]**4**.

- Enter the expression you want to sum in the placeholder to the right of the "Σ".

- Enter the index variable and summation range in the placeholders above and below the "Σ" as shown in Figure 16.

- Surround the entire expression with a selection box and press [**Shift**][**F9**].

The procedure is the same for a product over a range, except that you type [**Ctrl**][**Shift**]3 to get the product operator. If you use numerical limits in a summation or product range, be sure that the upper limit of the range is greater than or equal to the lower limit.

Note that as with all symbolic operations, the symbolic processor doesn't know about any variable definitions in your worksheet. Thus if you've defined a 10 element vector **v**, symbolic summation of v_i over the range i = 0 . . 9 will just give you the formal sum $v_0 + v_1 + \ldots + v_9$. If all you want is a numerical answer, use the sum and product operators described in Chapter 11.

Evaluating other functions and operators

In general, you can symbolically evaluate any of the Mathcad built-in functions described in the previous section. If the result can be computed exactly ($\sin(\pi)$ for example), you'll see an exact answer. Otherwise Mathcad will return the original expression as the answer. Figure 16 illustrates various results of symbolic evaluation.

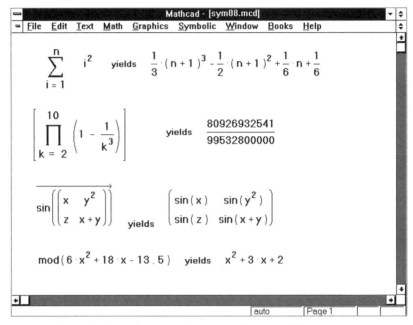

Figure 16: Symbolic evaluation of sums, products, and functions.

Symbolic calculus

This section describes how evaluate definite and indefinite integrals, how to evaluate derivatives and how to take limits.

Derivatives

To evaluate a derivative symbolically, you can use Mathcad's derivative operator as shown in Figure 17:

- Type **?** to create the derivative operator or type [**Ctrl**]**?** to create the higher order derivative operator.

- In the placeholders, enter the expression you want to differentiate and the variable with respect to which you are differentiating.

- Press [**Shift**][**F9**].

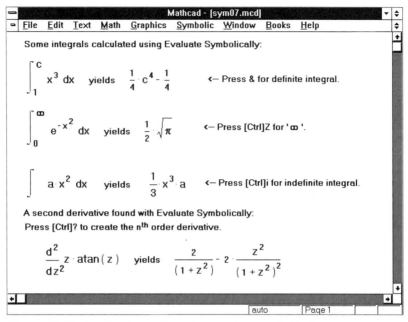

Figure 17: Evaluating integrals and derivatives symbolically.

Figure 18 shows you how to differentiate an expression without using the derivative operator. The menu command **Differentiate on Variable** differentiates an expression with respect to a selected variable. For example, to differentiate $2 \cdot x^2 + y$ with respect to x:

■ Select the x.

■ Choose **Differentiate on Variable** from the **Symbolic** menu. Mathcad will display the derivative, $4 \cdot x$.

If you selected the variable y instead of x, you would get the answer 1. Mathcad treats all variables except the one you've selected as constants.

If you've selected neither x nor y the menu command will be gray. Mathcad can't differentiate the expression because you haven't specified a differentiation variable.

If the expression in which you've selected a variable is one element of an array, Mathcad will differentiate only that array element. To differentiate an entire array, differentiate each element individually by selecting a variable in that element and choosing **Differentiate on Variable**.

The symbolic processor treats functions that are not on the list of built-in functions as unknown. When you differentiate such a function, the symbolic processor will usually express the answer in terms of derivative operators.

Indefinite integrals

Mathcad provides the symbolic indefinite integral operator shown in Figure 17. To use this operator:

- Type [Ctrl]I to insert the indefinite integral operator and its placeholders.

- Fill in the placeholder for the integrand.

- Place the integration variable in the placeholder next to the "*d*." This can be any variable name.

- Enclose the expression in a selection box.

- Press [Shift][F9].

Figure 18 shows how to integrate an expression without using the indefinite integral operator. The menu command **Integrate on Variable** integrates an expression with respect to a selected variable. For example, to integrate $2 \cdot x^2 + y$ with respect to x:

- Select the x.

- Choose **Integrate on Variable** from the **Symbolic** menu. Mathcad will display the integral.

The **Integrate on Variable** command integrates an expression with respect to a selected variable. If you don't have a variable selected, this command will be gray. Mathcad cannot integrate without knowing the variable of integration.

If the symbolic processor can't find a closed-form indefinite integral, you'll see the message "*No closed form found for integral.*" Keep in mind that many simple expressions don't have a closed-form indefinite integral that can be written in terms of polynomials or elementary functions. For example e^{-x^3} has no elementary integral. If the integral is too big to display, Mathcad puts the answer, in text form, on the clipboard. See the section "Long answers" on page 420 to learn what to do when this happens.

When evaluating an indefinite integral, remember that the answer to an integration problem is not unique. If $f(x)$ is an integral of a given function, so is $f(x) + C$ for any constant C. Thus, the answer you get from Mathcad may differ by a constant from the answer you find in tables. If you differentiate a function and then integrate the result, you won't necessarily get the original function back as your answer.

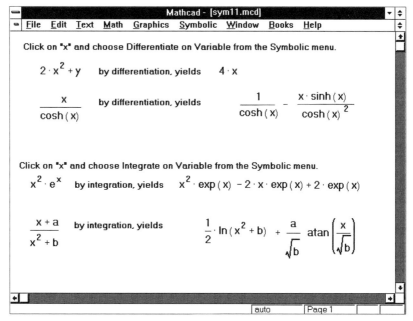

Figure 18: Differentiating and integrating expressions.

Definite integrals

To symbolically evaluate a definite integral:

- Type **&** to create the integral operator with its empty placeholders.

- Fill in the placeholders for the limits of integration. These can be variables, constants, or expressions.

- Fill in the placeholder for the integrand.

- Fill in the placeholder next to the "d." This is the variable of integration.

- Surround the entire expression with a selection box.

- Press **[Shift][F9]**.

The symbolic processor will attempt to find an indefinite integral of your integrand before substituting the limits you specified. If the symbolic processor can't find a closed form for the integral, you'll see an appropriate error message.

If the symbolic integration succeeds and the limits of integration are integers, fractions, or exact constants like π, you'll get an exact value for your integral. If the integrand or one of the limits contains a decimal point, the symbolic answer will be a number displayed with twenty significant digits.

This answer will in general agree with the answer you get by evaluating the same integral numerically. The symbolic and numerical answers are, however, obtained in very different ways. Mathcad's symbolic processor:

- Finds an indefinite integral.

- Subtracts its value at the lower limit of integration from its value at the upper limit.

The numerical integration routine, on the other hand:

- Samples the integrand at many points in the interval of integration.

- Uses these samples to approximate the integral.

The accuracy of this numerical integration depends on the value you set for the variable TOL and on the smoothness of the function you are integrating.

Of course, many functions do not have a closed form integral, and definite integrals involving these functions can *only* be calculated numerically. Integrals for which the integrand is not smooth (has a discontinuous derivative) might not be evaluated correctly by the symbolic processor. See Chapter 11 for more on Mathcad's numerical integration.

Limits

Mathcad PLUS provides three limit operators. These can only be evaluated symbolically. They cannot be evaluated numerically. To use the limit operators:

- Press [Ctrl]L to create the limit operator. To create operators for limits from the left or right, press [Ctrl]B or [Ctrl]A.

- Enter the expression in the placeholder to the right of the "lim."

- Enter the limiting variable in the left-hand placeholder below the "lim."

- Enter the limiting value in the right-hand placeholder below the "lim."

- Enclose the expression with a selection box.

- Press [Shift][F9].

Mathcad will return a result for the limit. If the limit does not exist, Mathcad returns an error message. Figure 19 shows some examples of evaluating limits.

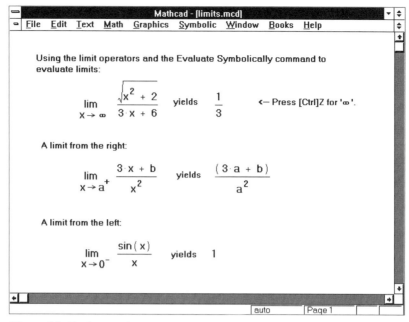

Using the limit operators and the Evaluate Symbolically command to evaluate limits:

$$\lim_{x \to \infty} \frac{\sqrt{x^2 + 2}}{3 \cdot x + 6} \quad \text{yields} \quad \frac{1}{3} \qquad \longleftarrow \text{Press [Ctrl]Z for '}\infty\text{'}.$$

A limit from the right:

$$\lim_{x \to a^+} \frac{3 \cdot x + b}{x^2} \quad \text{yields} \quad \frac{(3 \cdot a + b)}{a^2}$$

A limit from the left:

$$\lim_{x \to 0^-} \frac{\sin(x)}{x} \quad \text{yields} \quad 1$$

Figure 19: Evaluating limits.

Solving equations symbolically

This section discusses how to symbolically solve an equation for a variable, find the symbolic roots of an expression, and solve a system of equations symbolically. The **Solve for Variable** command from the **Symbolic** menu lets you solve an equation for a variable and find the roots of an expression.

This section also describes how to solve a system of equations symbolically using a solve block. To do this, you must be running Mathcad PLUS.

Solving equations symbolically is far more difficult than solving them numerically. You may find that the symbolic solver does not give a solution. This may happen for a variety of reasons discussed in the section "Limitations of symbolic solving" on page 420.

Solving an equation for a variable

To solve an equation for a variable:

- Type the equation. Make sure you use [**Ctrl**]= to create the equals sign.

- Select the variable you want to solve for by clicking on it.

- Choose **Solve for Variable** from the **Symbolic** menu.

Mathcad will solve for the variable and paste the result into your worksheet. Note that if the variable was squared in the original equation, you may get *two* answers back when you solve. Mathcad displays these in a vector. Figure 20 shows an example.

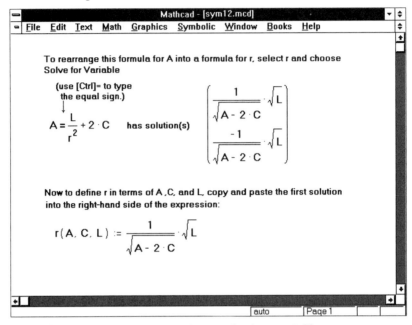

Figure 20: Rearranging an expression to solve for a variable.

You can also solve an inequality entered using the symbols <, >, ≤, and ≥. Solutions to inequalities will be displayed in terms of Mathcad boolean expressions. If there is more than one solution, Mathcad places them in a vector. A Mathcad boolean expression such as $x < 2$ has the value 1 if it is true and 0 if it is false. Thus the solution "x is less than 2 and greater than −2" would be represented by the expression $(x < 2) \cdot (-2 < x)$.

Finding the roots of an expression

The procedure for finding the roots of an expression is analogous to the more general problem of solving an equation for a variable. To find the roots of an expression:

■ Type the expression.

■ Select any occurrence of the variable for which you are solving.

■ Choose **Solve for Variable** from the **Symbolic** menu.

Note that there is no need to set the expression equal to zero. When Mathcad doesn't find an equals sign, it assumes you mean to set the expression equal to zero.

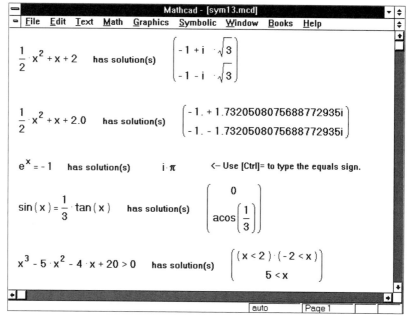

Figure 21: Examples of finding roots and solving inequalities.

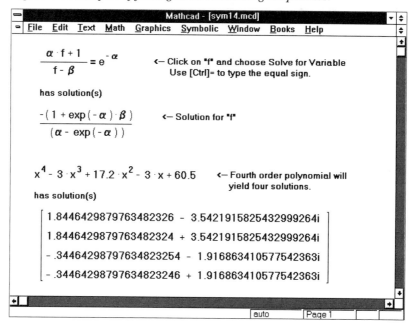

Figure 22: Some uses for symbolic solving.

Solving a system of equations symbolically

Mathcad
PLUS

In Chapter 15, "Solving Equations," you learned how to use a solve block to solve a system of equations. Using the *Find* function gave you numerical values for the unknowns in a system of equations. If you're using Mathcad PLUS, you'll be able to use a similar technique for finding *symbolic* answers for the unknowns in a system of equations.

To solve a system of equations symbolically:

- Type the word *Given*. This tells Mathcad that what follows is a system of equations. You can type *Given* in any combination of upper and lower case letters, and in any font. Just be sure you don't type it while in a text region or paragraph.

- Now type the equations in any order below the word *Given*. Make sure you press [Ctrl]= to type "=."

- Type the *Find* function as appropriate for your system of equations. This function is described on page 340. The arguments of the function are the variables for which you are solving.

- Press [Ctrl]. (the control key followed by a period). Mathcad displays the symbolic equal sign.

- Click outside the *Find* function.

Mathcad displays the solutions to the system of equations to the right of the arrow. If the *Find* function has one argument, Mathcad returns one result. If the *Find* has more than one argument, Mathcad returns a vector of results. For example, Find(*x*, *y*) returns a vector containing the expressions for *x* and *y* that solve the system of equations. Note that if your system is an overdetermined non-linear system, the *Find* function will not return a solution. Use the *Minerr* function instead of *Find*. *Minerr* will return an answer that minimizes the errors in the constraints.

Most of the guidelines for solve blocks described in Chapter 15 apply to the symbolic solution of systems of equations. The main difference is that when you solve equations symbolically, you need not enter guess values for the solutions.

Figure 23 shows an example of a solve block used to solve a system of equations symbolically. For more information on solve blocks, see Chapter 15, "Solving Equations."

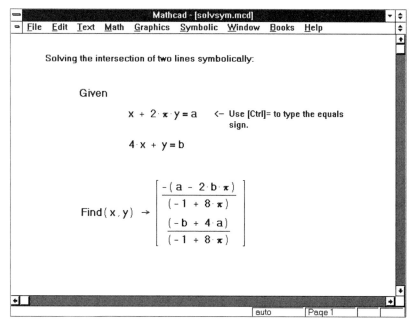

Figure 23: Solving a system of equations symbolically.

When you choose **Matrices** from the **Symbolic** menu, you'll see four commands on a pull-right menu. This section describes how to use these commands to find the symbolic transpose, inverse, and determinant of a matrix.

Before using these commands, make sure that a selection box encloses the entire matrix. Click anywhere in the matrix and press [**Space**] to enlarge the selection box until it encloses the matrix.

Finding the symbolic transpose

To find the symbolic transpose of a matrix:

■ Enclose the matrix in a selection box.

■ Choose **Matrix Operations**⇒**Transpose Matrix** from the **Symbolic** menu.

Mathcad returns the matrix with its rows and columns swapped.

Finding the symbolic inverse

To find the symbolic inverse of a square matrix:

■ Enclose the matrix in a selection box.

■ Choose **Matrix Operations**⇒**Invert Matrix** from the **Symbolic** menu.

Symbolic matrix manipulation   405

Mathcad will return a symbolic representation for the inverse of the selected matrix.

Finding the symbolic determinant

To find the symbolic determinant of a square matrix:

■ Enclose the matrix in a selection box.

■ Choose **Matrix Operations⇒Determinant of Matrix** from the **Symbolic** menu.

Mathcad will return a symbolic representation for the determinant of the selected matrix. Keep in mind that this is usually a lengthy expression.

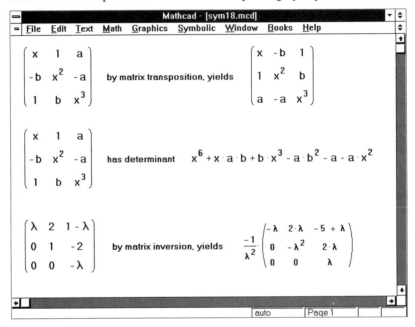

Figure 24: Symbolic matrix operations.

If you have Mathcad PLUS, you'll be able to symbolically perform certain integral transforms. If you choose **Transforms** from the **Symbolic** menu, you'll see six additional commands on a pull-right menu. This section describes how to use these commands to perform the Fourier, Laplace, and z-transforms, and their inverses.

Figure 25 shows some examples on how to use Mathcad's symbolic transformations. Note that the result may contain functions that are recognized by Mathcad's symbolic processor but not by its numeric processor. An example is the function *Dirac* at the bottom of Figure 25. You'll find numerical definitions for this and other such functions at the end of this chapter.

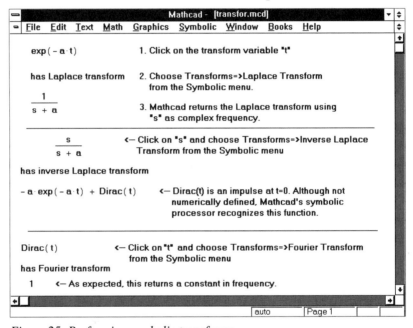

Figure 25: Performing symbolic transforms.

Fourier and inverse Fourier transformations

To evaluate the Fourier transform of a function:

- Enter the expression to be transformed.

- Click on the transform variable.

- Choose **Transforms⇒Fourier Transform** from the **Symbolic** menu.

Mathcad returns a function of ω given by:

$$\int_{-\infty}^{+\infty} f(t)\, e^{-i\omega t}\, dt$$

where $f(t)$ is the expression to be transformed.

Mathcad returns a function in the variable ω when you perform a Fourier transform since this is a commonly used variable name in this context. If the expression you are transforming already contains an ω, Mathcad avoids ambiguity by returning a function of the variable $\omega\omega$ instead.

You can substitute a different variable or expression for ω by placing the variable or expression on the clipboard, clicking on the ω and choosing **Substitute for Variable** from the **Symbolic** menu.

To evaluate the inverse Fourier transform of a function:

- Enter the expression to be transformed.

- Click on the transform variable.

- Choose **Transforms⇒Inverse Fourier Transform** from the **Symbolic** menu.

Mathcad returns a function of t given by:

$$\frac{1}{2\pi}\int_{-\infty}^{+\infty} F(\omega)\, e^{i\omega t}\, d\omega$$

where $F(\omega)$ is the expression to be transformed.

Mathcad returns a function in the variable t when you perform an inverse Fourier transform since this is a commonly used variable name in this context. If the expression you are transforming already contains a t, Mathcad avoids ambiguity by returning a function of the variable tt instead.

You can substitute a different variable or expression for t by placing the variable or expression on the clipboard, clicking on the t and choosing **Substitute for Variable** from the **Symbolic** menu.

Laplace and inverse Laplace transformations

To evaluate the Laplace transform of a function:

- Enter the expression to be transformed.

- Click on the transform variable.

- Choose **Transforms⇒Laplace Transform** from the **Symbolic** menu.

Mathcad returns a function of s given by:

$$\int_{0}^{+\infty} f(t)\, e^{-st}\, dt$$

where $f(t)$ is the expression to be transformed.

Mathcad returns a function in the variable s when you perform a Laplace transform since this is a commonly used variable name in this context. If the expression you are transforming already contains an s, Mathcad avoids ambiguity by returning a function of the variable ss instead.

You can substitute a different variable or expression for s by placing the variable or expression on the clipboard, clicking on the s and choosing **Substitute for Variable** from the **Symbolic** menu.

To evaluate the inverse Laplace transform of a function:

- Enter the expression to be transformed.

- Click on the transform variable.

- Choose **Transforms⇒Inverse Laplace Transform** from the **Symbolic** menu.

Mathcad returns a function of t given by:

$$\frac{1}{2\pi i} \int_{\sigma - i\infty}^{\sigma + i\infty} F(s) \, e^{st} \, ds$$

where $F(s)$ is the expression to be transformed and all singularities of $F(s)$ are to the left of the line $\mathrm{Re}(s) = \sigma$.

Mathcad returns a function in the variable t when you perform an inverse Laplace transform since this is a commonly used variable name in this context. If the expression you are transforming already contains a t, Mathcad avoids ambiguity by returning a function of the variable tt instead.

You can substitute a different variable or expression for t by placing the variable or expression on the clipboard, clicking on the t and choosing **Substitute for Variable** from the **Symbolic** menu.

z and inverse z-transformations

Mathcad
PLUS

To evaluate the z-transform of a function:

- Enter the expression to be transformed.

- Click on the transform variable.

- Choose **Transforms⇒z-Transform** from the **Symbolic** menu.

Mathcad returns a function of z given by:

$$\sum_{n=0}^{+\infty} f(n) z^{-n}$$

where $f(n)$ is the expression to be transformed.

Mathcad returns a function in the variable z when you perform a z-transform since this is a commonly used variable name in this context. If the expression you are transforming already contains a z, Mathcad avoids ambiguity by returning a function of the variable zz instead.

You can substitute a different variable or expression for z by placing the variable or expression on the clipboard, clicking on the z and choosing **Substitute for Variable** from the **Symbolic** menu.

To evaluate the inverse z-transform of a function:

- Enter the expression to be transformed.

- Click on the transform variable.

- Choose **Transforms⇒Inverse z-Transform** from the **Symbolic** menu.

Mathcad returns a function of n given by a contour integral around the origin:

$$\frac{1}{2\pi i}\int_C F(z)\, z^{n-1}\, dz$$

where $F(z)$ is the expression to be transformed and C is a contour enclosing all singularities of the integrand.

Mathcad returns a function in the variable n when you perform an inverse z-transform since this is a commonly used variable name in this context. If the expression you are transforming already contains an n, Mathcad avoids ambiguity by returning a function of the variable nn instead.

You can substitute a different variable or expression for n by placing the variable or expression on the clipboard, clicking on the n and choosing **Substitute for Variable** from the **Symbolic** menu.

Displaying symbolic results

Two commands from the **Symbolic** menu can be used to determine how symbolic results are presented. Before using any of the other commands from the **Symbolic** menu, you might want to use the **Derivation Format** or the **Derive in Place** commands first.

Derivation Format

If you're using the symbolic equal sign, "→", the result of a symbolic transformation will always go to the right of the "→". However, when you use the **Symbolic** menu, you can tell Mathcad to place the symbolic reults in one of the following ways:

- The symbolic result can go below the original expression.

- The symbolic result can go to the right of the original expression.

- The symbolic result can simply replace the original expression.

In addition, you can also choose whether or not you want Mathcad to generate text describing what had to be done to get from the original expression to the symbolic result. This text would go between the original expression and the symbolic result, in effect creating a narrative for the symbolic derivation. These text regions are referred to as "derivation comments."

To control both the placement of the symbolic result and the presence of narrative text, choose **Derivation Format** from the **Symbolic** menu. This brings up the following dialog box.

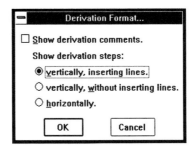

The check box at the top of the dialog box shows whether Mathcad will automatically generate derivation comments at each step of the derivation. Click in this box to toggle these comments on or off.

The three option buttons control where symbolic results are placed. These options do the following:

- *Show derivation steps vertically, without inserting lines* is useful when you want to show two parallel derivations side by side. In this mode, you can position expressions arbitrarily. New answers may, however, overwrite old ones.

- *Show derivation steps vertically, inserting lines* is useful when you expect lengthy intermediate results and you want to reserve an entire line for them.

- *Show derivation steps horizontally* is useful if you want to place the symbolic result to the right of the expression being transformed, click on the option button See Figure 26 for some examples.

Derive in Place

Sometimes you don't care about saving the steps of a derivation. You may just want to transform an expression in place, for example to make a substitution, or to factor the numerator of a fraction. In this case you can choose **Derive in Place** from the **Symbolic** menu. This tells Mathcad to replace the old expression with the new one. Under these circumstances, derivation comments are inappropriate and therefore omitted altogether.

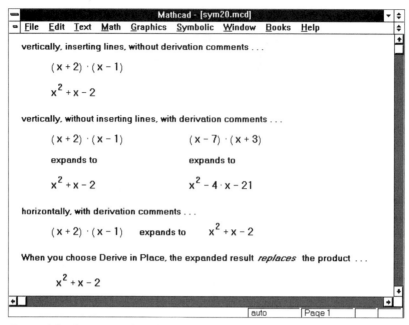

Figure 26: Placement of symbolic results and comments.

Symbolic optimization

Mathcad
PLUS

In general, Mathcad's symbolic processor and Mathcad's numerical processor don't communicate with one another. Because of this, it's possible to set up a complicated numerical calculation without knowing that you could have reduced it to an equivalent but much simpler problem by judicious use of the symbolic processor.

If you're using Mathcad PLUS however, you can make the numerical processor ask the symbolic processor for advice before starting what could be a needlessly complex calculation. In effect, the symbolic processor acts like the numerical processor's consultant, examining each expression and recommending a better way to evaluate it whenever possible. It does this for each expression in the worksheet except for those you specificaly tell it to ignore.

For example, if you were to evaluate an expression such as:

$$\int_0^u \int_0^v \int_0^w x^2 + y^2 + z^2 \, dx \, dy \, dz$$

Mathcad would undertake the laborious task of evaluating a numerical approximation of the triple integral even though one could arrive at an exact solution by first performing a few elementary calculus operations.

This happens because by itself, Mathcad's numerical processor does not know enough to simplify before plunging ahead into the calculation. Although Mathcad's symbolic processor knows all about simplifying complicated expressions, these two processors do not consult with each other.

If however you are running Mathcad PLUS, you can make these two processors talk to each other by choosing **Optimize** from the **Math** menu.

Once you've done this, Mathcad's live symbolic processor steps in and simplifies all expressions to the right of a ":=" *before* the numerical processor gets a chance to begin its calculations. It will continue to do so until you choose **Optimize** from the **Math** menu once more to remove the checkmark.

If Mathcad finds a simpler form for the expression, it responds by doing the following:

- It marks the region with a red asterisk.

- It *internally* replaces what you've typed with a simplified form. The expression you typed is left unchanged; Mathcad simply works with an equivalent expression that happens to be better suited for numerical analysis.

- Mathcad evaluates this equivalent expression instead of the expression you specified. To see this equivalent expression, double-click on the red asterisk beside the region.

In the previous example, the symbolic processor would examine the triple integral and return the equivalent, but much simpler expression:

$$\frac{1}{3}(w^3vu + wv^3u + wvu^3)$$

To see this expression in a pop-up window double-click on the red asterisk (see Figure 27). You can choose **Copy** from this pop-up window's **Edit** menu to put the simplified form on the clipboard. To dismiss the pop-up, click anywhere in your worksheet.

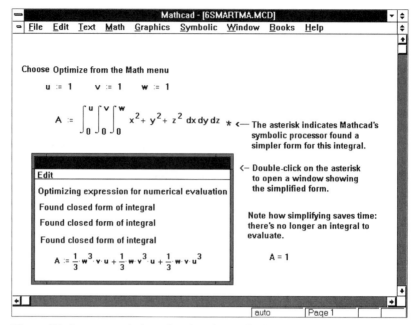

Figure 27: A pop-up window showing the equivalent expression that Mathcad actually evaluates.

Since this simplified form contains no integral, Mathcad's numerical processor no longer needs to use a lengthy numerical algorithm to evaluate the integral. This offers two advantages:

- By avoiding time-consuming integration, Mathcad's numerical processor can evaluate the expression far more quickly.

- Mathcad avoids all the computation issues inherent in numerical integration.

There may be times when you don't want Mathcad's symbolic processor to examine a particular equation. You may want to evaluate an expression exactly as you've typed it. To do so, precede the expression with the keyword **literally**. When the symbolic processor encounters this keyword, it makes no attempt to simplify the expression immediately following it.

Using functions and variables

Mathcad's symbolic processor does not treat functions and variables in exactly the same way as its numerical processor. These differences revolve around the answers to the following question:

- Does the symbolic processor "know" that a function or variable is defined elsewhere?

The answer to this depends on two things:

- Is the function or variable built-in or is it defined somewhere on the worksheet?

- Are you using the symbolic equal sign or a menu command?

The next two sections describe what Mathcad does with variables and functions in a symbolic transformation.

A related question is the converse. Symbolic transformations can sometimes return functions and constants which do not exist in Mathcad's list of built-in functions and constants. These are described in the last section, "Special functions".

Built-in functions and variables

As a general rule, built-in functions retain their meanings when used in symbolic transformations provided that it makes sense for them to do so. For example, functions like *sin* and *log* keep their meanings because these have a commonly accepted mathematical meaning. Other functions like *linterp* or *rnd* lack any commonly accepted meaning so Mathcad doesn't attempt to assign one.

Built-in functions that do retain their meanings when used in symbolic calculations include: trigonometric and hyperbolic functions and their inverses; logarithmic and exponential functions; the *Re* and *Im* functions; the *erf* function; the Γ function; the *mod* function; Φ (the Heaviside step function); *max* and *min*; and the *identity* and *eigenvals* functions for matrices..

In general, these functions mean the same thing for both numerical evaluations and symbolic transformations. There are three subtle differences:

- Unlike the numerical *mod* function, the symbolic *mod* function requires an integer modulus, and can accept a polynomial as its first argument (see Figure 16).

- Certain of the inverse trigonometric functions use different branches in the complex plane.

- The *eigenvals* function will work symbolically for complex as well as real matrices; numerical evaluation of *eigenvals* works only for real matrices.

As a general rule, built-in constants also retain their meanings when used in symbolic transformations provided that it makes sense for them to do so. The symbolic processor will recognize π, e and ∞. Moreover, these will have their exact meanings when used symbolically. When symbolic transformations are involved, there is no need to limit ∞ to 10^{307} or to limit π to only fifteen digits of precision.

Built-in constants lacking an intuitive mathematical meaning are not recognized by the symbolic processor. For example, *TOL* and *ORIGIN* will not have their usual meanings in symbolic transformations. They will be treated like any other undefined variable.

Figure 28 shows the difference in the way Mathcad treats functions in symbolic transformations. Note that the symbolic processor will recognize and evaluate the *sin* function, but when asked to evaluate *rnd*(3) the symbolic processor simply returns *rnd*(3).

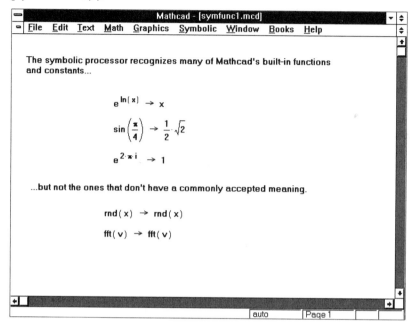

Figure 28: Some functions retain their numerical meanings while others lose them.

User-defined functions and variables

Functions and variables you define yourself *are* recognized by the symbolic processor when you use the symbolic equal sign discussed in the next section. They *are not*, however, recognized when you use menu commands. Figure 29 shows the difference.

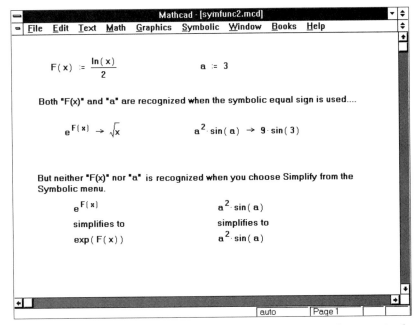

$$F(x) := \frac{\ln(x)}{2} \qquad\qquad a := 3$$

Both "F(x)" and "a" are recognized when the symbolic equal sign is used....

$$e^{F(x)} \rightarrow \sqrt{x} \qquad\qquad a^2 \cdot \sin(a) \rightarrow 9 \cdot \sin(3)$$

But neither "F(x)" nor "a" is recognized when you choose Simplify from the Symbolic menu.

$$e^{F(x)} \qquad\qquad\qquad a^2 \cdot \sin(a)$$

simplifies to   simplifies to

$$\exp(F(x)) \qquad\qquad\qquad a^2 \cdot \sin(a)$$

Figure 29: Functions and variables you define yourself are only recognized when you use the symbolic equal sign.

Special functions

A symbolic transformation sometimes comes back in terms of a function which isn't part of Mathcad's list of built-in functions. The list below gives definitions for those special functions. Except for *Ei, erf,* and *Zeta,* all of which involve infinite sums, and *W,* you can use these definitions to calculate numerical values.

γ is Euler's constant, approximately 0.5772156649.

$$\text{Chi}(x) = \gamma + \ln(x) + \int_0^x \frac{\cosh(t) - 1}{t} \, dt$$

$$\text{Ci}(x) = \gamma + \ln(x) + \int_0^x \frac{\cos(t) - 1}{t} \, dt$$

$\text{csgn}(z) = 1$ if $\text{Re}(z) > 0$ or $(\text{Re}(z) = 0$ and $\text{Im}(z) \geq 0)$; -1 otherwise. Define in Mathcad as: $\text{if}(\text{Re}(z) \neq 0, 2\Phi(\text{Re}(z)) - 1, 2\Phi(\text{Im}(z)) - 1)$

$$\text{dilog}(x) = \int_1^x \frac{\ln(t)}{1 - t} \, dt$$

$\text{Dirac}(x) = \infty$ if $x = 0$ and 0 otherwise.

$$\text{Ei}(x) = \gamma + \ln(x) + \sum_{n=1}^{\infty} \frac{x^n}{n \cdot n!} \quad (x > 0)$$

$$\text{erf}(z) = \frac{2}{\sqrt{\pi}} \sum_{n=0}^{\infty} \frac{(-1)^n z^{2n+1}}{n! \, (2n+1)} \quad \text{(for complex } z\text{)}$$

$$\text{FresnelC}(x) = \int_0^x \cos\left[\frac{\pi}{2} t^2\right] dt$$

$$\text{FresnelS}(x) = \int_0^x \sin\left[\frac{\pi}{2} t^2\right] dt$$

$$\text{LegendreE}(x, k) = \int_0^x \left[\frac{1 - k^2 \cdot t^2}{1 - t^2}\right]^{1/2} dt$$

$$\text{LegendreEc}(k) = \text{LegendreE}(1, k)$$

$$\text{LegendreEc1}(k) = \text{LegendreEc}\left[\sqrt{1 - k^2}\right]$$

$$\text{LegendreF}(x, k) = \int_0^x \frac{1}{\sqrt{(1 - t^2)(1 - k^2 \cdot t^2)}} dt$$

$$\text{LegendreKc}(k) = \text{LegendreF}(1, k)$$

$$\text{LegendreKc1}(k) = \text{LegendreKc}\left[\sqrt{1 - k^2}\right]$$

$$\text{LegendrePi}(x, n, k) = \int_0^x \frac{1}{(1 - n^2 \cdot t^2)\sqrt{(1 - t^2)(1 - k^2 \cdot t^2)}} dt$$

$$\text{LegendrePic}(n, k) = \text{LegendrePi}(1, n, k)$$

$$\text{LegendrePic1}(n, k) = \text{LegendrePic}\left[n, \sqrt{1 - k^2}\right]$$

$$\text{Psi}(n, x) = \frac{d^n \, \text{Psi}(x)}{dx^n}$$

$$\text{Psi}(x) = \frac{d \ln(\Gamma(x))}{dx}$$

$$\text{Shi}(x) = \int_0^x \frac{\sinh(t)}{t} dt$$

$$\text{Si}(x) = \int_0^x \frac{\sin(t)}{t} dt$$

signum(x) = 1 if $x = 0$, $x/|x|$ otherwise; calculate in Mathcad as $(x = 0) + x/|x|$

$W(x) = $ the principal branch of a function satisfying $W(x) \cdot \exp(W(x)) = x$.

$W(n, x) = $ the nth branch of $W(x)$.

$$\text{Zeta}(s) = \sum_{n=1}^{\infty} \frac{1}{n^s} \quad (s > 1)$$

The functions *arcsec, arccsc, arccot, arcsech, arcscsh, arccoth* can be calculated by taking reciprocals and using the Mathcad built-in functions *acos, asin,* etc. For example:

$$\texttt{arcsec(x)} := \texttt{acos}\left(\frac{1}{\texttt{x}}\right)$$

The *Psi* function and Γ appear frequently in the results of *indefinite* sums and products. If you use a single variable name rather than a full range in the index placeholder of a summation or product, and you choose **Evaluate Symbolically** or one of the other symbolic evaluation commands, Mathcad will attempt to calculate an indefinite sum or product of the expression in the main placeholder. The indefinite sum of $f(i)$ is an expression $S(i)$ for which

$$S(i+1) - S(i) = f(i)$$

The indefinite product of $f(i)$ is an expression $P(i)$ for which

$$\frac{P(i+1)}{P(i)} = f(i)$$

Limits to symbolic processing

As you work with the symbolic processor, you will undoubtedly discover two things:

- many problems can *only* be solved numerically, and

- many more problems yield such lengthy expressions that you'll wish you *had* solved them numerically.

For a computer, symbolic operations are, in general, much more difficult than the corresponding numerical operations. In fact, if you write down a complicated function at random, the chance is very small that either its roots or its integral can be expressed in a simple closed form. For example, there is no formula for the roots of a general polynomial of degree 5 or higher, even though exact roots can be found for some special cases.

Many deceptively simple-looking functions made up of elementary pieces like powers and roots, exponentials, logs, and trigonometric functions, have no closed-form integral that can be expressed in terms of these same functions.

Limitations of symbolic solving

As you use the symbolic solver, remember that symbolic solution is a very different operation from numerical solution. The symbolic solver may not find an solution even if one exists. This is because many equations that can easily be solved numerically have no exact symbolic solution. For example, there is no formula like the quadratic formula that gives the roots of a polynomial of degree 5 or higher. Even some simple equations like $x = \cos(x)$ can't be solved symbolically.

When an equation has several solutions, Mathcad sometimes returns only a partial solution and asks if you want this result placed in the clipboard. If you click "OK," Mathcad shows a vector containing the solutions found and the word "Root". In the clipboard, in place of the word "Root" you will see an expression of the form "RootOf (function_of_Z)". The roots of the indicated function are solutions of the original equation.

As with other symbolic operations, the answers you get depend on whether the constants in your equation contain decimal points. If your constants are pure rational numbers like 1/2 or 4, the symbolic solver will try to find an *exact* solution. For example, the solution to the first quadratic equation in Figure 21 is exact; in fact it's just the quadratic formula. But if you had typed ".5" instead of "1/2", Mathcad would have given approximate numerical values for the roots.

Long answers

Symbolic calculations can easily produce answers so long that they don't fit conveniently in your window. If the answer consists of the sum of several terms, you can reformat such an answer by using Mathcad's "Break with Plus" operator.

To break an expression with plus signs:

- Select the leftmost term.

- Press [↑] until the plus sign you want to break on and the term following it are included in the selection box.

- Press [Del]. The last plus sign in the selection box will be replaced with an operand placeholder.

- Now type [Ctrl][↵] to insert the plus with break.

You can repeat this process if there are several terms connected by plus signs.

Sometimes, a symbolic answer will be so long that you can't conveniently display it in your worksheet. When this happens, Mathcad will ask if you want the answer placed in the clipboard. If you click "OK," Mathcad places a string representing the answer on the clipboard. To see this string:

- Open the Main group in the Program Manager window.

- Double-click on the Clipboard icon.

You'll see an answer written in a Fortran-like syntax as shown in Figure 30. This syntax uses the following conventions:

- The symbols +, −, *, and / stand for the basic arithmetic operations. Exponentiation is denoted by "**".

- The derivative of $f(x)$ with respect to x is written "diff($f(x)$, x)". The nth derivative is "diff($f(x)$, $x\$n$)".

- A "D" also stands for the partial derivative operator. The nth derivative is "(D, n)". The partial derivative of a function with respect to its nth argument is "(D [n])".

- The integral of $f(x)$ with respect to x is written "int($f(x)$, x)".

- The summation and product operators appear as "sum( )" and "product( )".

- The operator "@" denotes function composition. For example, (sin@exp)(x) is the same as sin(exp(x)). A "@ @" represents repeated composition, so (f@ @2)(x) is the same as f($f(x)$).

- "RootOf(*equation*)" stands for any root of an algebraic equation. (For example, "RootOf(Z**2 + 1)" represents either i or $-i$.)

- You may see embedded font codes (like "MFNT_03_") preceding the variable name to indicate the font in which the variable name is to appear.

To insert the answer as text into your Mathcad worksheet:

- Click in an empty area.

- Choose **Paste** from the **Edit** menu.

To save a long clipboard answer as a separate text file, choose **Save As** from the Clipboard's **File** menu.

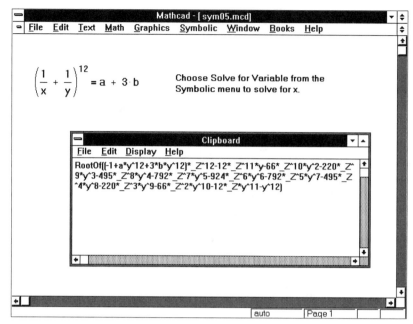

Figure 30: A long symbolic answer in the clipboard.

Chapter 18
Data Files

Mathcad reads and writes *data files* — ASCII text files containing numerical data. By reading data files, you can pull in data from other sources and analyze it in Mathcad. By writing data files, you can export Mathcad's results to word processors, spreadsheets, and other applications.

Mathcad includes two sets of functions for reading and writing data. *READ*, *WRITE*, and *APPEND* read or write a single value at a time. *READPRN*, *WRITEPRN*, and *APPENDPRN* read a whole matrix from a file with rows and columns of data or write such a file from a matrix in Mathcad.

This chapter contains the following sections:

Data files and file functions
Format of data files; description of file-access functions.

Importing data from other directories
Using the **Associate Filename** command to specify which file to read from or write to.

Unstructured files
How to use *READ*, *WRITE*, and *APPEND*.

Structured files
Reading and writing arrays with *READPRN*, *WRITEPRN*, and *APPENDPRN*.

Data files and file functions

A Mathcad data file must be a text file in plain ASCII format. Mathcad reads files that consist of numbers separated by commas, spaces, or carriage returns. The following are some examples of files that Mathcad can read, assuming they are in ASCII format:

■ A file containing experimental data captured with data-acquisition hardware and software.

■ A file created by printing from a spreadsheet program to the disk.

■ A column of numbers typed into a word processor and saved in plain ASCII format.

■ Output from a BASIC program.

■ Data downloaded from a mainframe database.

The numbers in the data files can be integers like **3** or **-1**, floating-point numbers like **2.54**, or E-format numbers like **4.51E-4** (for $4.51 \cdot 10^{-4}$).

For example, this list of numbers would be a valid line in a Mathcad data file:

$$200, \ 50 \ 25.1256, \ 16E-2, \ -16.125E15$$

Mathcad also saves data in ASCII files. Data files saved by Mathcad contain numbers separated by spaces and carriage returns.

Note: Mathcad documents themselves are not valid data files. The only way to create a data file from Mathcad is by using file-access functions as described in this chapter.

File-access functions

Mathcad includes six file access functions: *READ, WRITE, APPEND, READPRN, WRITEPRN,* and *APPENDPRN.* They share the following properties:

■ You must type the function name all in uppercase. Alternatively, you may insert the function into your document by using the **Choose Function** command from the **Math** menu and double-clicking on the function name.

■ If Mathcad cannot find a data file, it marks the file-access function with the message "*file not found.*" If Mathcad tries to read a file and the format is incorrect, it marks the function with the message "*file error.*"

■ The *WRITE, APPEND, WRITEPRN,* and *APPENDPRN* functions must appear alone on the left side of a definition.

■ Each new equation reopens the data file. When you read data, for example, each new equation starts reading at the beginning of the file.

- A file can only be opened once per equation. This means that if you use *READ* on the same argument twice in the same equation, the second *READ* will begin reading where the first left off. Since *READPRN* reads the entire file at once, this means you can't use *READPRN* on the same file more than once in an equation; there will be nothing left for the second *READPRN* to read.

- If two equations in the same document use *WRITE* or *WRITEPRN* with the same file variable, the data from the second equation will overwrite the data from the first. Use *APPEND* or *APPENDPRN* when you don't want to overwrite data. These functions add to an existing file instead of overwriting it.

The table below describes these six functions. In this table:

- **A** represents an array, either vector or matrix.

- v_i represent the individual elements of vector **v**.

- *file* is any valid filename on your file system.

- i is a range variable.

The functions *READ*, *WRITE* and *APPEND* can be used with range variables. The remaining functions never use range variables.

Function	Meaning
READ(*file*)	Read a value from a data file. Returns a scalar. Usually used as follows: $v_i := \text{READ}(\textit{file})$
WRITE(*file*)	Write a value to a data file. If file already exists, replace it with new file. Must be used in a definition of the following form: $\text{WRITE}(\textit{file}) := v_i$
APPEND(*file*)	Append a value to an existing file. Must be used in a definition of the following form: $\text{APPEND}(\textit{file}) := v_i$
READPRN(*file*)	Read a structured data file. Returns a matrix. Each line in the data file becomes a row in the matrix. The number of elements in each row must be the same. Usually used as follows: $\mathbf{A} := \text{READPRN}(\textit{file})$
WRITEPRN(*file*)	Write a matrix into a data file. Each row becomes a line in the file. Must be used in a definition of theform: $\text{WRITEPRN}(\textit{file}) := \mathbf{A}$
APPENDPRN(*file*)	Append a matrix to an existing file. Each row in the matrix becomes a new line in the data file. Must be used in a definition of the following form: $\text{APPENDPRN}(\textit{file}) := \mathbf{A}$ Existing data must have as many columns as **A**.

Arguments to file access functions

The arguments of all functions in the previous table are called file variables. When evaluated, a file variable doesn't return a number like most variables, it returns the name of a file. The name of the file returned is the file variable with either the extension **.dat** or **.prn** added.

The choice of extension depends on which file access function you are using. For example, if the file variable is *papageno* and you are using *READPRN* or *WRITEPRN*, then Mathcad will read from or write to a file called **papageno.prn** in the current directory. If instead you are using *READ* or *WRITE*, Mathcad will read from or write to a file called **papageno.dat** in the current directory.

You can override the default extensions **.dat** and **.prn** by using the complete filename as the file variable. For example, to read from a file named **papageno.txt** just type the full name as your file variable. The period will disappear and you'll see "*papageno$_{txt}$*" in your document. Read page 161 on literal subscripts to learn why this happens.

Be careful though of using file variables that are too long. Although Mathcad lets you create long file variable names like *resistance$_{parallel}$* these cannot correspond to filenames because there are too many characters. Instead, Mathcad looks for a file whose name is a truncated version of the file variable. For example, READPRN(*resistance$_{parallel}$*) tells Mathcad to read from a file named **resistan.par**.

If the file you want to read from or write to is located in a directory other than the default directory you cannot simply type its complete pathname between the parentheses of one of the file access functions. This is because when you type a file variable, you're in a math expression and as a result, Mathcad treats your keystrokes as if you were typing math. This means that whenever you type \ or : to indicate a drive letter or a directory Mathcad inserts a square root or a definition operator.

To circumvent this difficulty, Mathcad allows you to associate a filename with a file variable in much the same you have been associating a number with a variable all along. This procedure is discussed in the next section.

When you are editing a Mathcad document, the default directory is the directory from which you loaded the document or to which you have most recently saved it.

Mathcad's file access functions read from and write to the default directory. The default filename is the file variable with the extension `.dat` or `.prn`. Thus, if you use READPRN(*papageno*), Mathcad searches for **papageno.prn** in your default directory. If you use READ(*papageno*), Mathcad searches for **papageno.dat** in your default directory.

You can make a file-access function read from or write to a file other than the one that matches its argument in the default directory. The following example shows how to access a file called **papageno.dat** in the directory **c:\rem**:

- Choose **Associate Filename** from the **File** menu. A file dialog box appears, as shown below.

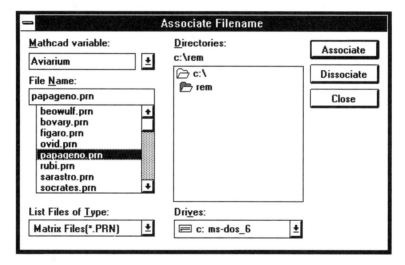

- In the text box under "Mathcad Variable," type the file variable. If, for example, you use READPRN(*Aviarium*) to access the data, the file variable is *Aviarium*. Keep in mind that Mathcad variable names are case-sensitive. You must type the variable name just as it appears in your document.

- Specify the directory path to the data file. In this example, the pathname is - **c:\rem\papageno.prn**. You can use the scrolling list of filenames to assist you in naming the file.

- Click the "Associate" button. Mathcad will now access the file named **c:\rem\papageno.prn** whenever it encounters a file access function with the file variable *Aviarium*.

- Choose **Calculate Document** from the **Math** menu to update your document.

Equations involving file access functions are not automatically updated like other equations. If you make a change to a data file or change a filename association, it will not affect calculations until you either click in the equation and press [F9], or choose **Calculate Document** from the **Math** menu. Think of file access functions as always being in manual mode.

Since Mathcad can have only a finite number of files open at once, you may want to sever the link between a variable and its associated file when it is no longer needed. This may be necessary if you see a "*too many files*" error message. To do so, Choose **Associate Filename** from the **File** menu and type the name of the variable you want to disassociate from a file on your disk. Then click the "Dissociate" button.

Unstructured files

This section discusses how to use *READ*, *WRITE*, and *APPEND* to read and write data in unstructured files. An unstructured data file is a file that contains numbers, but not necessarily in rows and columns.

Reading data with the READ function

Figure 1 shows two ways to use *READ* to read data from a file.

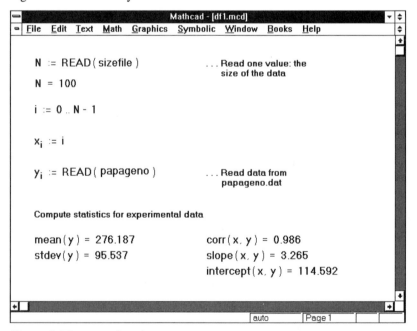

Figure 1: The READ function.

The first *READ* equation defines N as the first value in the data file `sizefile.dat`. The second *READ* equation fills the array **y** with the first 100 numbers in the data file `papageno.dat`.

When Mathcad reads data with the *READ* function:

- Each new equation reopens the file and starts reading from the beginning. You cannot read two successive sets of data from the same file by using two separate *READ* equations.

- In an equation with *READ* and a range variable, Mathcad reads one value for each value of the range variable. If the data runs out before the range variable, Mathcad just stops looking for more data. If the range variable ends before the end of the data, Mathcad ignores the extra data in the file.

- An equation cannot include more than one *READ* function.

- To read from a file other than the one that matches the variable name in parentheses, choose **Associate Filename** from the **File** menu. Also choose Associate Filename to read from a file that is not in your Mathcad directory. See the section "Importing data from other directories" earlier in this chapter for more information.

Writing data with the WRITE and APPEND functions

Figure 2 shows how to use the *WRITE* function to write data to a data file.

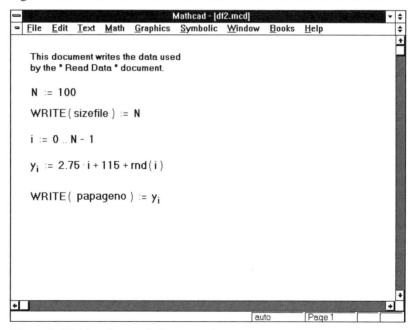

Figure 2: Writing data with the WRITE function.

The first *WRITE* equation writes a single number to the data file
`sizefile.dat`. The second *WRITE* equation writes N numbers to the data file
`papageno.dat`, one number for each value of the range variable *i*.

When Mathcad writes data to a file, it separates successive numbers with spaces.
Mathcad also inserts line breaks to keep the lines shorter than 80 characters.
When you use *WRITE*, all values are saved to the file with maximum precision,
regardless of the global format of the document.

Mathcad ignores units when it writes data to a data file.

Like the *READ* function, the *WRITE* function reopens the file and starts at the beginning for each new equation. If you want to write data to a file from several
different equations, use the *APPEND* function instead of the *WRITE* function in
the second and subsequent equations.

Warning: If you use the *WRITE* function on the same file in two separate equations, the data from the second equation will overwrite the data from the first
equation.

Figure 3 shows a document that reads data from a file, performs some computations, and writes the results out to another file.

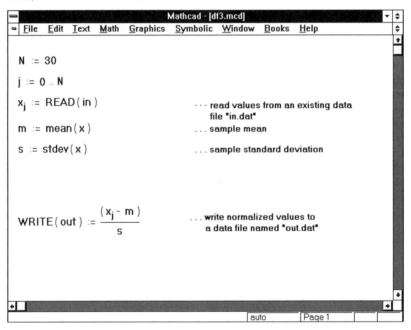

Figure 3: Reading and writing data files.

This section discusses how to use *READPRN*, *WRITEPRN*, and *APPENDPRN* to read and write data in structured files. A structured data file is a data file with a fixed number of values per line. For example, if you print a rectangular area from a spreadsheet into a file, the resulting rows and columns of numbers will be a structured file.

Reading a matrix with the READPRN function

Suppose you have an ASCII text file containing the data shown below. These numbers could come from a spreadsheet or from any other source.

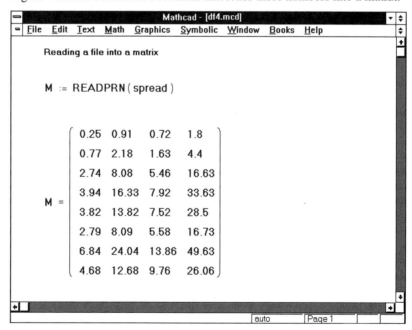

Figure 4 shows a Mathcad document that reads these numbers into a matrix.

Figure 4: Reading spreadsheet data into a matrix.

The *READPRN* function reads the entire data file, determines the number of rows and columns, and creates a matrix out of the data.

When Mathcad reads data with the *READPRN* function:

- Each instance of the *READPRN* function reads an entire data file.

- All lines in the data file must have the same number of values. (Lines containing no values are ignored.) If the lines in the file have differing numbers of values, Mathcad marks the *READPRN* equation with the message "*file error.*"

- The *READPRN* function ignores text in the data file.

- The result of reading the data file is an *m*-by-*n* matrix, where *m* is the number of lines containing data in the file and *n* is the number of values per line. To define a matrix out of the numbers in a data file, use an equation like **M** := *READPRN*(*file*). *Do not use subscripts on* **M**. *READPRN* returns a matrix, so no subscripts are necessary.

- To read from a file other than the one that matches the argument of *READPRN* or to read from a file that is not in your Mathcad directory, use the **Associate Filename** command on the **File** menu. See the section "Changing file associations," earlier in this chapter.

Warning: Each line in the data file must contain the same number of values. If you leave gaps where Mathcad expects numbers, the *READPRN* function will not be able to read the file. Mathcad determines where one number ends and the next begins by looking for spaces or commas.

Sometimes each column of values in a data file represents a different variable. Figure 5 shows how to use superscripts to create a vector from each column in the data file.

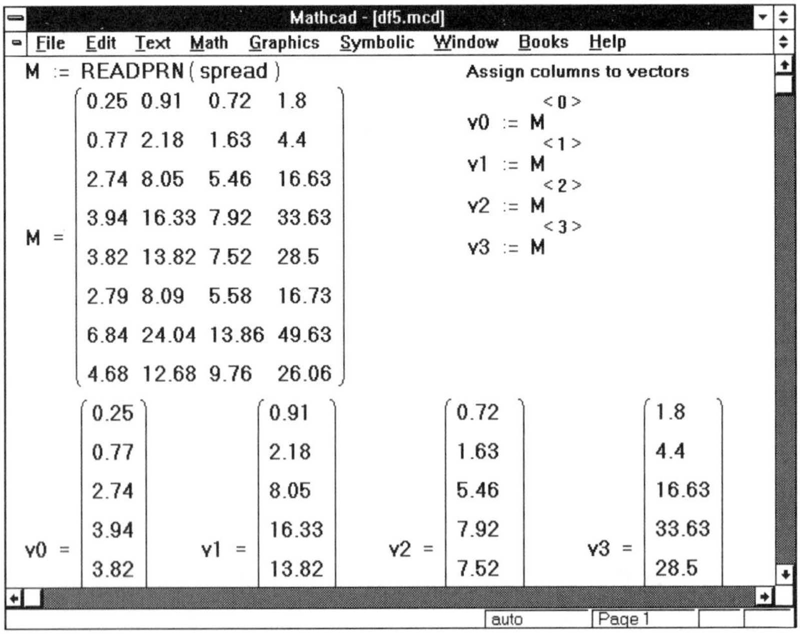

Figure 5: Assigning a variable to each column of data from a data file.

Writing data with the WRITEPRN and APPENDPRN functions

Figure 6 shows how to use the *WRITEPRN* function to write data to a structured data file.

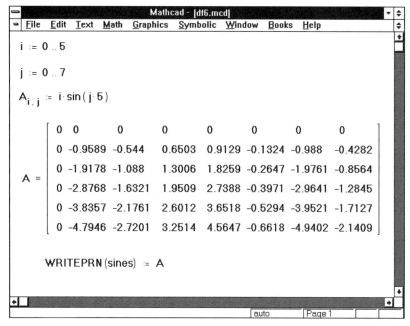

Figure 6: Writing data to a structured data file.

When you calculate the document in Figure 6, Mathcad creates a data file containing the following numbers:

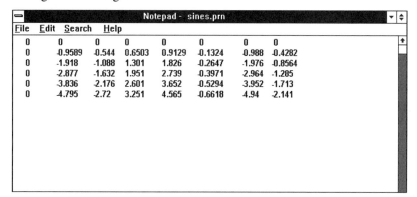

Unlike the *WRITE* function, the *WRITEPRN* function writes out the data in columns. Note that since the *PRNPRECISION* is set to four, the numbers are shown to four decimal places. Since *PRNCOLWIDTH* is set to eight, each column has space for eight characters. Since *PRNPRECISION* and *PRNCOLWIDTH* can be varied independently, you must take care to choose them in such a way that the column width can accommodate all the digits, together with a space to separate the columns.

When you use *WRITEPRN*:

- Equations using *WRITEPRN* must be in a specified form as follows: On the left should be WRITEPRN(*file*), where *file* is a variable name. This is followed by a definition symbol (:=) and a matrix expression. *Do not use range variables or subscripts with WRITEPRN.*

- Each new equation writes a new file. If two equations write to the same file, the data written by the second equation will overwrite the data written by the first. Use *APPENDPRN* if you want to append values to a file instead of overwriting the file.

- The built-in variables *PRNCOLWIDTH* and *PRNPRECISION* determine the format of the data file that Mathcad creates. The current value of *PRNCOL-WIDTH* specifies the width of the columns (in characters). The current value of *PRNPRECISION* specifies the number of significant digits used. By default, *PRNCOLWIDTH* = 8 and *PRNPRECISION* = 4. To change these values, choose **Built-In Variables** from the **Math** menu, or enter definitions in your Mathcad document above the *WRITEPRN* function, as shown in Figure 7.

- If the array you are writing is either a *nested* array (an array whose elements are themselves arrays) or a complex array (an array whose elements are complex) then *WRITEPRN* will *not* create a simple ASCII file. Instead, *WRITEPRN* creates a file using a special format unlikely to be readable by other applications. This file can, however, be read by Mathcad's *READPRN* function.

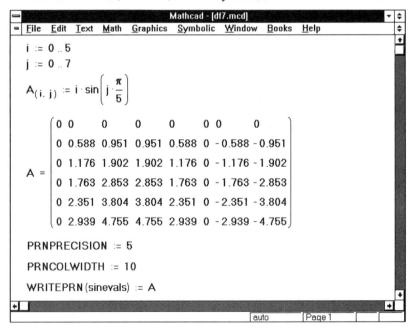

Figure 7: A document that creates a data file with columns 10 characters wide containing numbers with 5 significant digits.

By using the *augment* function, you can concatenate several variables and write them all to a data file. Figure 8 demonstrates how to do this.

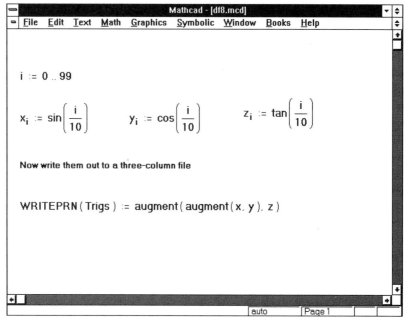

Figure 8: Writing several concatenated vectors.

Advantages of using READPRN and WRITEPRN

READPRN is generally preferable to *READ*. When the data values are regularly listed out in columns, *READPRN* brings the data into Mathcad in a readily accessible form.

If some lines in a data file have more data values than others, data values may be missing. Use a text editor to replace the missing values with zeros before you use *READPRN*.

READ is required for files in which numbers for a single variable are scattered across several lines in the file. This includes files created by the *WRITE* function, in which there are as many numbers on each line as will fit.

Remember: use a range variable subscript to read with *READ*; do *not* use a subscript to read with *READPRN*.

WRITEPRN generally produces more readable files than *WRITE* because the data values are neatly lined up in rows and columns. However, *WRITE* produces smaller files than *WRITEPRN* because it doesn't have to add spaces to line up the numbers.

Use *WRITE* instead of *WRITEPRN* when you want to crowd as many values as possible into a small data file. *WRITE* creates a data file with only one space between each value and the next.

Graphics Features

Chapter 19
Graphs

Mathcad graphs are both versatile and easy to use. To create a graph, click where you want to insert the graph, choose **Create X-Y Plot** from the **Graphics** menu, and fill in the placeholders. You can modify the format extensively, including reformatting the axes and curves and using a variety of different types of labels.

The following sections describe the use of Mathcad graphs:

Creating a graph

Basic steps in creating a graph.

Graphing functions

Procedures for graphing functions.

Graphing a vector

Procedures for graphing vectors.

Graphing more than one expression

Procedures for creating graphs with multiple traces.

Formatting the axes

Procedures for modifying the formats of the x- and y-axes.

Formatting individual curves

Procedures for modifying the formats of curves or traces in a graph.

Setting and restoring default formats

Procedures for using default format settings.

Labeling your graph

Procedures for working with titles, axis labels, and other labels.

Modifying the graph's perspective

Procedures for changing the size of the graph, zooming in on a portion of the graph, and finding coordinates in it.

Gallery of graphs

A set of sample graphs illustrating the options for creating graphs.

To create a graph:

- Click wherever you want the graph to appear.

- Choose **Create X-Y Plot** from the **Graphics** menu, or press **@**. Mathcad creates an empty graph with six placeholders, three on each axis.

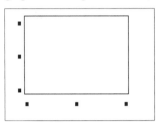

To see the graph, fill in the placeholders:

- The placeholder at the middle of the horizontal axis holds the variable to graph against. Enter a range variable, a subscripted variable, or any other expression involving a range variable in this placeholder.

- The placeholder at the middle of the vertical axis holds an expression to graph. Enter a range variable, subscripted variable, or any other expression involving the range variable on the horizontal axis.

- The other four placeholders can be used to override Mathcad's automatic choices of axis limits. For more information about axis limits, see the section "Setting limits for axes" on page 451.

Graphs typically have one or more expressions involving range variables on each axis. Mathcad graphs one point for each value of the range variable. Range variables are discussed in Chapter 10.

Be aware that it's usually an error to use two different range variables in the same curve, or *trace*, on a graph. If you use two range variables in the same trace, Mathcad tries to graph one point for each value of each range variable. For example, if i ranges through 20 points and j through 30, and you try to plot y_i against x_j, Mathcad tries to graph a total of 600 points. It is, however, permissible to use different range variables in different traces on the same graph.

Just as with an equation, Mathcad does not process a graph until you either press [**F9**] or, in automatic mode, click outside the graph region. When Mathcad processes the graph, it draws one point for each value of each range variable in the x or y axis expressions and, unless you specify otherwise, connects them with straight lines.

Figure 1 shows a typical graph with the placeholders filled in. Note the line that appears under the y_j. This indicates the trace type and color used to display the curve. See the section "Formatting individual curves" later in this chapter to learn how to control this.

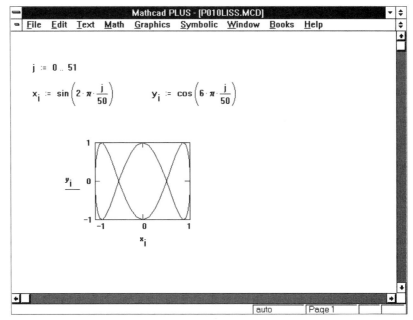

Figure 1: Mathcad graphs a Lissajous figure.

If an expression is complex, Mathcad graphs only the real part. The imaginary part is ignored. Note that no error message will be displayed.

Graphing functions

Each trace on a graph depends on a range variable. This range variable must appear in both the x-axis expression and the y-axis expression. Mathcad graphs one point for each value of the range variable.

Graphing a function

The easiest graph to create shows values of a function over a range. The first graph in Figure 2, below, illustrates this type of plot. To create this graph, do the following:

- Define a range variable x that ranges over the values you want to graph.

- Type the expression you want to plot in the middle placeholder of the y-axis and type x in the middle placeholder of the x-axis.

- Press [**F9**] to see the graph.

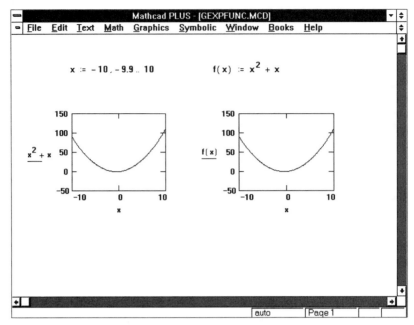

Figure 2: Graphing an expression against a range variable.

You can also define a function $f(x)$ and place it in the middle placeholder of the y-axis. This is particularly useful when the expression you want to plot becomes large and unwieldy. The second graph in Figure 2, above, shows the same plot as the first graph in the figure, except that it is made with a function definition.

You can drag, cut, copy and paste a graph just as you would an equation. See Chapter 2,"Editing Equations," for details.

To delete a graph from your worksheet:

■ Press and hold down the mouse button just outside the plot.

■ With the button still pressed, drag the mouse cursor so as to enclose the graphics region in the dashed selection rectangle.

■ Press [**Ctrl**]**X** to delete the graph. You can also choose **Cut** from the **Edit** menu if you prefer.

To move a graph, follow the instructions above for deleting it. Then click the mouse wherever you want the graph and choose **Paste** from the **Edit** menu. Alternatively, you can drag a plot as you would an equation. See Chapter 2 for details.

Using functions for polar plots

By creatively using the tools presented in this chapter, you can plot a wide variety of closed curves. The example in Figure 3 illustrates how to transform polar into rectangular coordinates. This technique lets you create polar plots, or even paths in the complex plane. In Figure 3, the equation for the cardioid in polar coordinates is given by $r(\theta)$. The equations for $x(\theta)$ and $y(\theta)$ are the usual transformation from polar to rectangular coordinates. See Chapter 20, "Polar Plots," for a description of Mathcad's built-in polar plotting capabilities.

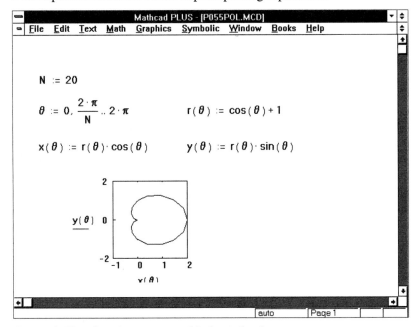

Figure 3: Two functions computed independently.

Graphing a vector

You can also graph the elements of a vector. Such a graph is shown in Figure 4 on the following page. To create this graph, do the following:

- Define a range variable i that references the subscript of each element you want to plot.

- Define a vector y_i. Use the left bracket key, [, to create the subscript.

- Press @ to create an empty plot region.

- Place y_i in the middle placeholder of the vertical axis and i in the middle placeholder of the horizontal axis.

- Press [F9] to see the graph.

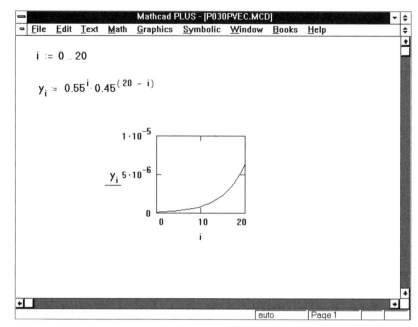

Figure 4: Graphing a vector.

Subscripts must be non-negative integers (or integers greater than or equal to ORIGIN, if ORIGIN $\neq 0$.) This means that the x-axis variable used in a graph like Figure 4 can run through whole-number values only. If you want to graph fractional or negative values on the *x*-axis, graph a function as in Figure 2, or graph two vectors as described in the next section.

If you have a handful of data points that don't have a convenient functional relationship as in Figure 4 but there are too few of them for you to use data files, you might want to use an input table to create a vector. For more information, see "Entering a table of numbers" on page 224.

Graphing one vector against another

Figure 5 shows how to graph two vectors against each other. The vectors need not be the same length. The only requirements are:

- The two vectors must share the same subscript. For example, you cannot plot x_i against y_j because *i* and *j* are not the same subscript.

- Each value of the subscript must correspond to an element in each vector. For example, if *x* has only two elements and *y* has eight elements, and the range variable goes from 0 through 7, you will get the error "*index out of bounds.*"

To create the plot shown in Figure 5, do the following:

- Define a range variable *i* that references on the subscript of each element you want to plot.

- Define the arrays x_i and y_i. Use the left bracket key, [, to create the subscript.

- Press @ to create an empty graph region.
- Place y_i in the middle placeholder of the y-axis and x_i in the middle placeholder of the x-axis.
- Press [**F9**] to see the graph.

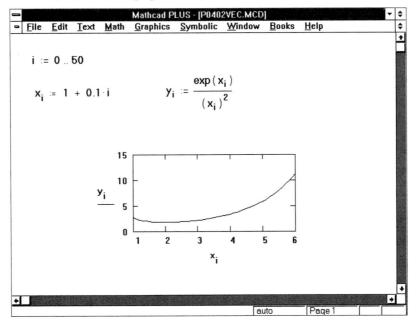

Figure 5: Graphing two vectors.

Although the x vector in Figure 5 is a list of evenly spaced values, this need not be the case. Only the i values are required to be evenly spaced integers. No such restriction exists for the x_i. This allows you to plot something besides integers on the x-axis while still satisfying the requirement for integers as subscripts.

In Figure 5, the y_i came directly from the x_i. Other applications might compute x and y independently from a third variable. As long as the two vectors use the same range variable, you can graph them on the same graph. Figure 6 shows a polar graph in which both x and y depend on the variables r and θ. Figure 6 uses vectors to do what was done with functions in Figure 3.

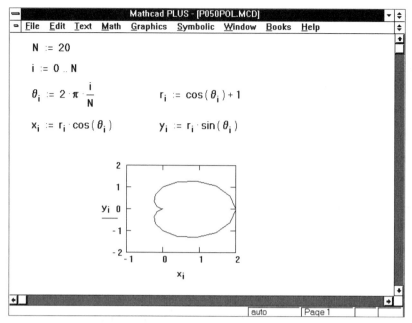

Figure 6: Two vectors computed independently.

Note that in Figure 6, the range variable i must have integer values and must be used to define a vector, namely θ, of equally spaced non-integer values. In Figure 3, however, we could define θ directly as a range variable. This is because functions do not require integer arguments the way vectors require integer subscripts.

Graphing data files

You don't have to use Mathcad to generate the vectors that you plot as shown in Figure 1. You can also use Mathcad's *READ* and *READPRN* functions to import data from ASCII text files generated from any spreadsheet, database, or word processing program capable of exporting data in ASCII format. Once imported, Mathcad plots the data just as it would data created in Mathcad.

For example, you can plot data from a spreadsheet by doing the following:

- Save the spreadsheet as an ASCII text file, with the extension **.prn**.

- Use the *READPRN* function to import the **.prn** file into Mathcad as a matrix. See the section "Reading a matrix with the *READPRN* function" in Chapter 18.

- Figure 7 shows the process for plotting vectors from the data imported from a **.prn** file.

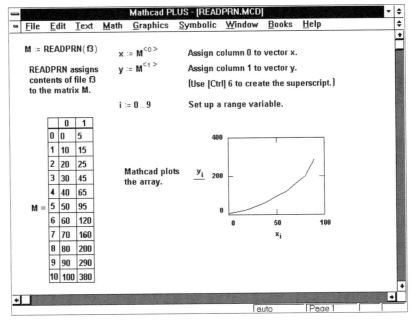

Figure 7: Plotting vectors from imported data.

See Chapter 18, "Data Files," for a detailed discussion of importing data files.

Graphing other expressions

Figures 2 through 6 show some of the most common types of graphs. However, graphs are not limited to following these examples. You can graph any expression against any other expression, as long as they share the same range variables. For example, see Figure 12 for an example of graphing a constant to be used as a marker on the graph of another function.

Graphing more than one expression

You can graph several traces on the same graph. A graph can show several *y*-axis expressions against the same *x*-axis expression, or it can match up several *y*-axis expressions with corresponding *x*-axis expressions.

To graph several *y*-axis expressions versus one *x*-axis expression, enter the first *y*-axis expression followed by a comma. You'll see a placeholder immediately below this first expression. Enter the second expression here, followed by another comma to get another empty placeholder. Enter the next expression. All the expressions should use the same range variable (Figure 8).

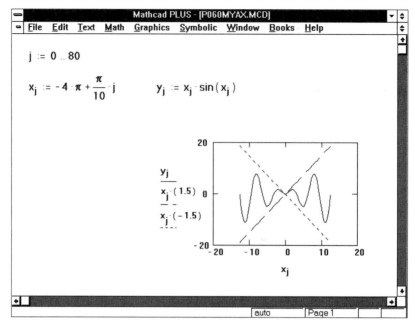

Figure 8: Graph with multiple y-axis expressions.

To graph several independent curves on the same set of axes, enter two or more expressions separated by commas on the *x*-axis and the same number of expressions on the *y*-axis. Mathcad matches up the expressions in pairs – first *x*-axis expression with first *y*-axis expression, the second with the second, and so on. It then draws a trace for each pair. Each matching pair of expressions should use the same range variable. The range variable for one pair need not match the range variables for the other pairs.

You can plot up to 16 arguments on the *y*-axis against 1 argument on the *x*-axis. However, if you have the same number of *x* arguments as *y* arguments, you can only plot up to 10 traces.

Figure 9 shows an example in which the range variables differ for each pair. Note however, that all traces on a graph share the same axis limits. For each axis, all expressions and limits on that axis must have compatible units.

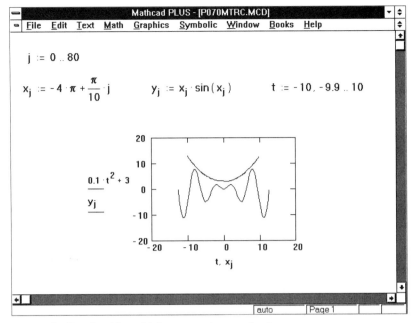

Figure 9: Graph with multiple expressions on both axes.

Formatting the axes

You can reformat your graph's axes, using the X-Y Axes page of the Formatting Currently Selected X-Y Plot dialog box.

To change a graph's format:

- Click in the graph to select it. Mathcad encloses the graph in a blue selection box and the **X-Y Plot** menu replaces the **Graphics** menu.

- Double-click in the graph. Alternatively, choose **Format** from the **X-Y Plot** menu. You'll see the dialog box for formatting X-Y plots.

- If necessary, click the X-Y Axes tab to display the X-Y Axes page, shown below.

- There is a complete group of settings for each axis. Change the appropriate settings.

- Click "OK" to accept your changes and close the dialog box. Mathcad redraws the graph with the new settings in effect. Alternatively, click "Apply" to see the graph redrawn without closing the dialog box. Click "Close" to close the dialog box.

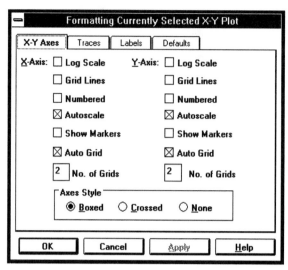

If you initiate this process by double-clicking on an axis, you'll see an equivalent dialog box for that axis alone.

The rest of this section describes the settings on the X-Y Axes page of the dialog box for formatting X-Y Plots. It then provides detailed discussions about options for setting axis limits and for adding horizontal and vertical reference lines to your graph.

Axis settings

Each axis has the following settings associated with it:

Log Scale
When this box is checked, the selected axis is logarithmic and the axis limits must be positive. The bottom-right-hand graph in Figure 16 on page 467 illustrates a graph with a logarithmic axis.

Grid Lines
When this box is checked, the tick marks on the selected axis are replaced by grid lines. The top-right-hand graph in Figure 16 on page 467 illustrates a graph that uses grid lines rather than tick marks.

Numbered
When this box is checked, the tick marks on the selected axis are numbered.

Autoscale
This controls axis limits that you don't otherwise specify. When this box is checked, Mathcad rounds the axis limit to the next major tick mark. When unchecked, Mathcad sets the axis limit to the data limit. For a discussion of Autoscale and the other ways to set axis limits, see "Setting limits for axes" later in this section.

Show Markers

When this box is checked, you can add reference lines to your graph. For a discussion of Show Markers and another way to create horizontal and vertical reference lines, see "Adding horizontal and vertical lines" later in this section.

Auto Grid

When this box is checked, Mathcad automatically selects the number of grid intervals created by tick marks or grid lines on the axes. When the box is unchecked, you choose the number of grid intervals by typing in the box labeled "No. of Grids". Enter a number from 2 to 99. You can specify the number of grid intervals only when Log Scale is unchecked. Figure 20 on page 469 illustrates the effect of Auto Grid.

In addition to these check boxes, the X-Y Axes page contains the following:

No. of Grids

When available, this text box indicates the number of grid intervals on the associated axis. You can enter a number between 2 and 99, inclusive. This box is only available when Auto Grid and Log Scale are unchecked.

Axes Style

These buttons define the style in which the graph will show the axes. Boxed axes are crossed in the bottom left corner of the graph. Crossed axes are crossed in the center of the graph. If you select None, no axes will be displayed on the graph. Figure 21 on page 469 illustrates the use of crossed axes.

See the section "Setting default formats," on page 457 to learn how to:

- Quickly restore the graph to its default format settings.

- Use a particular graph as a model for all future graphs.

Setting limits for axes

Mathcad provides the following ways to set limits for axes:

- Automatically, with Autoscale turned on.

- Automatically, with Autoscale turned off.

- Manually, by entering the limits directly on the graph.

- Manually, by entering the limits in the Axis Format dialog box.

By default, a plot you create in Mathcad is autoscaled. With Autoscale on, Mathcad automatically sets each axis limit to the first major tick mark beyond the end of the data. This will be a reasonably round number large enough to display every point being graphed. With Autoscale off, Mathcad automatically sets the axis limits exactly at the data limits.

Figure 10 shows how turning Autoscale on and then off changes the way the graph looks.

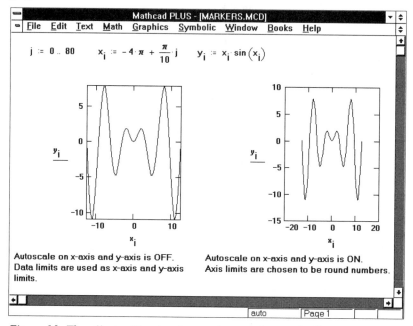

Figure 10: The effects of having Autoscale turned on and off.

To turn Autoscale off and have the axis limits automatically coincide with the end of the data:

- Click on the graph to select it and then choose **Format** from the **X-Y Plot** menu. Mathcad displays the dialog box for formatting X-Y graphs, shown on page 450. Click the X-Y Axes tab if the X-Y Axes page is not displayed. (You can also double-click on the axis itself to see a similar dialog box.)

- Click on Autoscale for the appropriate axis to remove the check and to toggle Autoscale off.

You may want to use axis limits other than those set by Mathcad. You can override Mathcad's automatic limits by entering limits directly on the graph. To do so:

- Click the graph to select it. Mathcad displays four additional numbers, one by each axis limit. These numbers are enclosed within corner symbols, as illustrated in the selected plot in Figure 11.

- To set the axis limit on the horizontal axis, click on the number underneath the appropriate *x*-axis limit and type the number at which you want the axis to end. To set an axis limit for the vertical axis, do the same thing to the number to the left of the appropriate *y*-axis limit.

- Click outside the graph. Mathcad redraws it using the axis limits you specified. Figure 11 shows the effect of manually setting limits on a graph.

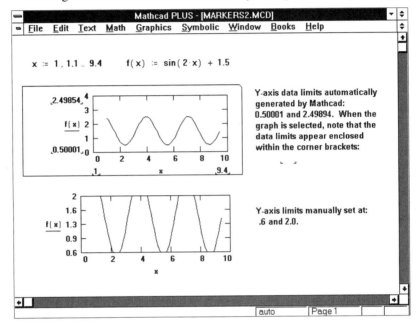

Figure 11: Data limits set manually and automatically.

Adding horizontal and vertical lines

Mathcad places linearly or logarithmically spaced tick marks or grid lines on a graph. The spaces between these markings are relatively round numbers that span the range of values on each axis. There may, however, be occasions when you need to place a line somewhere other than where Mathcad would normally place a grid line.

To add a horizontal or vertical line to a plot:

- Click in the plot to select it. The **X-Y Plot** menu replaces the **Graphics** menu.

- Choose **Format** from the **X-Y Plot** menu or double-click on the graph to bring up the dialog box for formatting X-Y graphs.

- If necessary, click on the X-Y Axes tab to display the X-Y Axes page, as shown on page 450.

- For a vertical line, click on Show Markers in the X-axis column to add a check; for a horizontal line, click on Show Markers in the Y-axis column to add a check. Click "OK". Mathcad shows two additional placeholders on each axis for which you have Show Markers checked.

- To add a vertical line, click on one of the placeholders under the *x*-axis and type in a value at which you want a line drawn. For a horizontal line, do the same thing in one of the placeholders under the *y*-axis.

When you click outside the graph, Mathcad draws a dashed line at each number you specify. The number you type appears at the end of the line. To move the dashed line, click on the number in the placeholder and change it. To delete the line, delete this number or click on Show Markers for the appropriate axis to uncheck it.

By using the Show Markers function, you can add to each axis one or two dashed lines stretching across the plot. When you need to place more than two lines or you need more control over the appearance of a line, you can add lines by plotting a constant expression.

- To create a horizontal line, place a range variable on the the middle placeholder of the *x*-axis and the constant expression on the *y*-axis. Mathcad will plot a horizontal line across the plot at whatever value the constant value happens to be. The expression you place on the *y*-axis need not depend on the range variable you place on the *x*-axis.

- To create a vertical reference line, reverse the roles of the *x*- and *y*-axes. Place a range variable on the middle placeholder of the *y*-axis and the constant expression on the *x*-axis.

Figure 12 compares graphs with vertical and horizontal lines created by plotting constant expressions and by using the Show Markers option.

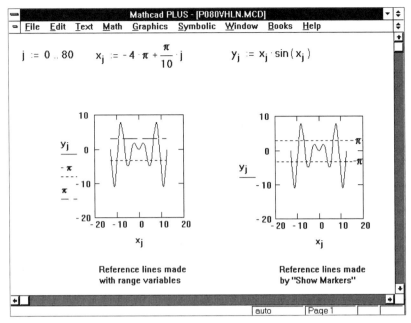

Figure 12: Graphs with reference lines.

Formatting individual curves

You can reformat the traces on your graph, using the Traces page of the dialog box for formatting X-Y graphs.

To reformat a graph's traces:

- Click in the graph to select it. Mathcad encloses the graph in a blue selection box and the **X-Y Plot** menu replaces the **Graphics** menu.

- Double-click in the graph. Alternatively, choose **Format** from the **X-Y Plot** menu. Mathcad displays the dialog box for formatting X-Y graphs.

- If necessary, click the Traces tab to display the Traces page.

- Click on the line in the scrolling list box for that trace. To change the name of the trace, type the new name in the text box under the "Legend Label" column. To change the symbol or marker, line type, color, trace type, or line weight of this trace, click on the arrow beside each text box to see a drop-down list of options, and then click on the option you want. See the next section, "Trace settings," for complete explanations of the various options in these lists.

- Click "OK" to accept your changes and close the dialog box. Mathcad redraws the graph with the new settings in effect. Alternatively, click "Apply" to preview your changes without closing the dialog box.

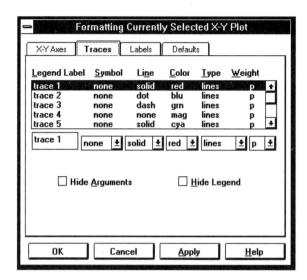

Trace settings

A graph can have up to sixteen individual traces. Each trace is described by a
line in the scrolling list. Mathcad uses these lines as needed, assigning one for
each trace in your graph. Each line has six fields:

Legend Label

This is the name of the trace as it would appear in the legend beneath the
plot. See the section "Displaying or hiding arguments and legends" on page
462 for more information about legends.

Symbol

This controls whether each point on the curve is marked with a symbol. You
can mark each point with either an "×", a "+", a hollow box, a hollow diamond, a circle, or no symbol at all. If you have a lot of points packed closely
together, you should probably select "none." Figure 18 on page 468 shows
an example in which each data point is marked by with an "×".

Line

This controls whether the line is solid, dotted, dashed, or whether it consists
of alternating dashes and dots. This feature provides a useful way to distinguish unmarked curves in black and white printouts.

Color

This controls whether the selected trace is red, blue, green, magenta, cyan (a
light blue), brown, black, or white. Mathcad ignores this on monochrome terminals.

Type

This controls the type of trace that will be displayed. Mathcad can generate the following types of plots: curves, bar charts, stepped curves, error bars, and points. For an example of a bar chart, see the bottom left-hand graph in Figure 16, on page 467. Figure 17 on page 467 has examples of step graphs and error bars.

Weight

This controls the weight or thickness of the trace. Select from 1 to 9 (thinnest to thickest). Select "p" for a trace that is one device pixel wide. Although this may look like weight 1 on your screen, a high resolution printer will print it as a very fine line. This field also controls the size of the symbols marking data points, if you have selected a symbol other than "none". If you have selected trace type points, this field sets the weight of the dot plotted at each data point.

See the "Setting default formats" section on page 457 to learn how to:

- Quickly restore the graph to its default format settings.

- Use a particular graph as a model for all future graphs.

In addition to the scrolling list and its associated text box and lists, the Trace page has two check boxes: Hide Arguments and Hide Legend. These are explained fully in the "Displaying or hiding arguments and legends" section on page 462.

Setting default formats

Mathcad uses default settings to format the axes and traces of new graphs as you create them. You can change these defaults in two ways:

- By saving as defaults the settings of your current graph.

- By using the Setting Default Formats for X-Y Plots dialog box, if you don't want to use an existing graph.

Changing defaults only affects new graphs; previously existing graphs are unaffected.

Copying defaults from an existing graph

One way to create a new set of defaults is to use the format settings of an existing graph. The advantage of this method is that you can actually see how the format settings look as you define them.

To use the format of a particular graph as the default graph format:

- Click in the graph to select it. Mathcad encloses the graph in a blue selection box and the **X-Y Plot** menu replaces the **Graphics** menu.

- Choose **Format** from the **X-Y Plot** menu or double-click on the selected graph. Mathcad displays the dialog box for formatting X-Y graphs. If necessary, click on the Defaults tab to see the Defaults page.

- If the Use for Defaults check box doesn't contain a check, click on it to add one. When you close the dialog box, Mathcad saves these settings as your default settings.

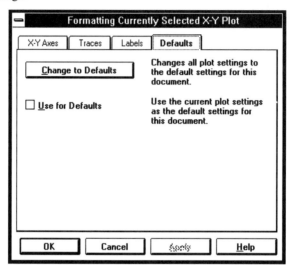

Setting defaults without using a graph

You don't have to use an existing graph to create or revise default formats. Instead, you can use the X-Y Axes page on the dialog box for setting X-Y plot defaults. To set defaults this way:

- Make sure that you don't have any graphs selected.

- Choose **X-Y Plot Format** from the **Graphics** menu. You'll see the dialog box for setting X-Y graph defaults. The following figure shows an example of this dialog box with the X-Y Axes page displayed.

- Change the appropriate settings on the X-Y Axes and Traces pages.

- Click "OK" to accept your changes and close the dialog box.

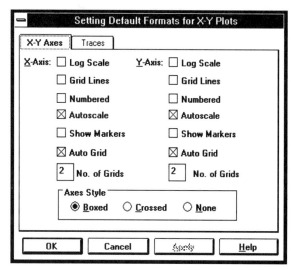

Setting Default Formats for X-Y Plots

| X-Y Axes | Traces |

X-Axis: ☐ Log Scale   Y-Axis: ☐ Log Scale
        ☐ Grid Lines   ☐ Grid Lines
        ☐ Numbered   ☐ Numbered
        ☒ Autoscale   ☒ Autoscale
        ☐ Show Markers   ☐ Show Markers
        ☒ Auto Grid   ☒ Auto Grid
        [2] No. of Grids   [2] No. of Grids

Axes Style
    ⦿ Boxed   ○ Crossed   ○ None

| OK | Cancel | Apply | Help |

Using default graph settings

If you want to reverse the format changes that have been made to a graph since it was created, you can restore its original default settings. To restore the original defaults:

- Click the Defaults tab on the dialog box for formatting X-Y graphs. (See the figure on page 458.)
- Click "Change to Defaults."
- Click "OK" to close the dialog box.

Mathcad redraws the graph, using the default format settings that were in place when the graph was first created. Mathcad does not use any defaults you might have set using the Use for Defaults check box at any time after the creation of this graph.

Labeling your graph

Mathcad provides several ways to help you to identify what it is that you've plotted. You can choose to display:

- A *title*, either above or below the graph.
- *Axis labels* to describe what's plotted on each axis.
- *Legends* to identify the individual traces.
- *Arguments* showing what you typed into the *x*- and *y*-axis place holders.

Figure 13 shows the relative locations of each of these types of labels on a boxed axes graph and on a crossed axes graph.

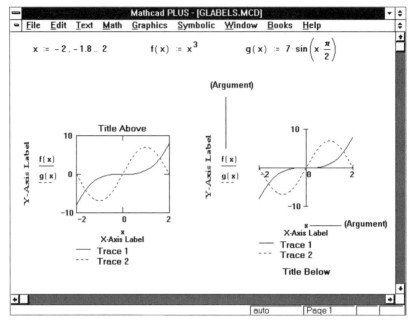

Figure 13: Graphs with different labels.

You can use these labels all together or in any combination. By default, Mathcad shows neither title nor axis labels, displays the arguments, and hides legends.

Working with titles

To add a title to a graph, follow these steps:

■ Click in the graph to select it. Mathcad encloses the graph in a blue selection box and the **X-Y Plot** menu replaces the **Graphics** menu.

■ Choose **Format** from the **X-Y Plot** menu or double-click on the selected graph. Mathcad displays the dialog box for formatting X-Y graphs. If necessary, click on the Labels tab.

■ Type a title for your graph into the Title text box.

■ Click on either the Above or Below button, depending upon where you want to put the title. Note, however, that Mathcad doesn't display the title until you click "Apply" or close the dialog box.

■ Make sure that the Show Title check box is checked. If it isn't, Mathcad still remembers the title but won't display it.

■ Click "OK" to accept your changes. Mathcad redraws the graph with the title in place. Alternatively, click "Apply" to preview your title without closing the dialog box.

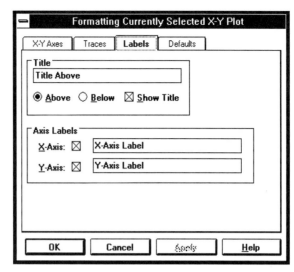

To edit a graph's title, follow these steps:

- Click in the graph to select it. Mathcad encloses the graph in a blue selection box and the **X-Y Plot** menu replaces the **Graphics** menu.

- Choose **Format** from the **X-Y Plot** menu or double-click on the selected graph. Mathcad displays the dialog box for formatting X-Y graphs. If necessary, click the Labels page. (You can also double-click on the title itself to display an equivalent dialog box.)

- Edit the information for the title as appropriate.

- Backspace over the title to delete it.

- Click "OK" to close the dialog box.

Labeling axes on a graph

You can also label one or both axes of a graph in much the same way as you add a title to a graph. The x-axis label appears directly below the x-axis, and the y-axis label appears just to the left of the y-axis. To label an axis, follow these steps:

- Click in the graph to select it. Mathcad encloses it in a blue selection box and the **X-Y Plot** menu replaces the **Graphics** menu.

- Choose **Format** from the **X-Y Plot** menu or double-click on the selected graph. Mathcad displays the dialog box for formatting X-Y graphs. If necessary, click on the Labels tab to see that page, as shown in the preceding section.

- Type the axis labels into the appropriate text boxes.

- To save the label name without having it appear on the graph, click X-Axis or Y-Axis to remove the check.

Labeling your graph

- Click "OK" to accept your changes and close the dialog box. Mathcad redraws the graph with the new settings in effect. Alternatively, click "Apply" to preview your changes without closing the dialog box.

To edit an axis label, follow these steps:

- Click in the graph to select it. Mathcad encloses the graph in a blue selection box and the **Graphics** menu changes to the **X-Y Plot** menu.

- Choose **Format** from the **X-Y Plot** menu or double-click on the selected graph. Mathcad displays the dialog box for formatting X-Y graphs. If necessary, click the Labels page. (You can also double-click on the label itself to display an equivalent dialog box.)

- Edit the information for the title as appropriate.

- To remove a label, delete it from the text box.

- Click "OK" to close the dialog box.

Displaying or hiding arguments and legends

Mathcad provides both arguments and legends for identifying specific traces on a graph:

- Arguments are the expressions that you typed into the placeholders of the x- and y-axes to create the graph. By default, Mathcad displays arguments.

- Legends are labels that appear underneath the graph containing a name and an example of the line and symbols used to draw the trace. By default, legends are hidden.

To display or hide arguments and legends:

- Click on the graph to select it.

- Choose **Format** from the **X-Y Format** menu or double-click on the graph. Mathcad displays the dialog box for formatting X-Y graphs, as shown below. If necessary, click on the Traces tab.

- To suppress the display of the arguments, click on Hide Arguments to add a check.

- To show the legend, click on Hide Legend to remove the check.

Modifying your graph's perspective

Mathcad provides options for manipulating the presentation of your graph:

- You can resize the graph, making it proportionally larger or smaller or stretching the x-axis or y-axis for emphasis.

- You can zoom in on a portion of the graph.

- You can get the coordinates for any point that was plotted to construct the graph.

- You can get the coordinates for any location within the graph.

The rest of this section shows how to use these features.

Resizing a graph

Resizing a graph is very much like resizing a window:

- Click the mouse just outside the graphics region. This anchors one corner of the selection rectangle.

- Press and hold down the left mouse button and drag the mouse pointer towards the graph. A dashed selection rectangle emerges from the anchor point.

- When the selection rectangle just encloses the graphics region, let go of the left mouse button.

- Move the mouse pointer on the selection rectangle to the right or bottom edge of the selection rectangle. It will change to a double-headed arrow.

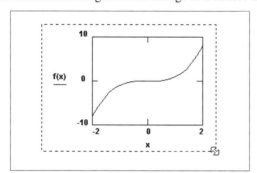

- Press and hold down the mouse button and move the mouse in the direction that you want the graph's dimension to change.

- Once the graphics region is the right size, let go of the mouse button.

- Click outside the graph to deselect it.

Note that when you change the size of a graph that is using Auto Grid, Mathcad may add or delete tick marks or grid lines to maintain the default spacing.

Zooming in on a graph

Mathcad allows you to select a region of a graph and magnify it. To zoom in on a portion of a graph, follow these steps:

- With the cursor in the graph region, click the mouse so the graph is enclosed in a blue selection box. The **X-Y Plot** menu replaces the **Graphics** menu.

- Choose **Zoom** from the the **X-Y Plot** menu. The X-Y Zoom dialog box appears.

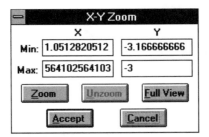

- If necessary, reposition the X-Y Zoom dialog box so that you can see the entire region of the graph you want to zoom.

- In the graph region, click the mouse at one corner of the region you want to magnify.

- Press and hold down the left mouse button and drag the mouse. A dashed selection rectangle emerges from the anchor point.

- When the selection rectangle just encloses the region you want to magnify, let go of the left mouse button.

- The coordinates of the selected region are listed in the Min: and Max: text boxes of the X-Y Zoom dialog box. Click the "Zoom" button to redraw the graph. The axis limits are temporarily set to the coordinates specified in the X-Y Zoom dialog box. To make these axis limits permanent, click "Accept."

Before you make these axis limits permanent, you can select another region to zoom by enclosing another selection rectangle around a new region. Press "Unzoom" to undo the zoom you've just made. If you're working with a graph that has already been zoomed, you may want to view the original graph as it was before any zooming took place. To do so, click on "Full View."

Figure 14 shows the effects of zooming in on a portion of a graph.

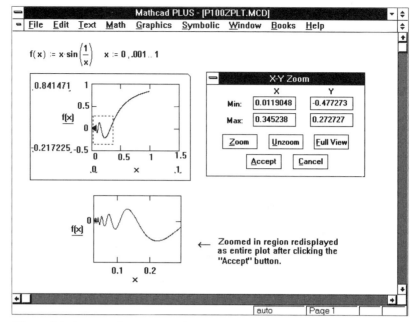

Figure 14: A zoomed-in region of a graph.

Getting a readout of graph coordinates

To see a readout of graph coordinates of the specific points that make up a trace, follow these steps:

- Click the mouse in the graph to enclose it in a blue selection box. The **X-Y Plot** menu replaces the **Graphics** menu.

- Choose **Trace** from the the **X-Y Plot** menu to show the X-Y Trace dialog box. Note that the Track Data Points check box is checked.

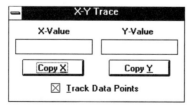

- If necessary, reposition the X-Y Trace dialog box so that you can see the entire region of the graph.

- In the graph region, click and drag the mouse along the trace whose coordinates you want to see. A dotted crosshair jumps from one point to the next as you move the pointer along the trace.

- If you release the mouse button, you can now use the left and right arrows to move to the previous and next data points. Use the up and down arrows to move to other traces.

- As the pointer reaches each point on the trace, Mathcad displays the x and y values of that point in the X-Value and Y-Value boxes.

- The x and y values of the last point selected are shown in the X-Value and Y-Value boxes. The crosshair remains until you click outside the graph.

To copy a coordinate to the clipboard,

- Click "Copy X" or "Copy Y". You can then paste that value into a math region or a text region on your Mathcad worksheet, into a spreadsheet, or into any other application that allows pasting from the clipboard.

- Double-click on the control box in the upper-left-hand corner to close the X-Y Trace dialog box. The crosshair will remain on your graph until you click anywhere outside the graph.

To see a readout of graph coordinates for any location in a graph:

- Follow the above procedures to call up the X-Y Trace dialog box.

- Click on Track Data Points to uncheck it.

- In the graph region, click and drag the mouse pointer over the points whose coordinates you want to see. A dotted crosshair follows the pointer as you drag it over the graph. Mathcad displays the coordinates of the pointer in the X-Value and Y-Value boxes. The x and y values change continuously to reflect the current pointer position.

- When you release the mouse button, the X-Value and Y-Value boxes show the x and y values of the last pixel selected.

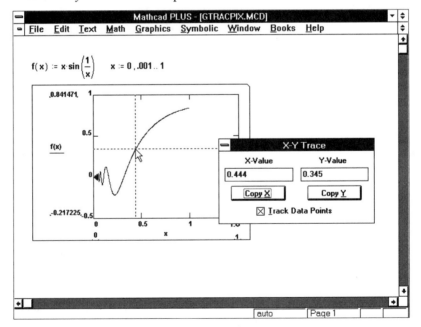

Figure 15: Reading coordinates from a graph.

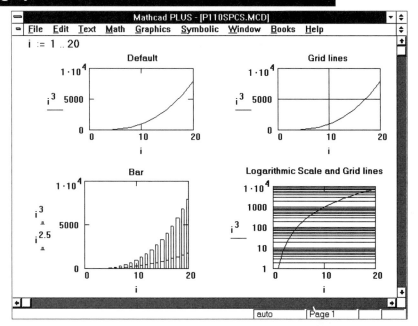

Figure 16: Different graph formats on the same graph.

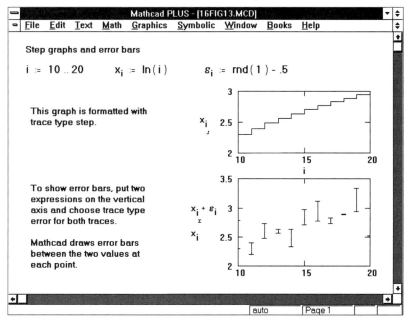

Figure 17: Step graphs and error bars from the scrolling list under "Trace type."

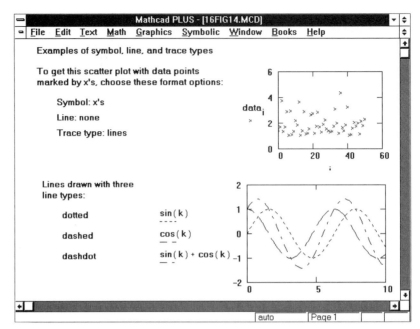

Figure 18: Choosing from the scrolling lists under "Line" and "Symbol."

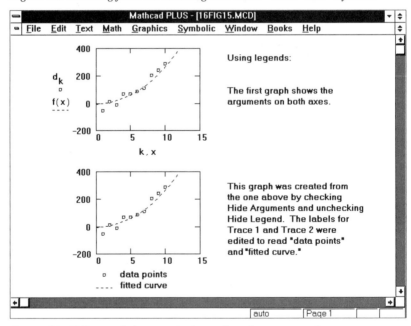

Figure 19: Hiding and showing the legend on the same graph.

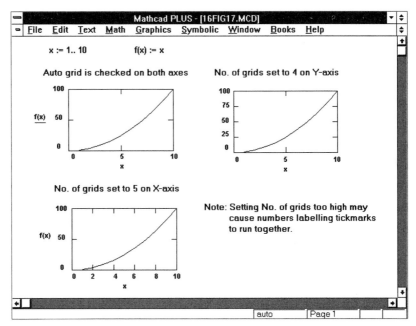

Figure 20: Unchecking Auto Grid option to vary the number of tick marks.

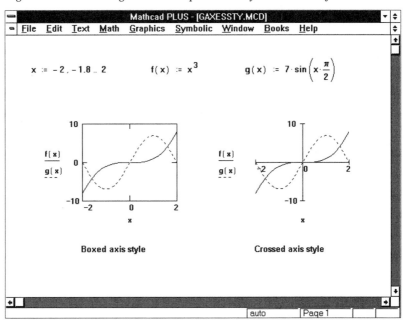

Figure 21: Using the "Crossed Axes" option to cross axes in the center of the plot.

Chapter 20
Polar Plots

In addition to Cartesian plots, Mathcad worksheets can contain polar plots. Using polar coordinates, you can quickly and easily display angle-dependent data.

The following sections describe how to create, use, and format polar plots:

Creating a polar plot
Basic steps in creating a polar plot.

Plotting more than one expression
Procedures for creating polar plots with multiple traces.

Formatting the axes
Procedures for modifying the radial and angular axes.

Formatting individual curves
Procedures for modifying curves or traces in a polar plot.

Setting and restoring default formats
Procedures for using default format settings for polar plots.

Labeling your polar plot
Procedures for working with titles, legends, and other labels.

Modifying the polar plot's perspective
Procedures for changing the size of the plot, zooming in on a portion of the plot, and finding coordinates in it.

Gallery of polar plots
A set of sample polar plots illustrating the options for creating polar plots.

You can easily use Mathcad to plot functions that do not lend themselves well to Cartesian coordinates. For example, you could plot circular antenna patterns or electric field intensities around an object.

To create a polar plot:

- Click where you want the polar plot to appear.

- Choose **Create Polar Plot** from the **Graphics** menu. Mathcad shows a circle with four placeholders as shown in Figure 1.

- Above the plot region, define an angle θ and a function of the angle, $r(\theta)$.

- The bottom placeholder holds the angle variable to plot against. Enter a range variable or any expression involving a range variable in this placeholder.

- The left placeholder holds a radial expression to plot.

- The two placeholders to the right hold the upper and lower radial limits. Mathcad fills in these placeholders by default. If you want, you can modify these limits. See the section "Formatting the axes."

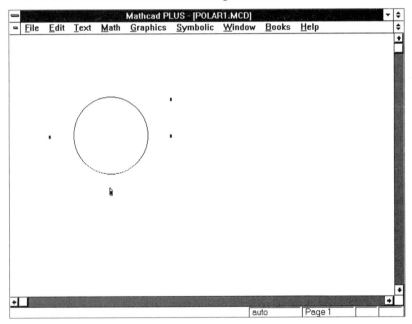

Figure 1: Empty placeholders in a polar plot region.

Just as with an equation, Mathcad will not process the polar plot until you either press [**F9**] or, in automatic mode, click outside of the region.

In Mathcad, polar plots are drawn by mapping r and θ onto x and y using the standard transformations $x = r\cos(\theta)$ and $y = r\sin(\theta)$. r and θ can assume positive or negative values.

You can specify many of the characteristics of the polar plot including the size, the number of grid lines and the upper and lower radial axis limits. The procedures for specifying these characteristics are later in this chapter.

A typical polar plot shows the value of a radial expression versus an angular expression. To see such a plot, you must first create a function, then create a polar plot of that function. Here are the typical steps in plotting a function like the one shown in Figure 2:

- Define a range.

- Define an increment for θ.

- Define $r(\theta)$, a function of θ.

- Show $r(\theta)$ in a polar plot.

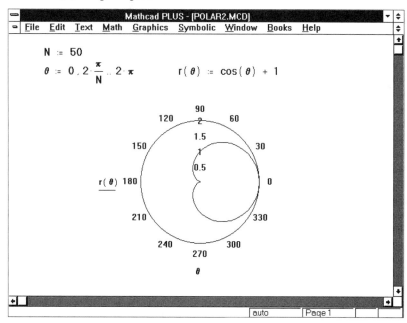

Figure 2: Polar plot of a function of θ.

Graphing more than one expression

Just as you can graph several expressions on a Cartesian plot, you can graph several expressions on the same polar plot. Each expression generates a *trace*. A polar plot can show several *r* expressions against the same θ expression, or it can match up several *r* expressions with corresponding θ expressions.

To graph several *r* expressions versus one θ expression, enter the first *r* expression followed by a comma. You'll see a placeholder immediately below this first expression. Enter the second expression here, followed by another comma to get another empty placeholder. All the expressions should use the same range variable, as shown in Figure 3. Figure 3 also shows how to define an angle range in degrees.

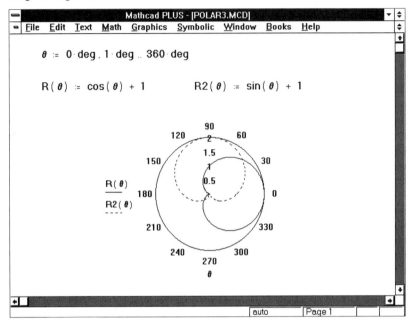

Figure 3: Polar plot with multiple expressions.

To graph several independent curves on the same polar plot, enter two or more expressions separated by commas in the bottom placeholder and the same number of expressions in the left placeholder. For example, to plot $r(\theta)$ against θ and $s(\phi)$ against φ you could type "$r(\theta)$, $s(\phi)$" in one placeholder and "θ, φ" in the other. Mathcad matches the expressions in pairs—$r(\theta)$ with θ and $s(\phi)$ with φ. It then draws a trace for each pair. Each matching pair of expressions should use the same range variable. The range variable for one pair need not match the range variables for the other pairs.

As with *x-y* plots, you can plot one vector of values against another, using a range variable to index the two vectors. This is illustrated in Figure 4.

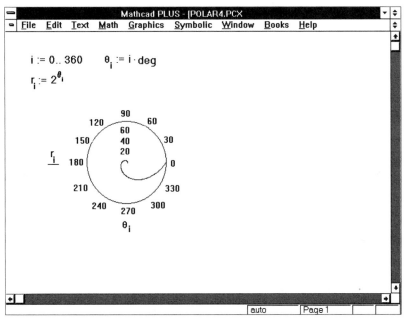

Figure 4: Plotting one vector against another.

Formatting the axes

You can reformat your polar plot's axes, using the Polar Axes page of the dialog box for formatting polar plots.

To change a polar plot's format:

- Click in the polar plot to select it. Mathcad encloses the plot in a blue selection box and the **Polar Plot** menu replaces the **Graphics** menu.

- Double-click in the polar plot. Alternatively, choose **Format** from the **Polar Plot** menu. You'll see the dialog box for formatting polar plots.

- If necessary, click the Polar Axes tab.

- There is a complete group of settings for each axis. Change the appropriate settings.

- Click "OK" to accept your changes and close the dialog box. Mathcad redraws the polar plot with the new settings in effect. Alternatively, click "Apply" to see the plot redrawn without closing the dialog box.

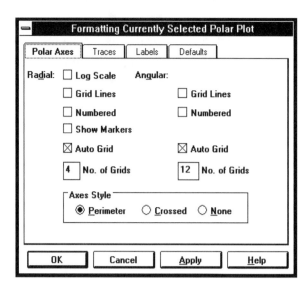

Axis settings

Each axis has the following settings associated with it:

Log Scale

When this box is checked, the radial axis is logarithmic. Axis limits must be positive. This setting is available only for the radial axis. Figure 13 on page 492 illustrates a polar plot with a logarithmic axis.

Grid Lines

When this box is checked, the tick marks on the selected axis are replaced by grid lines. If the axis is logarithmic, then logarithmically spaced grid lines are added if space permits. Radial grid lines are circles of fixed radius; angular grid lines radiate out from the origin at a fixed angle. Figure 11 on page 491 compares a plot with tick marks to the same plot with grid lines.

Numbered

When this box is checked, the selected grid lines are numbered. Figure 11 on page 491 illustrates numbers being used with grid lines.

Show Markers

When this box is checked, you can add reference lines to your polar plot. For a discussion of Show Markers, see "Adding radial reference lines" later in this section.

Auto Grid

When this box is checked, Mathcad automatically selects the number of grid markings (tick marks or grid lines). When the box is unchecked, you choose the number of grid markings (from 2 to 99) by typing a number in the No. of Grids text box. You can specify the number of grid markings only when Log Scale is unchecked. Figure 12 on page 491 illustrates the effect of Auto Grid.

In addition to these check boxes, the dialog boxes contain the following:

No. of Grids

When available, this text box indicates the number of tick marks or grid lines on the associated axis. You can enter a number between 2 and 99, inclusive. This box is only available when Auto Grid and Log Scale are unchecked. Figure 12 on page 491 shows the effects of defining the number of grid lines on both the radial and the angular axes.

Axes Style

These buttons let you choose between crossed axes, no axes at all, and a plot enclosed by a circle (perimeter). Figure 14 on page 492 illustrates the difference between perimeter and crossed axes.

See the section "Setting default formats" on page 481 to learn how to:

- Quickly restore a polar plot to its default format settings.

- Use a particular plot as a model for all future polar plots.

Setting limits for axes

Mathcad sets the upper and lower radial axis limits by default. For a linear scale, the upper limit is the maximum radial value of whatever is plotted. The lower limit is zero. For a logarithmic scale, the upper limit is set to the next higher integer power of ten above the maximum of the data. The lower limit on a logarithmic scale is set to the next integer power of ten below the minimum of the data.

You may want to use axis limits other than those set by Mathcad. You can override Mathcad's limits by entering limits directly on the graph. To do so:

- Click in the polar plot to select it. Mathcad shows two additional numbers on the upper right of the polar plot. These numbers are enclosed within corner symbols, as illustrated by the selected plot in Figure 5, below.

- Mathcad treats a negative radial limit as a positive value. To set the maximum value of the radial axis, click on the number in the top placeholder and type in a new number. While there's rarely a reason to change the minimum value, you can do this by clicking on the lower number and typing a new number.

- Click outside the plot, Mathcad immediately redraws it using the axis limits you specify. Figure 5 shows the effect of manually setting limits on a polar plot.

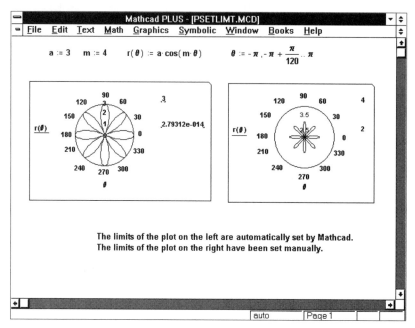

Figure 5: Manually setting axis limits.

Adding radial reference lines

Mathcad places linearly or logarithmically spaced radial grid lines on a polar plot. The spaces between grid lines are relatively round numbers that span the range of values on the angular axis. There may, however, be occasions when you need to place a radial line somewhere other than where Mathcad would normally place a grid line.

To add a radial reference line to the polar plot:

- Click in the polar plot to select it. The **Polar Plot** menu replaces the **Graphics** menu.

- Choose **Format** from the **Polar Plot** menu or double-click on the plot to display the dialog box for formatting polar plots. If necessary, click on the Polar Axes page.

- Click the Show Markers check box in the radial axis column to add a check. Click "OK". Mathcad shows two additional placeholders on the upper-left side of the plot.

- Click on one of the placeholders and type in the value at which you want the radial reference line drawn. Repeat this process with the other placeholder to add two radial reference lines.

When you click outside the graph, Mathcad draws a dashed circle at each number that you specified. The number that you typed appears on this dashed circle. To move the dashed circle, click on the appropriate number and change it. To delete the circle, delete this number or click on the Show Markers check box to remove the check. Figure 6 illustrates the use of radial reference lines.

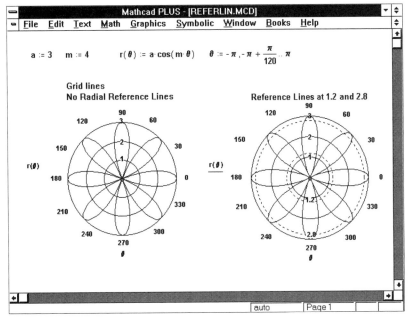

Figure 6: Adding radial reference lines to a polar plot.

Formatting individual curves

You can reformat the traces on your polar plot, using the Traces page of the dialog box for formatting polar plots.

To reformat a plot's traces:

■ Click in the polar plot to select it. Mathcad encloses the plot in a blue selection box. The **Polar Plot** menu replaces the **Graphics** menu.

■ Double-click in the polar plot. Alternatively, choose **Format** from the **Polar Plot** menu. Mathcad displays the dialog box for formatting polar plots.

■ If necessary, click the Traces tab.

- Click on the appropriate line in the scrolling list box to select a trace. To change the name of the trace, type the new name in the text box under the "Legend Label" column. To assign a symbol or marker, line type, color, trace type, and line weight to this trace, click on the arrow beside each text box to see a drop-down list of options, and then click on the option you want. See the next section, "Trace settings," for complete explanations of these fields.

- Click "OK" to accept your changes and close the dialog box. Mathcad redraws the plot with the new settings in effect. Alternatively, click "Apply" to preview your changes without closing the dialog box.

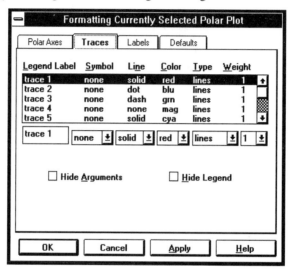

Trace settings

A graph can have up to sixteen individual traces. Each trace is described by a line in the scrolling list. Mathcad uses these lines as needed, assigning one for each trace in your plot. Each line has six fields:

Legend Label

This is the name of the trace as it would appear in the legend beneath the plot. See the section "Displaying or hiding arguments and legends" on page 485 for more information about legends.

Symbol

This controls whether each point on the curve is marked with a symbol. If y you choose, you can mark each point with either an "×", a "+", a hollow box, or a hollow diamond. If you have a lot of points packed closely together, you should probably select "none." Figure 15 on page 493 shows an example in which each data point is marked by with an "×".

Line

This controls whether the line is solid, dotted, or dashed or whether it consists of alternating dashes and dots. This feature provides a useful way to distinguish unmarked curves in black and white printouts.

Color

This controls whether the selected trace is red, blue, green, magenta, cyan (a light blue), brown, black, or white. Mathcad ignores this on monochrome terminals.

Type

This controls the type of trace that will be displayed. Mathcad can generate the following types of plots: curves, bar charts, stepped curves, error bars, and points. (You must have at least two traces to use error bars.) Figure 16 on page 493 illustrates the same polar plot, displayed with a variety of trace types.

Weight

This controls the weight or thickness of the trace. Select from 1 to 9 (thinnest to thickest). Select "p" for the lightest (single-pixel) trace. Although this may look like weight 1 on your screen, a high resolution printer will print it as a very fine line. This field also controls the size of the symbols marking data points, if you have selected a symbol other than "none". If you have selected trace type points, this field sets the weight of the dot plotted at each data point.

See "Setting default formats" on page 481 to learn how to:

- Quickly restore a polar plot to its default format settings.

- Use a particular plot as a model for all future polar plots.

In addition to the scrolling list and its associated text box and lists, the Trace page has two check boxes: Hide Arguments and Hide Legend. These are explained fully in the section "Displaying or hiding arguments and legends" on page 485 .

Setting default formats

Mathcad uses default settings to format the axes and traces of new polar plots as you create them. You can change these defaults in two ways:

- By saving as defaults the settings of your current plot.

- By using the Setting Default Formats for Polar Plots dialog box to set defaults, if you don't want to use an existing plot.

Changing defaults only affects new polar plots; previously existing plots are unaffected.

Copying defaults from an existing plot

One way to create a new set of defaults is to use the format settings of an existing polar plot. The advantage of this method is that you can use "Apply" to see how the format settings look while you define them.

To use the format of a particular polar plot as the default polar plot settings:

- Select the graph by clicking on it.

- Click the Defaults tab on the dialog box for formatting polar plots. The Defaults page appears, as shown below.

- If the Use for Defaults check box isn't checked, click on it to add one. When you close the dialog box, Mathcad saves these settings as your default settings.

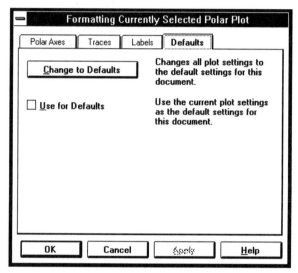

Setting defaults without using a polar plot

You don't have to use an existing polar plot to create or revise default formats. Instead, you can use the dialog box for polar plot defaults. To set defaults this way:

- Make sure that you don't have any plots selected.

- Choose **Polar Plot Format** from the **Graphics** menu. You'll see the dialog box for polar plot defaults. The following figure shows an example of this dialog box with the Polar Axes page displayed.

- Change the appropriate settings on the Polar Axes and Traces pages.

- Click "OK" to accept your changes and close the dialog box.

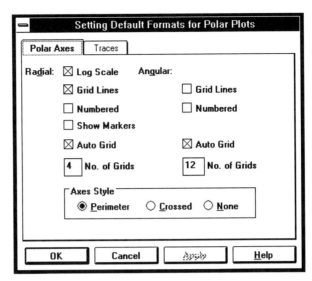

Using default graph settings

If you don't want the format changes made to your polar plot since creating the last set of default settings, you can restore the plot to its current default settings. To do so:

- Click the Defaults tab on the dialog box for polar plots.

- Click "Change to Defaults".

- Click "OK" to close the dialog box.

Mathcad redraws the plot, using the most recent set of default format settings. Mathcad does not use any defaults you might have set using the Use for Defaults check box at any time after the creation of this plot.

Labeling your polar plot

Mathcad provides several ways to help you to identify what it is you've plotted. You can display:

- A *title* centered above or below the polar plot.

- A *legend* identifying each trace.

- The arguments you used to create the plot.

Figure 7 shows the relative locations of each of these labels on a perimeter graph and on a crossed axes graph.

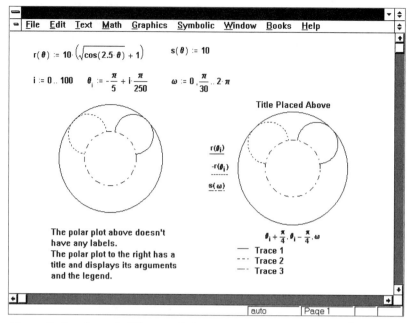

Figure 7: Graphs with different labels.

You can use these labels all together or in any combination. By default, Mathcad hides the title, displays arguments, and hides the legend.

Working with titles

To add a title to a polar plot, follow these steps:

- Click in the polar plot to select it. Mathcad encloses it in a selection box and the **Polar Plot** menu replaces the **Graphics** menu.

- Choose **Format** from the **Polar Plot** menu or double-click on the selected plot. Mathcad displays the dialog box for formatting polar plots. If necessary, click on the Labels tab to see the Labels page, as shown below.

- Type a title for your polar plot into the Title text box.

- Click on either the Above or Below button, depending upon where you want to put the title.

- Make sure that the Show Title check box is checked. If it isn't, Mathcad still remembers the title but won't display it.

- Click "OK" to accept your changes. Mathcad redraws the polar plot with the title in place. Alternatively, click "Apply" to preview your title without closing the dialog box.

To change the title's text or position, edit the information in the Title group as appropriate. To delete the title, highlight it in the text box and press **[Del]**.

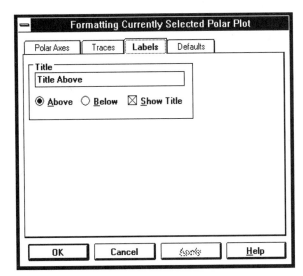

Displaying or hiding arguments and legends

Mathcad provides both arguments and legends for identifying specific traces on a polar plot:

- Arguments are the expressions that you typed into the placeholders to create the polar plot. By default, Mathcad displays arguments.
- Legends are labels that appear underneath the polar plot. They contain a name and an example of the line and symbols used to draw the trace. By default, Mathcad hides legends.

To display or hide arguments and legends:

- Click on the polar plot to select it. Mathcad encloses it in a selection box and the **Polar Plot** menu replaces the **Graphics** menu.
- Choose **Format** from the **Polar Plot** menu or double-click on the graph. Mathcad displays the dialog box for formatting polar plots. If necessary, click on the Traces tab.
- To suppress the display of the arguments, click on the Hide Arguments check box to add a check.
- To show the legend, click on the Hide Legend check box to remove the check.

Modifying your polar plot's perspective

Mathcad provides options for manipulating the presentation of your polar plot:

- You can make the plot larger or smaller.

- You can zoom in on a portion of the plot.

- You can get the coordinates for any point that was plotted to construct the plot.

- You can get the coordinates for any location within the plot.

The rest of this section shows how to use these features.

Resizing a polar plot

Resizing a polar plot is very much like resizing a window:

- Click the mouse just outside the plot region. This anchors one corner of the selection rectangle.

- Press and hold down the left mouse button and drag the mouse pointer towards the plot. A dashed selection rectangle emerges from the anchor point.

- When the selection rectangle just encloses the graphics region, let go of the mouse button.

- Move the mouse pointer to the lower right corner of the selection rectangle. It will change to a double-headed arrow.

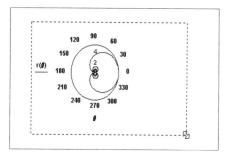

- Press and hold down the left mouse button and move the mouse in the direction in which you want the plot's dimensions to change.

- Once the plot is the right size, let go of the mouse button.

- Click outside the plot to deselect it.

Zooming in on a polar plot

Mathcad allows you to select a region of a polar plot and magnify it. To zoom in on a portion of a plot, follow these steps:

- With the cursor in the polar plot region, click the mouse so the plot is enclosed in a blue selection box and the **Polar Plot** menu replaces the **Graphics** menu.

- Choose **Zoom** from the **Polar Plot** menu. The Polar Zoom dialog box appears.

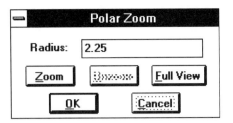

- If necessary, reposition the Polar Zoom dialog box so that you can see the entire region of the graph you want to zoom.

- Click in the polar plot region and drag the mouse while holding down the left mouse button. A dashed selection circle is centered in the plot.

- When the selection circle just encloses the region you want to magnify, let go of the left mouse button.

- The radius of the selected region is shown in the Radius box of the Polar Plot Zoom dialog box. Click the "Zoom" button to redraw the plot. The axis limits are temporarily set to the coordinates specified in the Polar Plot Zoom dialog box.

Before you make these axis limits permanent, you can select another region to zoom by enclosing another selection circle around the new region. Click "Unzoom" to start the zooming process over. If you're working with a plot that has already been zoomed, you may want to view the original plot as it looked before any zooming took place. To do so, click on "Full View".

Figure 8 shows the effects of zooming in on a portion of a polar plot.

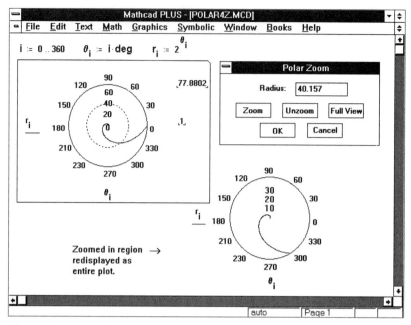

Figure 8: A zoomed-in region of a polar plot.

Getting a readout of polar plot coordinates

To see a readout of polar plot coordinates of the specific points that make up a trace, follow these steps:

- Click the mouse in the polar plot to enclose it in a blue selection box. The **Polar Plot** menu replaces the **Graphics** menu.

- Choose **Trace** from the the **Polar Plot** menu to show the Polar Trace dialog box.

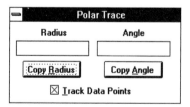

- If necessary, reposition the Polar Trace dialog box so that you can see the entire region of the graph.

- Drag the mouse along the trace whose coordinates you want to see. A dotted crosshair jumps from one point to the next as you move the pointer along the trace.

- Use the left and right arrows to move to the previous and next data points. Use the up and down arrows to move to other traces.

- As the pointer reaches each point on the trace, Mathcad displays the coordinates of the pointer location in the Radius and Angle boxes.

- When you release the mouse button, the radius and angle settings of the last point selected are shown in the Radius and Angle boxes. The crosshair remains until you click outside the polar plot.

- Double-click on the control box in the upper-left-hand corner to close the Polar Trace dialog box. The crosshair will remain on your plot until you click anywhere outside it.

To copy a coordinate to the clipboard:

- Click "Copy Radius" or "Copy Angle".

- You can then paste that value into either a math or text region of your Mathcad worksheet, into a spreadsheet, or into any other application that allows pasting from the clipboard.

To see a readout of coordinates for any location in a polar plot:

- Follow the above procedures to call up the Polar Trace dialog box.

- Click on Track Data Points to uncheck it.

- In the polar plot region, click and drag the mouse pointer over the points whose coordinates you want to see. A dotted crosshair follows the pointer as you drag it over the plot. Mathcad displays the coordinates of the pointer in the Radius and Angle boxes. The radius and angle values change continuously to reflect the current pointer position.

- When you release the mouse button, the Radius and Angle boxes show the r and θ values of the last pixel selected.

Figure 9 shows an example of the Trace option being used.

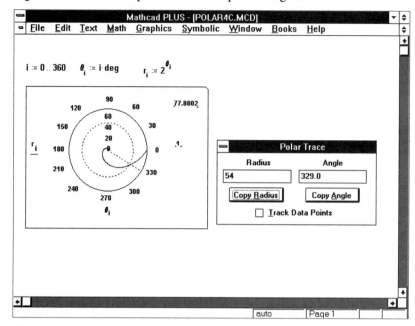

Figure 9: Reading coordinates from a polar plot using the Polar Trace dialog box.

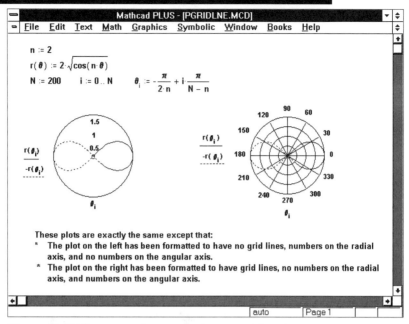

Figure 10: Different axis formats on the same polar plot.

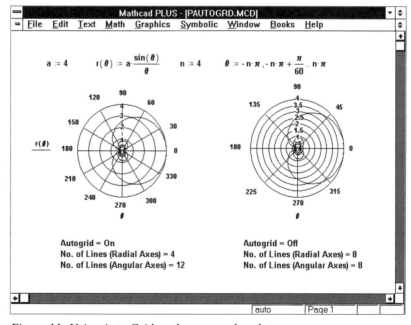

Figure 11: Using Auto Grid on the same polar plot.

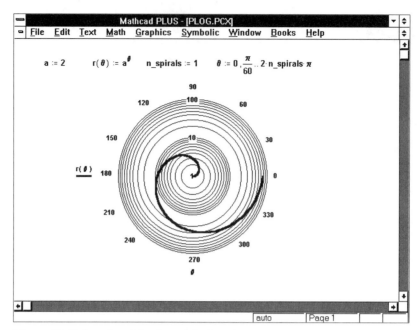

Figure 12: Polar plot with a logarithmic axis.

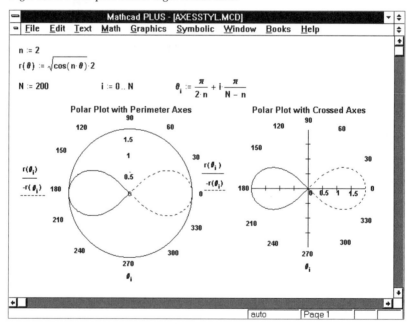

Figure 13: Using perimeter and crossed axes styles on the same polar plot.

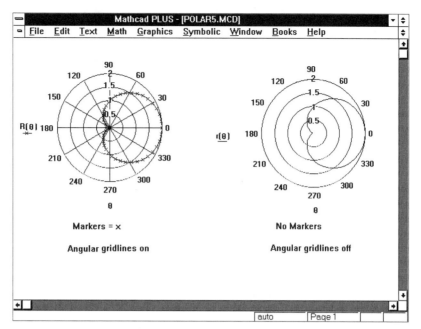

Figure 14: Using symbols and lines on the same polar chart.

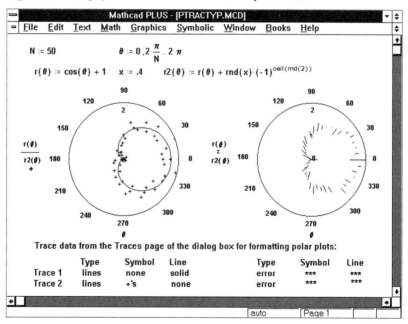

Figure 15: Presenting the same plot formatted as lines and symbols and then as error bars.

Chapter 21
Surface Plots

Mathcad worksheets can include both two-dimensional plots and three-dimensional plots. Unlike the two-dimensional plots, which work with range variables and functions, three-dimensional plots require a matrix of values. This chapter shows how a matrix can be represented as a surface plot in which you can see a three-dimensional illustration of its values.

This chapter describes how to create, use, and format three-dimensional surface plots. The chapters that follow describe how to work with the other types of plots.

This chapter contains the following sections:

Creating a surface plot

Basic steps for creating surface plots; procedures for creating surface plots for functions of two variables and for creating parametric surface plots.

Resizing surface plots

Procedures for changing the size of surface plots.

Formatting surface plots

Procedures for changing surface plots: setting the viewpoint, size, and magnification; adding labels; and formatting lines, colors, and axes.

To create a surface plot:

■ Define a matrix of values to plot. Mathcad will use the rows and column numbers of the matrix as *x*- and *y*-axes. The matrix elements will be plotted as heights above or below the *xy* plane.

■ Choose **Create Surface Plot** from the **Graphics** menu. Alternatively, you can press [**Ctrl**]**2**. Mathcad shows a box with a single placeholder, as shown below in Figure 1.

■ Type the name of the matrix in the placeholder. Just as with an equation, Mathcad will not process the surface plot until you either press [**F9**] or, in automatic mode, click outside the region.

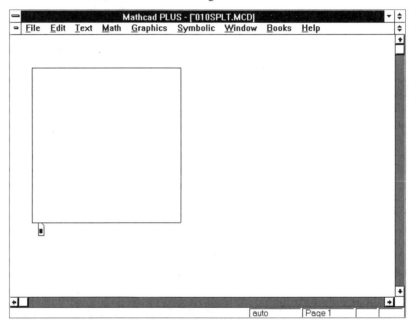

Figure 1: An empty placeholder in a surface plot region awaits the name of a matrix.

What you see is a visual representation of the matrix. Mathcad draws a perspective view of the matrix as a two-dimensional grid lying flat in three-dimensional space. Each matrix element is represented as a point at a specified height above or below this grid. The height is proportional to the value of the matrix element. In the default perspective, the first row of the matrix extends from the back left corner of the grid to the right, while the first column extends from the back left corner out toward the viewer.

Mathcad draws lines to connect the points in the plot. These lines define the surface. The perspective for this rendering of the surface depends on the location of the viewer with respect to the surface. You can specify this view by changing the plot's tilt or rotation, as described in the subsection "Changing your view of the surface plot," later in this chapter.

Plotting a function of two variables

A typical surface plot shows the values of a function of two variables. To see such a plot, you must first create a matrix that holds the values of the function, then create a surface plot of that matrix. Here are the typical steps in plotting a function of two variables such as that shown in Figure 2:

- Define a function of two variables.

- Decide how many points you want to plot in the x and y directions. Set up range variables i and j to index these points. For example, if you want to plot 10 points in each direction, enter:

$$i := 0 \mathinner{.\,.} 9 \qquad j := 0 \mathinner{.\,.} 9$$

- Define x_i and y_j as evenly spaced points on the x- and y-axes.

- Fill the matrix **M** with the values of $f(x_i, y_j)$.

- Choose **Create Surface Plot** from the **Graphics** menu.

- Type **M** in the placeholder and click outside the region.

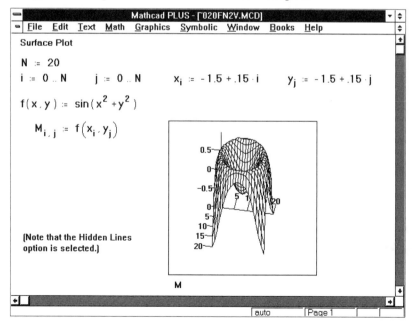

Figure 2: Surface plot of a function of two variables.

Creating parametric surface plots

To use Mathcad's surface plot operator to draw parametric surface plots:

- Type the names of three matrices having the same number of rows and columns into the placeholders at the bottom of the surface plot.

- Mathcad interprets these three matrices as the *x*-, *y*-, and *z*-coordinates of points on a surface and draws this surface from the viewing angle prescribed by the Rotation and Tilt settings.

The underlying parameter space is a rectangular sheet covered by a uniform mesh. In effect, the three matrices map this sheet into three-dimensional space. For example, the matrices **X**, **Y**, and **Z** defined in Figure 3 carry out a mapping that rolls the sheet into a tube and then joins the ends of the tube to form a torus.

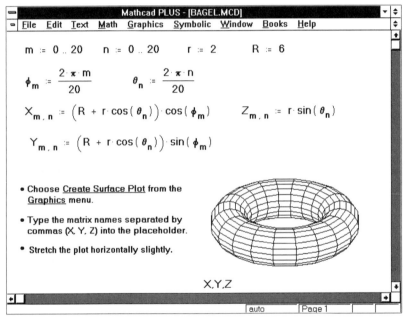

Figure 3: Parametric surface plots.

You can't convert parametric surface plots into any other type of 3D plot.

Resizing surface plots

To change the size of a surface plot, follow these steps:

- Click the mouse just outside the surface plot region. This anchors one corner of the selection rectangle.

- Press and hold down the left mouse button. While holding down the button, drag the mouse. A selection rectangle framed by dashed lines emerges from the anchor point.

- When the selection rectangle just encloses the surface plot region, let go of the left mouse button.

- Move the mouse pointer to the right or bottom edge or to the lower right corner of the selection rectangle. It should change to a double-headed arrow.

- Press and hold down the mouse button. While holding down the button, move the mouse. The surface plot region will be stretched in the direction of motion.

- Once the surface plot is the right size, let go of the mouse button.

- Click outside the surface plot to deselect it.

Formatting surface plots

Mathcad provides many ways to change the way a surface plot looks. These can be categorized in four groups:

- Viewing characteristics: the type of plot being displayed; the perspective or point of view from which you see the surface; how "bumpy" the surface looks; and the presence or absence of borders, enclosing boxes, axes, and co-ordinate planes.

- Color and line formatting: whether the z-coordinates of the surface are indicated by shades of gray or by color; whether the surface is opaque or transparent; and whether the surface patches form a smooth surface or form parallel patches.

- Axis formatting: whether to show tick marks or grid marks on each axis.

- Title characteristics: how the surface plot will display titles.

To change any of these plot characteristics, start with the 3D Plot Format dialog box:

- Choose **3D Plot Format** from the **Graphics** menu. Alternatively, double-click on the plot itself. Mathcad brings up the 3D Plot Format dialog box. The View Page of this dialog box is shown below. The remaining three tabs take you to three additional pages.

- If necessary, click the tab for the page you want to work with.

- Make the appropriate changes in the dialog box.

- To see the effect of your changes *without* closing the dialog box, click "Apply". When you're satisfied, click "Close".

- When you're finished, close the dialog by clicking "OK" or "Close".

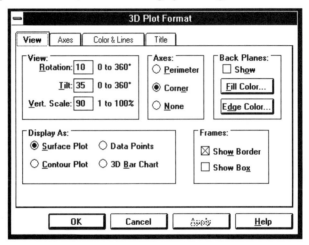

Changing your view of the surface plot

The View page of the 3D Plot Format dialog box lets you modify the general presentation of your plot.

To change your plot from a surface plot to another type of 3D plot, click on the appropriate button in the Display As group. You can convert any surface plot (except for parametric plots) into a contour plot or a 3D bar chart. These plot types are fully discussed in the corresponding chapters of this *User's Guide*. You can also display just the points making up the surface without displaying the surface itself. To do so, click on Data Points. You can change how the points look by using the Colors and Lines tab of this dialog box. For more information, see Chapter 24, "Surface plots."

To change the perspective, or point of view, from which you see the surface of your plot, adjust the figures in the Rotation and Tilt text boxes. Use an integer between 0 to 360 degrees. Figure 4 shows the effects of varying the rotation and tilt (as well as the scale) of a surface plot.

- Increasing the rotation turns the plot clockwise. When the rotation is set to 0, you look straight down the first column of the matrix. The first row of the matrix points to the right. When the rotation is set to 90, you look straight down the first row of the matrix. The first column points to the left.

- Increasing the tilt raises you higher above the plot's surface. When the tilt is set to 0, you look edge on at the plane of the matrix. When the tilt is set to 90, you look straight down on the surface. Think of how a mountain range looks when you're on the ground (tilt equals 0) and when you're flying directly above (tilt equals 90).

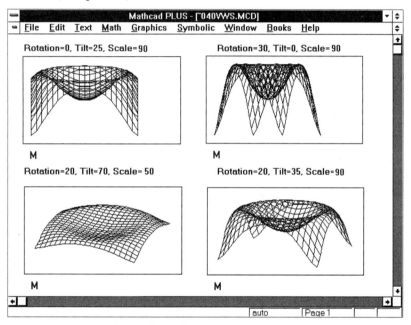

Figure 4: Different views of a surface.

To control how bumpy the plot looks, adjust the magnification of the vertical scale by changing the number in the Vert. Scale text box. This is an integer between 1 and 100. When the vertical scale is small, the variations in height of the surface will be barely perceptible. At 100, the variations are shown at full scale. Figure 4 shows the effects of varying the scale (as well as the rotation and tilt) of a surface plot.

To add or remove a border around the surface plot region, click on Show Border in the Frames group to add or remove a check. The border is a two-dimensional frame around the surface plot region.

To enclose the surface and and the axes within a three-dimensional bounding box, click on Show Box in the Frames group to add a check.

You can add back planes to your surface plots:

- To show the *xy*, *xz*, and *yz* back planes, click on Show in the Back Planes group.

- To color the surface of the back planes, click on "Fill Color".

- To outline the edges of the back planes in a particular color, click on "Edge Color".

Figure 5 shows a surface plot with a border around it and with back planes showing and the same plot enclosed within a box without showing back planes.

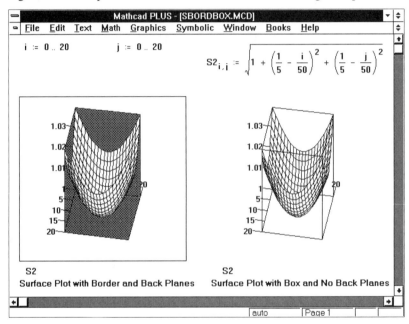

Figure 5: Using a border or a bounding box on a surface plot.

Changing the shading of the surface

You can often make a surface plot communicate more effectively by using different colors to represent different values of z. Alternatively, if you intend to print on a black and white printer, you can achieve a similar effect by using different shades of gray to represent the different values of z. Use the Color and Lines page of the 3D Plot Format dialog box.

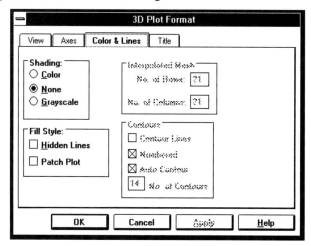

To specify the shading of your plot, click the appropriate button in the Shading group:

- None: The surface won't have any shading, regardless of where it is.

- Grayscale: The largest values of the matrix will be in white and the smallest values will be in black. Intermediate values will be in shades of gray.

- Color: The largest values of the matrix will be in red and the smallest values will be in blue. Intermediate values will range from yellow through green.

Figure 6 shows the same surface plot displayed without shading and in grayscale.

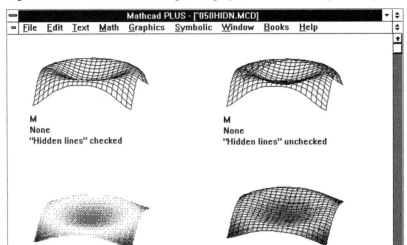

Figure 6: Surface plots showing display options for lines and meshes.

If you've chosen to leave the surface without shading ("None"), you'll be able to see through the surface as if it were transparent. Depending on the surface and on your viewpoint, you may find it distracting to see through the surface. When this happens, you may want to render the surface opaque. Note that this option is unnecessary when a surface is rendered in color or in shades of gray. Such surfaces are inherently opaque.

- To make the surface opaque, click Hidden Lines to add a check. Mathcad hides any lines that are behind the surface. Such a plot takes longer to draw since Mathcad has to determine which parts of the surface are concealed.

- To make the surface transparent, click Hidden Lines to remove the check. If you uncheck Hidden Lines, the surface shows lines that are behind it. Such a plot will draw more quickly than if lines were hidden, but it may be more difficult to interpret.

The upper two surface plots in Figure 6 show the same surface with and without lines showing.

By default, Mathcad overlays a mesh on colored and grayscale surfaces. The intersections of the lines making up this mesh correspond to the elements of the underlying matrix. Each patch created by this mesh gets a color corresponding to the value of the underlying matrix element.

As the number of matrix elements increases, this mesh can become so dense that it begins to obscure the colors. When this happens you may want to hide the mesh. To do so, click Hide Mesh in the Fill Style group to add a check.

Note that Hide Mesh is only available for colored and grayscale plots. Hiding the mesh of a plot that doesn't have any shading would make that plot invisible. The lower two surface plots in Figure 6 show the same surface plot with the mesh showing and with it hidden.

By default, the patches making up the surface are free to tilt in whatever direction necessary to connect them to their neighboring patches. The result is a continuous surface. In this case, each point at which grid lines intersect is associated with a matrix element. This means that for an $m \times n$ matrix, there will be $(m - 1)(n - 1)$ patches.

To constrain these patches to be horizontal, click Patch Plot in the Fill Style group for regular surface plots and Alternative Mesh for parametric surface plots to add a check. The resultant discontinuous surface shows a patch for each matrix element. This means that for an $m \times n$ matrix, there will be mn patches.

Figure 7 shows an example of the same matrix being plotted with Patch Plot checked and not checked.

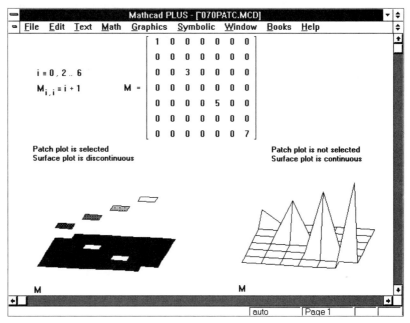

Figure 7: Patch plots.

Formatting the axes

The Axes page of the 3D Plot Format dialog box lets you modify the format of the axes of your plot. Each axis is described by its own set of check boxes and text boxes.

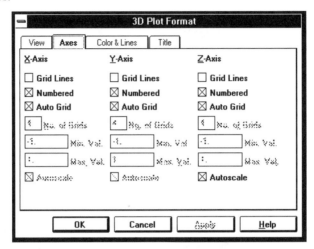

Mathcad generates grid lines for surface plots by extending tick marks up and down the two back planes adjacent to a given axis. Thus, x-axis grid lines represent lines of constant x drawn on the xz plane and the xy plane, the two orthogonal planes whose intersections form the x-axis. The y-axis grid lines and z-axis grid lines are defined similarly.

Note that this makes it impossible to draw lines of constant x on only the xz plane. Clicking Grid Lines always results in grid lines being drawn on two of the three back planes.

To choose between using tick marks or grid lines on a selected axis, use the Grid Lines check box for that axis. When Grid Lines is checked, Mathcad will extend the tick marks on the selected axis into grid lines on each adjacent back plane. For example, checking this on the z-axis will result in lines of constant z on both the yz and the xz back planes. If you are showing grid lines, you should seriously consider showing back planes as well. See "Changing your view of the surface plot" on page 500. Figure 8 shows an example of a surface plot that uses grid lines rather than tick marks.

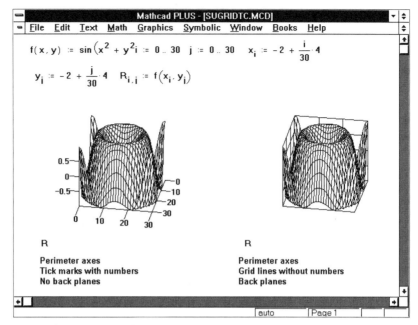

Figure 8: Using the different options for tick marks.

To add or remove numbers for the tick marks on an axis, use the Numbered check box for that axis. Figure 8 shows the differences between having numbers on the tick marks and not having numbers.

You can have Mathcad automatically select the number of grid intervals on an axis or you can specify the number yourself. Grid intervals are the spaces between tick marks or grid lines.

- To have Mathcad select the number of grid intervals, use the Auto Grid check box. When Auto Grid is checked, Mathcad will automatically select the number of grid intervals on the specified axis.

- To specify the number of grid intervals on an axis *yourself* enter an integer from 1 to 99 in the No. of Grids text box. This text box is only available when Auto Grid is unchecked.

By default, Mathcad autoscales the z-axis according to the range of values in the matrix you are plotting. Sometimes you will want to fix the scaling yourself, for example, if you are comparing views of related data or setting up a surface animation sequence. To set the z-axis limits manually, click on the Autoscale box in the z-axis column of the Axes page to uncheck it. Then enter the maximum and minimum values in the Max. Val. and Min. Val. text boxes.

Since a surface plot is made by plotting the elements of a matrix, Mathcad cannot "know" anything about x and y coordinates. By default, the coordinates on the x- and y-axes of a surface plot will simply be rows and columns. To change the numbers used to label the x- and y-axis, enter the new limits in the Max. Val. and Min. Val. text boxes. If you've made a parametric surface plot, you won't be able to use these text boxes. This is because the x and y values are themselves passed in as the first two matrices of the three matrices required for a parametric surface plot.

Labeling the surface plot

The Title page of the 3D Plot Format dialog box, shown below, lets you add and modify a title for your surface plot.

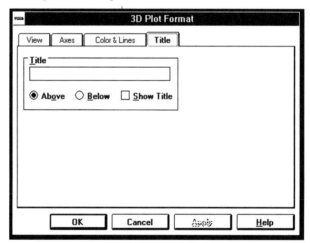

To add or edit a title for your surface plot:

- Type the title for your plot into the Title text box.

- To display the title, click on Show Title to insert a check. To conceal the title without deleting it, click on Show Title to remove the check.

- To position the title, click on either the Above or Below button. Mathcad places the title either directly above or below your plot. Figure 9 shows the options for positioning labels on your plot.

- To change the title's text or position, edit the information in the Title group as appropriate.

- Click "OK" to close the dialog box when you have finished.

- To delete the title, highlight it in the Title text box and press [Del].

If you initiate this process by double-clicking on the title itself, you'll see an equivalent dialog box.

Chapter 21 Surface Plots

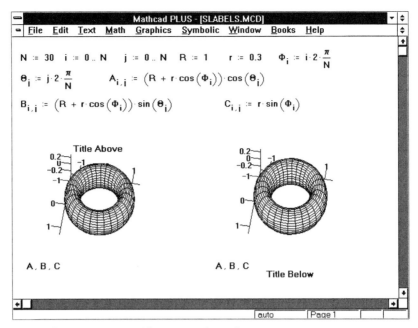

Figure 9: Positioning a title on a surface plot.

Chapter 21 Surface Plots

Chapter 22
Contour Plots

A contour plot lets you quickly visualize level curves. These are curves along which a particular quantity is constant. Using Mathcad, you make a contour plot in the same way you make a surface plot: by passing a matrix of z-values in which each row and column corresponds to a particular x and y value. This chapter describes how a matrix can be represented as a contour plot.

This chapter contains the following sections:

Creating a contour plot

Basic steps in creating a contour plot; what the plot actually shows.

Resizing a contour plot

Procedures for changing the size of contour plots.

Formatting contour plots

Procedures for changing contour plots: formatting contours and axes and adding labels.

Creating a contour plot

To create a contour plot:

- Define a matrix of values to plot. Mathcad will assume that the rows and columns represent equally spaced intervals on the axes. Mathcad then linearly interpolates the values of this matrix to form level curves. Such level curves can represent isotherms, isobars, equipotentials, streamlines, and many other physical phenomena.

- Choose **Create Contour Plot** from the **Graphics** menu. Mathcad shows a box with a single placeholder as shown in Figure 1.

- Type the name of the matrix in the placeholder. Just as with an equation, Mathcad will not process the contour plot until you either press [**F9**] or, in automatic mode, click outside out of the region.

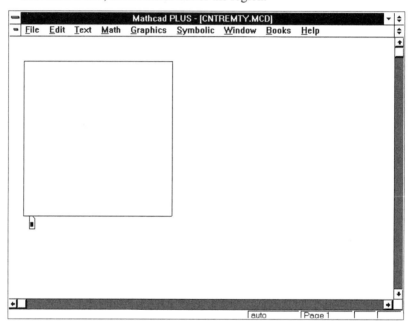

Figure 1: An empty placeholder in a contour plot region awaits the name of a matrix.

What you see is a visual representation of the matrix's level curves. Each level curve, or contour, is formed in such a way that no two cross. By default, the contours are labeled with their height above or below the *xy* plane. Mathcad plots the matrix by rotating it so that the (0,0) element is at the lower-left corner. Thus the rows of the matrix correspond to values on the *x* axis, increasing to the right, and the columns correspond to values along the *y* axis, increasing toward the top.

You can specify whether or not the contours are to be numbered, how many contours there are, and what labels and grid lines appear on the axes by formatting the contour plot. This is described in the section "Formatting contour plots," later in this chapter.

Level curves of a function of two variables

A typical contour plot shows the level curves of a function of two variables. To see such a plot, you must first create a matrix that holds the values of the function, then create a contour plot of that matrix. Here are the typical steps in plotting a function of two variables such as that shown in Figure 2:

- Define a function of two variables.

- Decide how many points you want to plot in the x and y directions. Set up range variables i and j to index these points. For example, if you want to plot 10 points in each direction, enter:

$$i := 0 .. 9 \qquad j := 0 .. 9$$

- Define x_i and y_j as evenly spaced points on the x- and y-axes.

- Fill the matrix $\mathbf{M}$ with the values of $f(x_i, y_j)$.

- Show $\mathbf{M}$ in a contour plot.

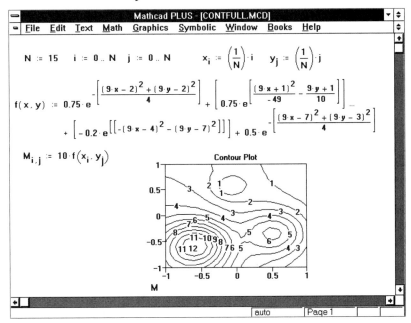

Figure 2: Contour plot of a function of two variables.

Note that if you plot a function as described here, the positive x-axis of the plot extends to the right and the positive y-axis extends toward the top of the window. Since the contour plot is created by putting the heights above the xy plane into a matrix, Mathcad has no way of knowing the actual values of the x and y axes. For this reason, the axes on contour plots are by default normalized to extend from 1 to −1. You can manually change the axis limits from these default values by choosing **3D Plot Format** from the **Graphics** menu with the contour plot selected or by double-clicking on the plot. Then set the values you want in the Min. Val. and Max. Val. text boxes on the Axes page.

Resizing a contour plot

To change the size of a contour plot, follow these steps:

- Click the mouse just outside the contour plot region. This anchors one corner of the selection rectangle.

- Press and hold down the left mouse button. While holding down the button, drag the mouse. A selection rectangle framed by dashed lines emerges from the anchor point.

- When the selection rectangle just encloses the contour plot region, release the left mouse button.

- Move the mouse pointer to the right or bottom edge or to the lower right corner of the selection rectangle. It should change to a double headed arrow.

- Press and hold down the mouse button. While holding down the button, move the mouse. The contour plot will stretch in the direction of motion.

- Once the contour plot is the right size, let go of the mouse button.

- Click outside the contour plot to deselect it.

Mathcad gives you control over many of the visual characteristics of contour plots. These can be categorized in four groups:

- Viewing characteristics: the type of plot being displayed.

- Axis formatting: whether to show tick marks or grid lines on each axis.

- Color and line formatting: whether the plot uses grayscale or color to show the height of a section and how the plot shows contours.

- Title characteristics: how the plot will display titles.

To change any of these plot characteristics, start with the 3-D Plot Format dialog box:

- Click on the plot to select it.

- Choose **3D Plot Format** from the **Graphics** menu. Alternatively, double-click on the plot itself. Mathcad brings up the 3D Plot Format dialog box. The View Page of this dialog box is shown below. The remaining three tabs take you to three additional pages.

- If necessary, click the tab for the page you want to work with.

- Change the appropriate characteristics in the dialog box.

- To see the effect of your changes *without* closing the dialog box, click "Apply".

- When you're finished, close the dialog by clicking "OK" or "Close".

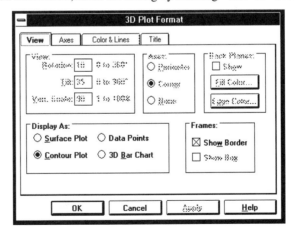

Changing your view of the contour plot

The View page of the 3D Plot Format dialog box lets you modify the general presentation of your plot.

To change your plot from a contour plot to another type of 3-D plot, click on the appropriate button in the Display As group. You can convert a contour plot into a Surface Plot or a 3D Bar Chart. These plot types are fully discussed in the corresponding chapters in this *User's Guide*. You can also display just the points making up the contours without displaying the contours themselves. To do so, click on Data Points. You can then change how the points look by using the Colors & Lines tab of this dialog box. For more information, see Chapter 24, "3D Scatter Plots."

Figure 3 shows the same matrix being plotted as a surface plot and as a contour plot.

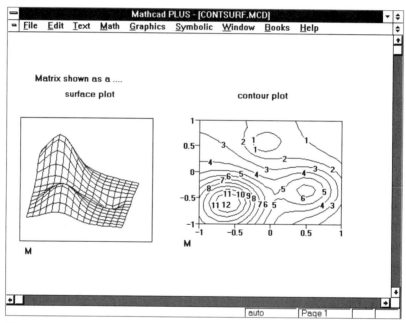

Figure 3: Matrix shown as both a surface plot and as a contour plot.

Changing the shading of the contours

You can often make a contour plot communicate more effectively by using different colors to represent different values of z. Alternatively, if you intend to print on a black and white printer, you can achieve a similar effect by using different shades of gray to represent different values of z. Use the Color and Lines page of the 3D Plot Format dialog box.

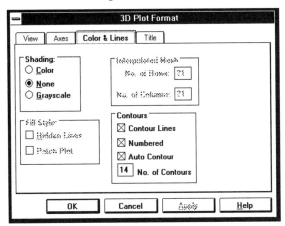

To specify the shading of your plot, click the appropriate button in the Shading group:

- Color: The bands between contour lines are colored. The largest values of the matrix will be in red and the smallest values will be in blue. Intermediate values will range from yellow through green.

- None: The bands between contour lines don't have any shading. Be sure the Contour Lines check box is checked or you won't see any contours at all.

- Grayscale: The bands between contour lines are in shades of gray. The largest values of the matrix will be in white and the smallest values will be in black. Intermediate values will be in shades of gray.

Figure 4 shows the same contour plot displayed without shading and in grayscale.

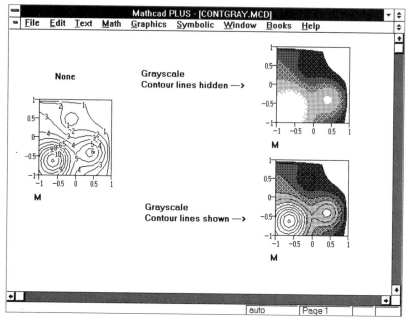

Figure 4: No shading and grayscale versions of a contour plot.

Besides varying the colors of a contour plot, you can also choose to hide the contours themselves. If you've chosen to leave the surface without shading ("None"), you should have the contour lines showing. If the plot is colored or grayscale, you can hide the contour lines and let the colors or gray shades show the contours. To show or hide the contour lines, click Contour Lines to add or remove the checkmark. Figure 4 shows the same contour plot with the contour lines hidden and showing.

Contours can be numbered to indicate the value associated with that contour. To add or remove numbers on most contours, use the Numbered check box. Figure 5 shows the same contour plot with numbered and unnumbered contour lines. Note that Mathcad doesn't number every contour when to do so would result in overcrowding.

Chapter 22 Contour Plots

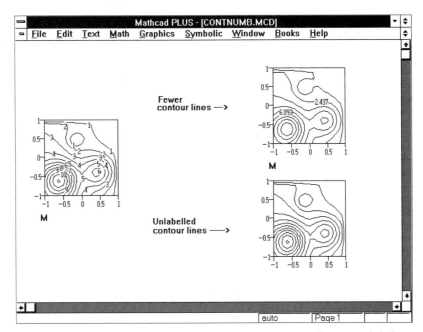

Figure 5: Changing the number of contours and turning off contour labeling.

To have Mathcad automatically select the number of contours to display, use the Auto Contour check box. When checked, Mathcad will automatically select the number of contours. When unchecked, you select the number of contours.

To specify the number of contours, enter an integer into the No. of Contours text box. This text box is only available when Auto Contour is unchecked. Figure 5 shows the same contour plot with contours automatically selected by Mathcad and with a specified number of contours.

Formatting the axes

The Axes page of the 3D Plot Format dialog box, shown below, lets you modify the format of the *x*- and *y*-axis of your plot. Each axis is described by its own set of check boxes and text boxes.

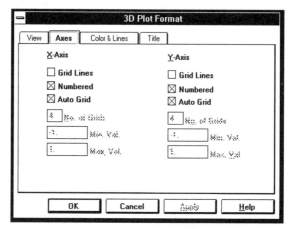

Mathcad generates grid lines on the plot at the same positions as the tick marks. To choose between seeing tick marks or grid lines on a selected axis, use the Grid Lines check box. When Grid Lines is checked, Mathcad adds grid lines to the plot. Figure 6 shows the same contour plot with and without grid lines.

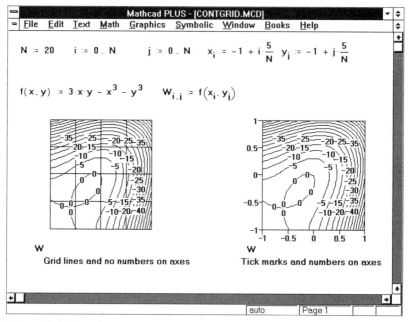

Figure 6: Effect of using the different options for tick marks.

To add or remove numbers for the tick marks on an axis, use the Numbered check box for that axis. The plot with grid lines in Figure 6 doesn't have numbers on the axes while the plot without grid lines does have them.

You can have Mathcad automatically select the number of grid intervals on an axis or you can specify the number yourself. Grid intervals are the spaces between tick marks or grid lines.

- To have Mathcad select the number of grid intervals, use the Auto Grid check box. When Auto Grid is checked, Mathcad will automatically select the number of grid intervals on the specified axis.

- To specify the number of grid intervals on an axis *yourself* enter an integer from 1 to 99 in the No. of Grids text box. This text box is only available when Auto Grid is unchecked.

To set limits on the maximum or minimum values of the *x*- or *y*-axis, enter the limit in the Max. Val. or Min. Val. text box. However, since the surface of the plot is stored as rows and columns in a matrix, these numbers have no significance as coordinates. They affect the display only. By default, Min and Max are set to −1 and 1 respectively.

Labeling the contour plot

The Title page of the 3D Plot Format dialog box, shown below, lets you add and modify labels on your contour plot.

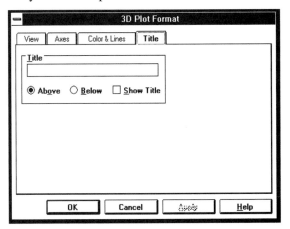

To add or edit a title for your contour plot:

- Type the title for your plot into the Title text box.

- To display the title, click on Show Title to insert a check. To conceal the title without deleting it, click on Show Title to remove the check.

- To position the title, click on either the Above or Below button. Mathcad places the title either directly above or below your plot.

- Click "OK" or "Close" to close the dialog box when you have finished.

To change the title's text or position, edit the information in the Title group as appropriate. To delete the title, highlight it in the text box and press [**Del**].

If you initiate this process by using the **Title** option from the **Contour Plot** menu or by double clicking on the title itself, you'll see an equivalent dialog box.

Figure 7 shows how Mathcad positions a title on a contour plot.

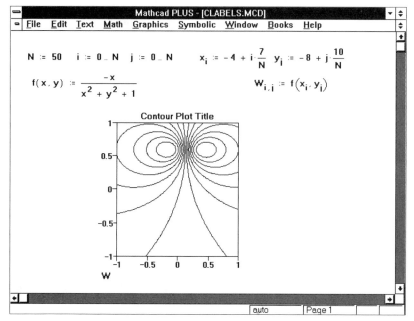

Figure 7: A title on a contour plot.

Chapter 23
3D Bar Charts

Three-dimensional bar charts offer you additional flexibility when displaying data. You can use them to visualize a matrix not as a surface plot but as bars of varying heights. You can show the bars either where they are in the matrix, stacked one on top of another, or laid out side-by-side.

This chapter contains the following sections:

Creating a 3D bar chart

Basic steps for creating bar charts and for creating bar charts for functions of two variables.

Resizing 3D bar charts

Procedures for changing the size of bar charts.

Formatting 3D bar charts

Procedures for changing bar charts: setting the viewpoint, size, and magnification; adding titles; and formatting lines, colors, and axes.

Creating a 3D bar chart

To create a bar chart:

- Define a matrix of values to display. Mathcad will use the rows and column numbers of the matrix as *x*- and *y*-axes. The matrix elements will be shown as columns extending from the *xy* plane to the appropriate height.

- Choose **Create 3D Bar Chart** from the **Graphics** menu. Mathcad shows a box with a single placeholder, as shown below in Figure 1.

- Type the name of the matrix in the placeholder. Just as with an equation, Mathcad will not display anything until you either press [**F9**] or, in automatic mode, click outside out of the region.

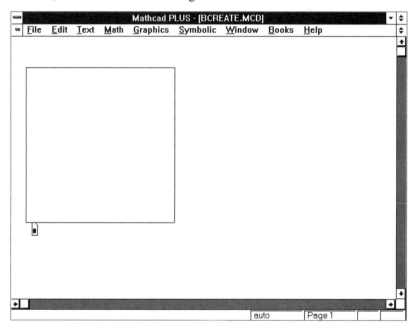

Figure 1: An empty placeholder in a bar chart region awaits the name of a matrix.

What you see is a visual representation of the matrix. Mathcad draws a perspective view of the matrix as a two-dimensional grid lying flat in three-dimensional space. Each matrix element is represented as a column extending above or below this grid by an amount proportional to the value of the matrix element. In the default perspective, the first row of the matrix extends from the back left corner of the grid to the right, while the first column extends from the back left corner out toward the viewer.

The perspective on the bar chart depends on the location of the viewer with respect to the surface. You can specify this view by changing the chart's tilt or rotation, as described in the subsection "Changing your view of the 3D bar chart," later in this chapter.

Displaying a function of two variables

A typical 3D bar chart shows the values of a function of two variables. To see such a chart, you must first create a matrix that holds the values of the function, then create a bar chart of that matrix. Here are the typical steps in plotting a function of two variables such as that shown in Figure 2:

- Define a function of two variables.

- Decide how many points you want to display in the x and y directions. Set up range variables i and j to index these points. For example, if you want to display 10 points in each direction, enter:

$$i := 0 .. 9 \qquad j := 0 .. 9$$

- Define x_i and y_j as evenly spaced points on the x- and y-axes.

- Fill the matrix **M** with the values of $f(x_i, y_j)$

- Choose **Create 3D Bar Chart** from the **Graphics** menu.

- Type **M** in the placeholder. Then press [**F9**] or, in automatic mode, click outside of the region.

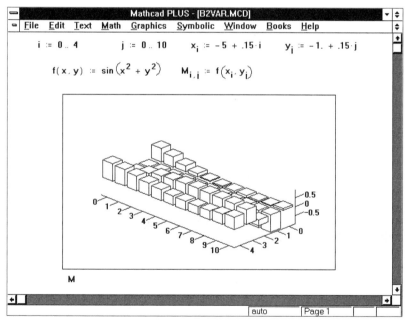

Figure 2: 3D bar chart of a function of two variables.

Resizing 3D bar charts

To change the size of a bar chart, follow these steps:

- Click the mouse just outside the bar chart. This anchors one corner of the selection rectangle.

- Press and hold down the left mouse button. While holding down the button, drag the mouse. A selection rectangle framed by dashed lines emerges from the anchor point.

- When the selection rectangle just encloses the bar chart, let go of the left mouse button.

- Move the mouse pointer to the right or bottom edge or to the lower right corner of the selection rectangle. It should change to a double-headed arrow.

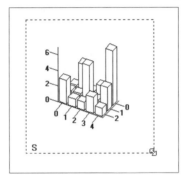

- Press and hold down the mouse button. While holding down the button, move the mouse. The bar chart will stretch in the direction of motion.

- Once the bar chart is the right size, let go of the mouse button.

- Click outside the bar chart to deselect it.

Formatting 3D bar charts

Mathcad provides many ways to change the way a bar chart looks. These can be categorized in four groups:

- Viewing characteristics: the type of plot being displayed; the perspective or point of view; how tall the tallest bars are; and the presence or absence of borders, enclosing boxes, axes, and coordinate planes.

- Color and line formatting: how the bars are colored; how the bars are laid out; spacing between the bars.

- Axis formatting: whether to show tick marks or grid lines on each axis.

- Title characteristics: how the bar chart will display titles.

To change any of these characteristics, start with the 3D Plot Format dialog box:

■ Click on a bar chart to select it.

■ Choose **3D Plot Format** from the **Graphics** menu. Alternatively, double-click on the chart itself. Mathcad brings up the 3D Plot Format dialog box. The View Page of this dialog box is shown below. The remaining three tabs take you to three additional pages.

■ If necessary, click the tab for the page you want to work with.

■ Make the appropriate changes in the dialog box.

■ To see the effect of your changes *without* closing the dialog box, click "Apply".

■ When you're finished, close the dialog by clicking "OK" or "Close".

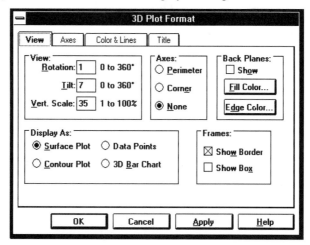

Changing your view of the 3D bar chart

The View page of the 3D Plot Format dialog box lets you modify the general presentation of your bar chart.

To change from a bar chart to another type of 3D plot, click on the appropriate button in the Display As group. You can convert a bar chart into a surface plot or a contour plot. These plot types are fully discussed in the corresponding chapters of this *User's Guide*. You can also display just the points at the top of the bars. To do so, click on Data Points. You can change how the points look by using the Colors & Lines tab of this dialog box. For more information, see Chapter 24, "3D Scatter Plots."

To change the perspective, or point of view, from which you see the bars on your chart, adjust the figures in the Rotation and Tilt text boxes. Use an integer between 0 to 360 degrees. Figure 4 shows the effects of varying the rotation and tilt (as well as the vertical scale) of a bar chart.

- Increasing the vertical rotation turns the chart clockwise. When the rotation is set to 0, you look straight down the first column of the matrix. The first row of the matrix points to the right. When the rotation is set to 90, you look straight down the first row of the matrix. The first column points to the left.

- Increasing the tilt raises you higher above the chart's surface. When the tilt is set to 0, you look edge on at the plane of the matrix. When the tilt is set to 90, you look straight down on the tops of the bars. Think of how tall buildings look when you're on the ground (tilt equals 0) and when you're flying directly above (tilt equals 90).

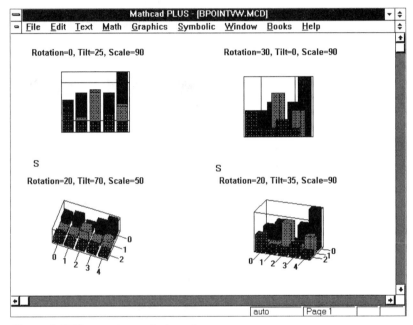

Figure 4: Different views of a bar chart.

To control how tall the tallest bars look, adjust the vertical scale by changing the number in the Vert. Scale text box. This is an integer between 1 and 100. When the vertical scale is small, the variations among the bars will barely be perceptible. At 100, the variations are such that the chart fills almost the entire frame. Figure 4 shows the effects of varying the scale (as well as the rotation and tilt) of a bar chart.

To add or remove a border around the bar chart, click on Show Border in the Frames group. The border is a two-dimensional frame around the bar chart.

To enclose the surface and and the axes within a three-dimensional bounding box, click on Show Box in the Frames group.

To show the xy, xz, and yz back planes:

- Click on Show in the Back Planes group.

- To color the surface of the back planes, click on "Fill Color".

■ To outline the edges of the back planes in a particular color, click on "Edge Color".

Figure 5 shows the same bar chart with back planes, with a border, and with a bounding box.

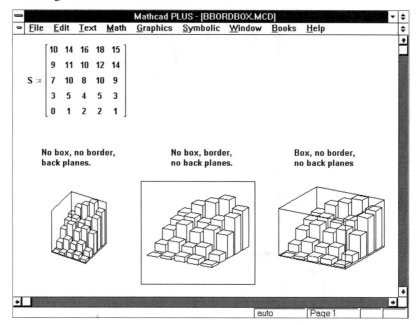

Figure 5: Using a border or a bounding box on a bar chart.

Changing the color and layout of the bars

You can often make a 3D bar chart communicate more effectively by using different colors. In addition, you can switch among several layouts of the bars to show your data most effectively. Use the Color & Lines page of the 3D Plot Format dialog box.

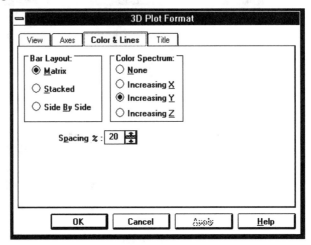

To specify the color of your chart, click the appropriate button in the Color Spectrum group:

- None: The bar chart doesn't show any colors.

- Increasing X: The largest values along the *x*-axis will be in red and the smallest values will be in blue. Intermediate values will range from yellow through green.

- Increasing Y: The largest values along the *y*-axis will be in red and the smallest values will be in blue. Intermediate values will range from yellow through green.

- Increasing Z: The largest values along the *z*-axis will be in red and the smallest values will be in blue. Intermediate values will range from yellow through green.

Use the Spacing text box to increase the space between adjacent bars on your plot. This text box measures spacing as the percentage of the size of the grid on which the bars are placed. The default spacing is 20%; the maximum spacing is 99%. As you increase the percentage, Mathcad makes the bars progressively skinnier. Figure 6 shows different spacing for plots of the same matrix.

Figure 6 shows the same bar chart using each of the Color Spectrum options.

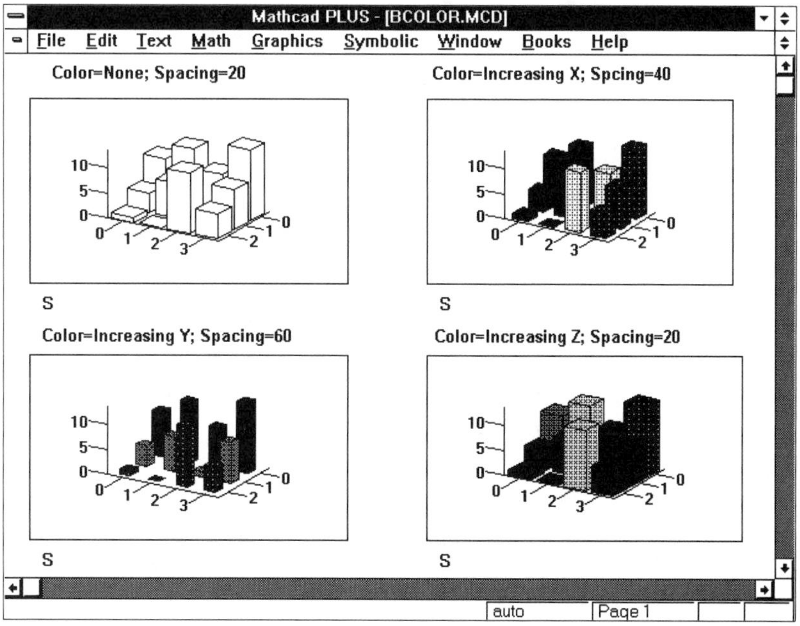

Figure 6: Color and spacing options for bar plots.

You can also control the placement of the bars relative to one another using the Bar Layout buttons. The three options are:

- Matrix: The bars are arranged exactly as the corresponding numbers in the underlying matrix.

- Stacked: All the bars coming from the same column of the matrix are stacked one on top of another. An $m \times n$ matrix would therefore appear as n bar clusters, each formed by stacking m bars one on top of another.

- Side by Side: All the bars coming from the same column of the matrix are clustered together side-by-side. An $m \times n$ matrix would therefore appear as n bar clusters, each of which contains m bars.

Figure 7 shows a $m \times n$ matrix being displayed using each of these three layout options. Note that if you want to swap rows and columns, you can simply plot the transpose of the matrix.

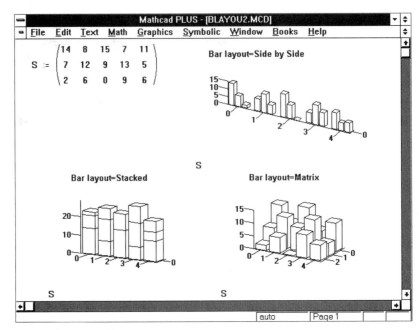

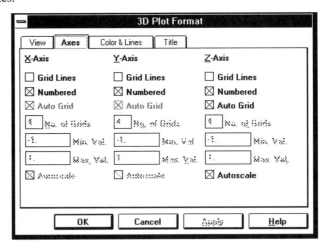

Figure 7: Different bar layouts with the same bar chart matrix.

Formatting the axes

The Axes page of the 3D Plot Format dialog box lets you modify the format of the axes of your plot. Each axis is described by its own set of check boxes and text boxes.

Mathcad generates grid lines for bar charts by extending tick marks up and down the two back planes adjacent to a given axis. Thus, *x*-axis grid lines represent lines of constant *x* drawn on the *xz* plane and the *xy* plane, the two orthogonal planes whose intersections form the *x*-axis. The *y*-axis grid lines and *z*-axis grid lines are defined similarly.

To choose between using tick marks or grid lines on a selected axis, use the Grid Lines check box for that axis. When Grid Lines is checked, Mathcad will extend the tick marks on the selected axis into grid lines on each adjacent back plane. For example, checking this on the z-axis will result in lines of constant z on both the yz and the xz back planes. If you are showing grid lines, you should seriously consider showing back planes as well. See "Changing your view of the 3D bar chart." Figure 8 shows an example of a bar chart that uses grid lines rather than tick marks.

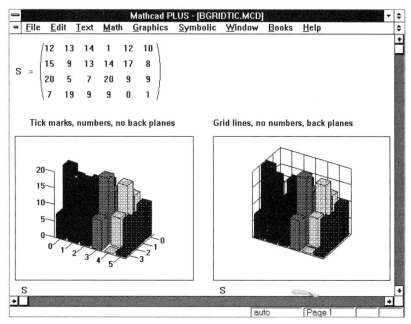

Figure 8: Using the different options for tick marks.

To add or remove numbers for the tick marks on an axis, use the Numbered check box for that axis. Figure 8 shows the differences between having numbers on the tick marks and not having numbers.

For bar charts, you can have Mathcad automatically select the number of grid intervals on the z-axis. The grid intervals on the x and y axes always match the rows and columns of the matrix whose elements constitute the bars being plotted.

- To have Mathcad select the number of grid intervals on the z-axis, use the Auto Grid check box. When Auto Grid is checked, Mathcad will automatically select the number of grid intervals on the specified axis.

- To specify the number of grid intervals on an axis *yourself* enter an integer from 1 to 99 in the No. of Grids text box. This text box is only available when Auto Grid is unchecked.

By default, Mathcad autoscales the z-axis according to the range of values in the matrix you are plotting. Sometimes you will want to fix the scaling yourself, for example, if you are comparing views of related data or setting up a surface animation sequence. To set the z-axis limits manually, click on the Autoscale box in the z-axis column of the Axes page to uncheck it. Then enter the maximum and minimum values in the Max. Val. and Min. Val. text boxes.

Labeling 3D bar charts

The Title page of the 3D Plot Format dialog box, shown below, lets you add and modify the title on your bar chart.

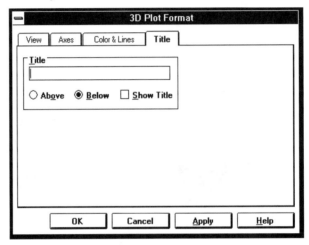

To add or edit a title for your bar chart:

- Type the title for your plot into the Title text box.

- To display the title, click on Show Title to insert a check. To conceal the title without deleting it, click on Show Title to remove the check.

- To position the title, click on either the Above or Below button. Mathcad places the title either directly above or below your plot.

- To change the title's text or position, edit the information in the Title group as appropriate.

- Click "OK" to close the dialog box when you have finished.

- To delete the title, highlight it in the Title text box and press [Del].

If you initiate this process by double-clicking on the title itself, you'll see an equivalent dialog box.

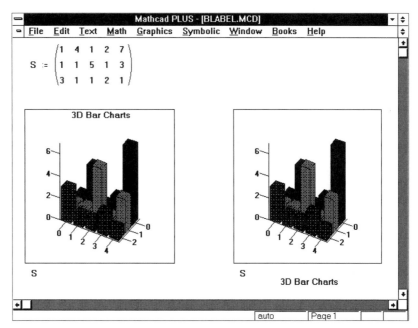

Figure 9: Titles on a bar chart.

Chapter 23 3D Bar Charts

Chapter 24
3D Scatter Plots

When using other types of 3D plots, you need to make a matrix in which rows and columns correspond to x and y values and the value of the matrix element is the z value. Scatter plots, on the other hand, let you specify x, y, and z coordinates directly. This makes them useful for drawing parametric curves or for observing clusters of data in a 3D space. This chapter shows how three vectors can be used to build a scatter plot.

This chapter contains the following sections:

Creating a 3D scatter plot

Basic steps in creating a scatter plot.

Resizing scatter plots

Procedures for changing the size of scatter plots.

Formatting scatter plots

Procedures for changing scatter plots: setting the viewpoint and the presentation; adding labels; and formatting markers, lines, and axes.

Creating a 3D scatter plot

Scatter plots allow you to plot an arbitrary collection of points in a three-dimensional space. This is particularly useful for such tasks as identifying data clusters or tracing a trajectory of a point. Scatter plots differ from all other 3D plots as follows:

- In all other 3D plots, you create a matrix in which the rows and columns correspond to x and y coordinates and the value of the matrix element is the corresponding z coordinate.

- In scatter plots, you create three vectors with as many elements as there are points to plot. The x, y, and z coordinates of a point go into the three elements of the corresponding vectors.

Unlike other 3D plots, you can easily have several z values corresponding to the same x and y value. This is often necessary in statistical applications in which you take the same measurement more than once. You can also easily create parametric curves through a three-dimensional space since the indices of the vectors are themselves natural parameters to use.

To create a 3D scatter plot:

- Define three vectors, each having as many elements as you have points to plot. Each vector contains either the x, y, or z coordinates of all the points.

- Choose **Create 3D Scatter Plot** from the **Graphics** menu. Mathcad shows a box with a single placeholder as shown in Figure 1.

- Type the names of the vectors, separated by commas, in the placeholder. Just as with an equation, Mathcad will not process the scatter plot until you either press [**F9**] or, in automatic mode, click outside out of the region.

If you have a matrix of rows and columns corresponding to the x and y coordinates that you want to show as a set of points, create a *surface plot* and select Data Points in the Display As group on the View page. For more information, see page 496.

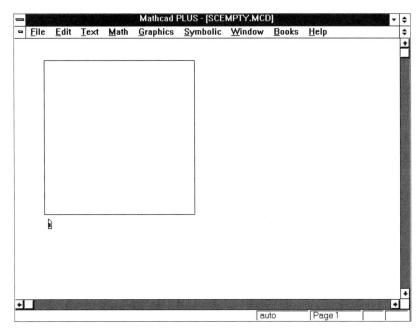

Figure 1: An empty placeholder in a scatter plot region awaits the name of a matrix.

Resizing scatter plots

To change the size of a scatter plot, follow these steps:

- Click the mouse just outside the scatter plot region. This anchors one corner of the selection rectangle.

- Press and hold down the left mouse button. While holding down the button, drag the mouse. A selection rectangle framed by dashed lines emerges from the anchor point.

- When the selection rectangle just encloses the scatter plot region, release the left mouse button.

- Move the mouse pointer to the right or bottom edge or to the lower right corner of the selection rectangle. It should change to a double-headed arrow.

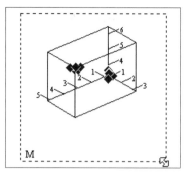

- Press and hold down the mouse button. While holding down the button, move the mouse. The scatter plot will stretch in the direction of motion.

- Once the scatter plot is the right size, let go of the mouse button.

- Click outside the scatter plot to deselect it.

Formatting scatter plots

Mathcad gives you control over many of the visual characteristics of scatter plots. These can be categorized in four groups:

- Viewing characteristics: the type of plot being displayed, the perspective or point of view from which you see the plot, and the presence or absence of borders, enclosing boxes, axes, and back planes.

- Color and line formatting: how the plot will mark points; how markers will be connected; and the format of any lines connecting markers.

- Axis formatting: whether to show tick marks or grid lines on each axis.

- Title characteristics: how the plot will display titles.

To change any of these plot characteristics, start with the 3D Plot Format dialog box:

- Click on the plot to select it.

- Choose **3D Plot Format** from the **Graphics** menu. Alternatively, double-click on the plot itself. Mathcad brings up the 3D Plot Format dialog box. The View Page of this dialog box is shown below. The remaining three tabs take you to three additional pages.

- If necessary, click the tab for the page you want to work with.

- Make the appropriate changes in the dialog box.

- To see the effect of your changes *without* closing the dialog box, click "Apply".

- When you're finished, close the dialog by clicking "OK" or "Close".

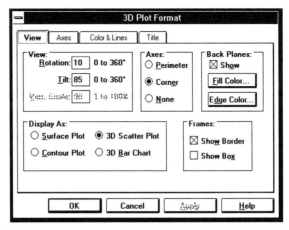

Changing your view of the scatter plot

The View page of the 3D Plot Format dialog box lets you modify the general presentation of your 3D scatter plot.

To change your plot from a scatter plot to another type of 3D plot, click on the appropriate button in the Display As group. You can convert a scatter plot into a Surface Plot, Contour Plot, or a 3D Bar Chart. These plot types are fully discussed in the corresponding chapters in this *User's Guide*.

When you view a scatter plot as a surface or contour plot or a 3D bar chart, Mathcad actually *interpolates* a surface that approximates your scatter data, using a 21 by 21 mesh by default. To change the density of this mesh, click on the Color & Lines tab and edit the number of rows and columns in the Interpolated Mesh group. If your data is not well approximated by a surface, Mathcad may be unable to compile a useful interpolation. If this occurs, Mathcad will signal this fact with a message in the status line.

As you view your scatter plot, you may not be able to perceive any patterns in your data. However, by examining the plot from another perspective, you may be able to isolate clusters of data. To change the perspective, or point of view, from which you see the scatter plot, change the numbers in the Rotation and Tilt text boxes. Use an integer between 0 to 360 degrees. Figure 2 shows the effects of varying the rotation and tilt (as well as the scale) of a scatter plot.

■ Increasing the rotation turns the plot clockwise.

■ Tilt controls whether you see the data edge on or whether you look down from directly overhead.

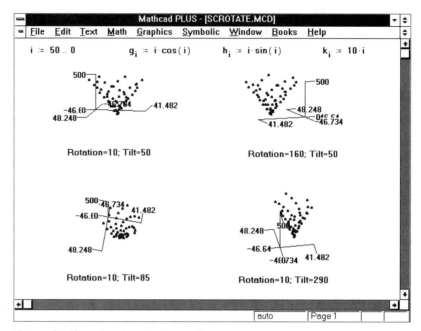

Figure 2: Changing the rotation and tilt.

To add or remove a border around the scatter plot region, click on Show Border. The border is a two-dimensional frame around the scatter plot region.

To enclose the plot and the axes within a three-dimensional bounding box, click on Show Box in the Frames group to add a check.

To show the *xy*, *xz*, and *yz* back planes:

- Click on Show in the Back Planes group.

- To color the surface of the back planes, click on "Fill Color".

- To outline the edges of the back planes in a particular color, click on "Edge Color".

Figure 3 shows a scatter plot with a border around it and with back planes showing together with the same plot enclosed within a box without showing back planes.

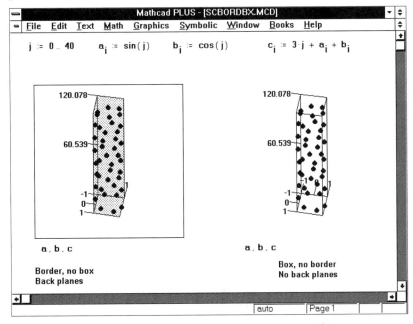

Figure 3: Using a border or an enclosing box on a scatter plot.

Changing the format of the markers

You can often make your scatter plot communicate more effectively by changing one of the following:

■ You can mark the points with a symbol.

■ You can connect the points with a line.

To do either of these, use the Color & Lines page of the 3D Plot Format dialog box.

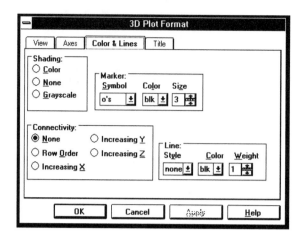

To specify the type of marker your plot will use, select an option from each of the following drop-down lists:

- Symbol: Each point in the scatter plot is marked by a symbol. Select among o's, ×'s, +'s, boxes, and diamonds. You can also select "none"; however, if you do and you aren't using a connecting line, your plot will be blank.

- Color: The markers can be any of the colors listed on the drop-down list, for example, red, blue, green, magenta, cyan, brown, black, and white.

- Size: Markers can range in size from 1 (thinnest) to 10 (thickest).

Figure 4 shows the same plot with markers formatted in several ways.

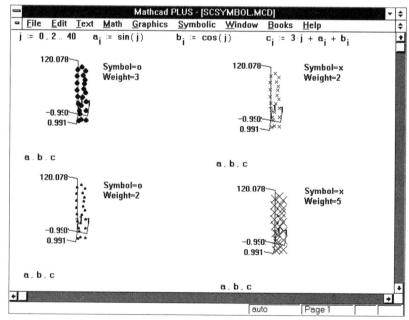

Figure 4: Selecting different formatting options for the markers.

If you are plotting data that shows progressive movement in a direction (for example, points in a trajectory), you may want to connect the data points with a line. Mathcad provides several options for connecting the data points:

- No line

- The order in which the points occur in the matrix (row order)

- Increasing x values

- Increasing y values

- Increasing z values

Use the buttons in the Connectivity group to choose which of these options Mathcad should use to connect the data points.

Once you've decided on the order for connecting the points, you can specify the way the line connecting them will look. Use the buttons in the Line group to choose:

- Style: The connecting line can be solid, dashed, dotted, or alternatingly dashed and dotted. You can also select "none"; however, if you do so and aren't using markers, your plot will be blank.

- Color: The lines can be any of the colors on the drop-down list.

- Weight: Lines can range in size from 1 (lightest) to 10 (the heaviest).

Figure 5 shows the same plot connected in different orders.

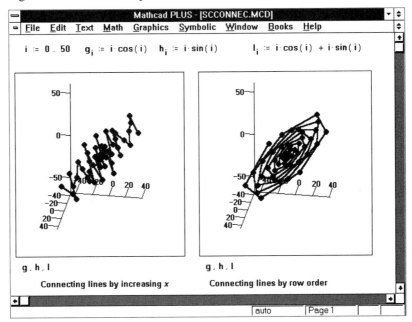

Figure 5: Passing a line through points on a scatter plot.

Formatting the axes

The Axes page of the 3D Plot Format dialog box lets you modify the format of the x, y, and z axes of your plot. Each axis is described by its own set of check boxes and text boxes.

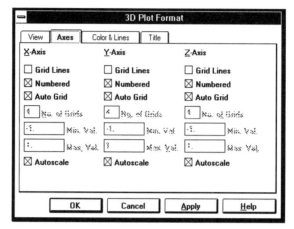

Mathcad generates grid lines on the plot at the same positions as the tick marks. To choose between using tick marks or grid lines on a selected axis, use the Grid Lines check box. When Grid Lines is checked, Mathcad adds grid lines to the plot. Figure 6 shows the same scatter plot with and without grid lines.

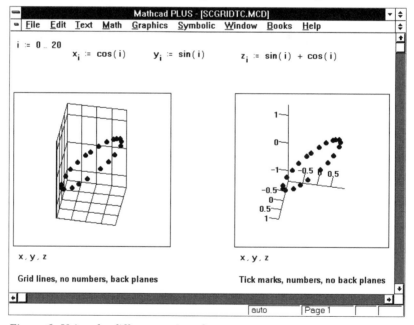

Figure 6: Using the different options for axes.

Chapter 24 3D Scatter Plots

To add or remove numbers for the tick marks on an axis, use the Numbered check box for that axis. The plot with grid lines in Figure 6 doesn't have numbers on the axes while the plot without grid lines does have them.

You can have Mathcad automatically select the number of grid intervals on an axis or you can specify the number yourself. Grid intervals are the spaces between tick marks or grid lines.

■ To have Mathcad select the number of grid intervals, use the Auto Grid check box. When Auto Grid is checked, Mathcad will automatically select the number of grid intervals on the specified axis.

■ To specify the number of grid intervals on an axis *yourself* enter an integer from 1 to 99 in the No. of Grids text box. This text box is only available when Auto Grid is unchecked.

By default, Mathcad sets the axis limits according to the data ranges in the three input vectors. However, you can set these limits by hand as follows:

■ Click on the Autoscale box in the appropriate axis columns of the Axes page to uncheck it.

■ Enter the maximum and minimum values in the Max. Val. and Min. Val. text boxes.

Fixing the axis limits in this way is useful when you are comparing plots of related data sets or setting up an animation sequence.

Labeling the scatter plot

The Title page of the 3D Plot Format dialog box, shown below, lets you add and modify labels on your scatter plot.

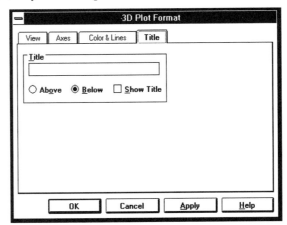

To add or edit a title for your scatter plot:

■ Type the title for your plot into the Title text box.

- To display the title, click on Show Title to insert a check. To conceal the title without deleting it, click on Show Title to remove the check.

- To position the title, click on either the Above or Below button. Mathcad places the title either directly above or below your plot.

- To change the title's text, edit the information in the Title group as appropriate.

- Click "OK" to close the dialog box when you have finished.

- To delete the title, highlight it and press [Del].

If you initiate this process by double-clicking on the title itself, you'll see an equivalent dialog box.

Figure 7 shows how Mathcad positions titles on a scatter plot.

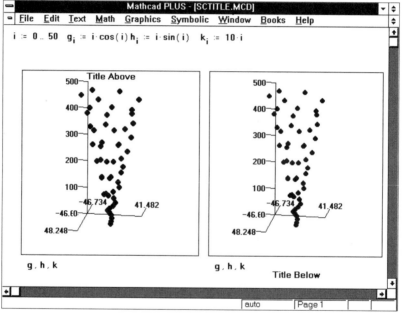

Figure 7: Titles on a scatter plot.

Chapter 25
Vector Field Plots

This chapter describes how to plot a two-dimensional vector field by representing x and y components of a vector as complex numbers.

This chapter contains the following sections:

Creating a vector field plot

Basic steps in creating a vector field plot.

Resizing vector field plots

Procedure for changing the size of vector field plots.

Formatting vector field plots

Procedures for changing vector field plots: formatting the vector fields and axes and adding labels.

Creating a vector field plot

In a vector field plot, each point in the xy plane is assigned a two-dimensional vector. To create a vector field plot, you must define a rectangular array of points and assign a vector to each point. You can do this by creating a matrix of complex numbers in which:

- The rows and columns represent x and y coordinates.

- The real part of each matrix element is the x component of the vector associated with that row and column.

- The imaginary part of each element is the y component of the vector associated with that row and column.

To create a vector field plot:

- Create a matrix as described above.

- Choose **Create Vector Field Plot** from the **Graphics** menu. Mathcad shows a box with a single placeholder as shown in Figure 1.

- Type the name of the matrix in the placeholder.

Just as with an equation, Mathcad will not process the vector field plot until you either press [**F9**] or, in automatic mode, click outside out of the region.

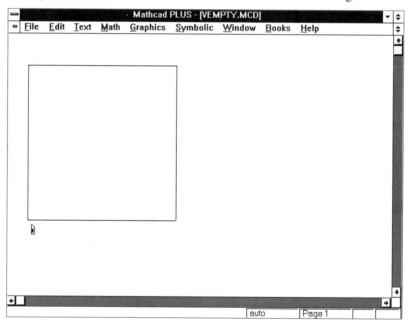

Figure 1: An empty placeholder in a vector field plot region awaits the name of a matrix.

Mathcad plots the matrix by rotating it so that the (0,0) element is at the lower-left corner. Thus the rows of the matrix correspond to values on the *x* axis, increasing to the right, and the columns correspond to values along the *y* axis, increasing toward the top.

What you'll see is a collection of *m·n* vectors as shown in Figure 2. The base of each vector sits on the *x* and *y* values corresponding to its row and column. The magnitude and direction of each vector are derived from the real and imaginary parts of the matrix element.

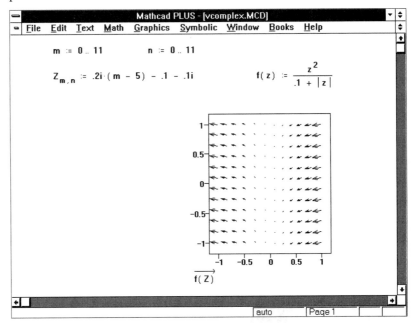

Figure 2: A sample vector plot from a complex matrix.

You can also create a vector field plot by using two matrices of real numbers rather than a single matrix of complex members. The two matrices must have the same number of rows and columns. The first matrix should have the *x* components of the vectors; the second should have the *y* components. Figure 3 shows the same vector field as that shown in Figure 2, but it is plotted using two real matrices rather than a single complex matrix.

Creating a vector field plot   551

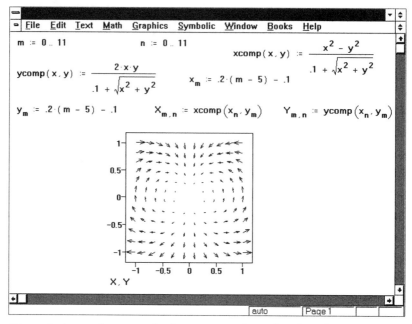

Figure 3: A sample vector plot from two matrices of real numbers.

You can specify what labels and grid lines appear on the axes by formatting the vector field plot. This is described in the section "Formatting vector field plots," later in this chapter.

Resizing vector field plots

To change the size of a vector field plot, follow these steps:

- Click the mouse just outside the plot region. This anchors one corner of the selection rectangle.

- Press and hold down the left mouse button. While holding down the button, drag the mouse. A selection rectangle framed by dashed lines emerges from the anchor point.

- When the selection rectangle just encloses the plot region, release the left mouse button.

- Move the mouse pointer to the right or bottom edge or to the lower right corner of the selection rectangle. It should change to a double-headed arrow.

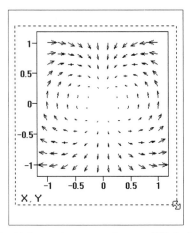

- Press and hold down the mouse button. While holding down the button, move the mouse. The plot will stretch in the direction of motion.

- Once the plot is the right size, let go of the mouse button.

- Click outside the vector field plot to deselect it.

Formatting vector field plots

Mathcad gives you control over many of the visual characteristics of vector field plots. These can be categorized in three groups:

- Axis formatting: whether to show tick marks or grid lines on each axis.

- Title characteristics: how the plot will display titles.

To change any of these plot characteristics, start with the 3D Plot Format dialog box:

- Click on the plot to select it.

- Choose **3D Plot Format** from the **Graphics** menu. Alternatively, double-click on the plot itself. Mathcad brings up the 3D Plot Format dialog box. The Axes Page of this dialog box is shown below. The remaining tab takes you to the Title page. The View and the Color & Lines pages are not used for these plots.

- If necessary, click the tab for the page you want to work with.

- Change the appropriate characteristics in the dialog box.

- To see the effect of your changes *without* closing the dialog box, click "Apply".

- When you're finished, close the dialog by clicking "OK" or "Close".

The Axes page of the 3D Plot Format dialog box, shown below, lets you modify the format of the *x*- and *y*-axis of your plot. Each axis is described by its own set of check boxes and text boxes.

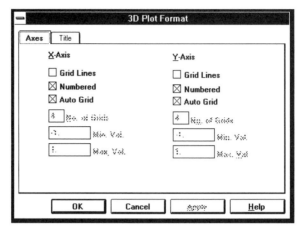

Mathcad generates grid lines on the plot at the same positions as the tick marks. To choose between using tick marks or grid lines on a selected axis, use the Grid Lines check box. When Grid Lines is checked, Mathcad adds grid lines to the plot. Figure 4 shows the same vector field plot with and without grid lines.

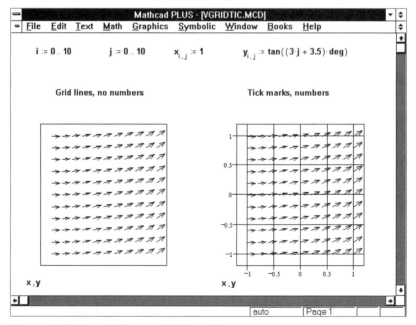

Figure 4: Using grid lines and tick marks.

To add or remove numbers for the tick marks on an axis, use the Numbered check box for that axis. The plot with grid lines in Figure 4 doesn't have numbers on the axes while the plot without grid lines does have them.

You can have Mathcad automatically select the number of grid intervals on an axis or you can specify the number yourself. Grid intervals are the spaces between tick marks or grid lines.

- To have Mathcad select the number of grid intervals, use the Auto Grid check box. When Auto Grid is checked, Mathcad will automatically select the number of grid intervals on the specified axis.

- To specify the number of grid intervals on an axis *yourself* enter an integer from 1 to 99 in the No. of Grids text box. This text box is only available when Auto Grid is unchecked.

Since a vector field plot is made by plotting the elements of a matrix, Mathcad cannot "know" anything about x and y coordinates. All it knows is the vector associated with a particular row and column. By default, the coordinates on the x- and y-axes of a vector field plot will simply be rows and columns.

To change the limits on the maximum or minimum values to be plotted on the x- and y-axis, enter the new limit in the Max. Val. or Min. Val. text box.

Labeling the vector field plot

The Title page of the 3D Plot Format dialog box lets you add and modify a title on your vector field plot.

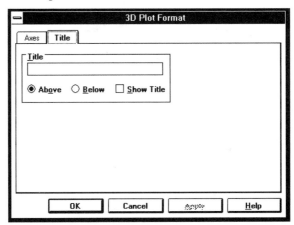

To add or edit a title for your vector field plot:

- Type the title for your plot into the Title text box.

- To display the title, click on Show Title to insert a check. To conceal the title without deleting it, click on Show Title to remove the check.

- To position the title, click on either the Above or Below button. Mathcad places the title either directly above or below your plot.

- Click "OK" to close the dialog box when you have finished.

To change the title's text or position, edit the information in the Title group as appropriate. To delete the title, highlight it in the text box and press [**Del**].

If you initiate this process by double-clicking on the title itself, you'll see an equivalent dialog box.

Figure 5 shows how Mathcad positions a title on a vector field plot.

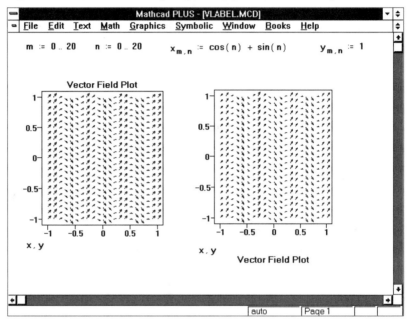

Figure 5: Titles on a vector field plot.

Chapter 25 Vector Field Plots

Chapter 26
Animation

This chapter describes how to use Mathcad PLUS to create and play short animation clips by using the built-in variable FRAME. Anything that can be made to depend on this variable can be animated. This includes not only plots but numerical results as well. You can play back the animation clips at different speeds or save them for use by other applications.

The following sections make up this chapter:

Creating an animation clip

How to use the FRAME variable to create a sequence of images and how to string this sequence together into a movie.

Playing an animation clip

Using the animation player to play back your movie.

Gallery of animations

A collection of examples showing what you can do with animation.

Creating an animation clip

Mathcad comes with a predefined constant called FRAME whose sole purpose is to drive animations. The steps in creating any animation are as follows:

- Create an expression or plot whose appearance ultimately depends on the value of FRAME as shown in Figure 1. This expression need not be a graph as shown. It can be anything at all.

- Choose **Animation⇒Create** from the **Windows** menu to bring up the following dialog box.

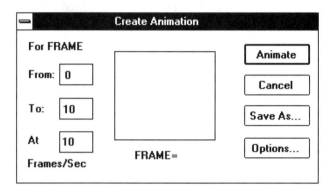

- Enclose whatever portion of your worksheet you want to animate inside a selection rectangle as shown in Figure 2.

- In the dialog box, set the upper and lower limits for FRAME. The FRAME variable will increment by one as it proceeds from the lower limit to the upper limit.

- In the Frames/Sec. text box, enter the playback speed.

- Click the "Animate" button in the dialog box. You'll see a miniature rendition of your selection inside the dialog box as shown in Figure 3. Mathcad redraws this once for each value of FRAME. This won't necessarily match the playback speed since at this point, you're just *creating* the animation, you're not yet playing it back.

At this point, an animation has been created. You can now do one of two things with it:

- You can save it as a Windows AVI file for use by other Windows applications.

- You can play it back immediately.

To save your animation clip as a Windows AVI file, click the Save As button in the dialog box. You'll see the usual Save As dialog box. Since animation clips tend to take considerable disk space, Mathcad saves them in compressed format. Before creating the animation, you may want to select what compression method to use or whether to compress at all. To do so, click on the Options button.

To play the animation sequence back, follow the instructions in the next section.

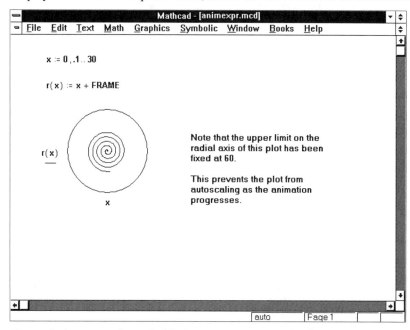

Figure 1: An expression suitable for animation. Note the dependence of the plot on FRAME.

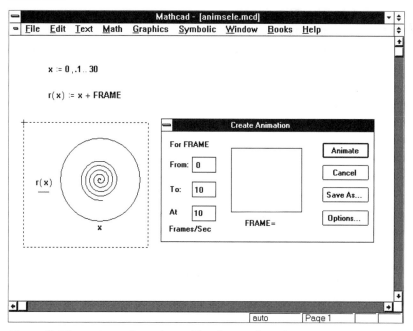

Figure 2: The region to be animated has been selected.

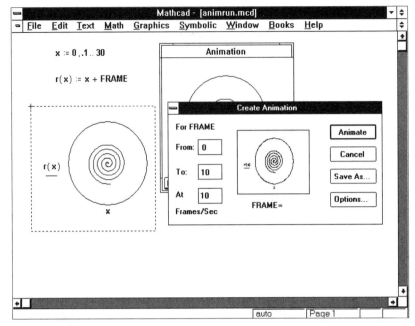

Figure 3: The animation clip has been created and is ready for playback.

Playing an animation clip

As soon as you've created an animation clip as described in the previous section, Mathcad brings up the following window:

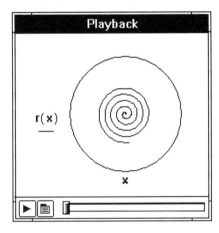

Chapter 26 Animation

Note that the first frame of the animation clip you just created is already in the window. To play back the animation clip, click on the arrow button at the lower left corner of the window. The arrow will turn into a square and the animation will begin to play. You can control the playback speed by clicking on the button to the right of the play button, choosing **Speed** from the menu and adjusting the slider control.

You can also play back the animation clip on a frame by frame basis, either forward or backward. To do so, drag the slider below the animated picture to the left or right.

You can resize this window the way you would any window, by dragging a corner in the appropriate direction. Keep in mind, however, that the image in the window is a bitmap and therefore subject to distortion when resized. You can minimize this distortion by keeping the aspect ratio (height to width) constant when you resize. To do this conveniently, click on the button to the right of the play button and choose **View** from the menu.

Playing a previously saved animation

If you have an existing Windows AVI file on your disk, you'll be able to play it within Mathcad. To do so:

■ Choose **Animation⇒Playback** from the **Windows** menu to bring up the following dialog box:

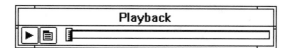

The window is collapsed shut since no animation clip has been opened. To open one, click on the button to the right of the play button and choose **Open** from the menu. You'll see an Open File dialog box which you can use to locate and open the Windows AVI file you want to play.

Once you've loaded a Windows AVI file, you can proceed as described in the previous section.

The following figures show some of the things you can do with animation using Mathcad's different plot types (polar, *x-y*, 3D scatter, vector field, parametric surface, bar and contour). Choose **QuickSheets** from the **Help** menu and look for "Animation examples" to see some more.

Note that since Mathcad's plots autoscale by default, you'll almost always have to change the plot format to show the animation you want. For example, when animating an *x-y* plot or a polar plot you should enter values into the axis limit placeholders to fix the extent of each axis and preserve the plot scaling throughout the course of the animation. Similarly, when an animation involves a 3D plot, you should fix the axis limits by double-clicking on the plot to bring up the 3D Plot Format dialog box, unchecking Autoscale on the Axes page, and setting the axis limit on each axis in such a way that all points generated in the course of the animation are within the axis limits.

In the examples in this chapter, Figure 1 has a maximum radius in the placeholder for the radial axis limit; Figures 6 and 8 have autoscale turned off on all axes and appropriate limits entered.

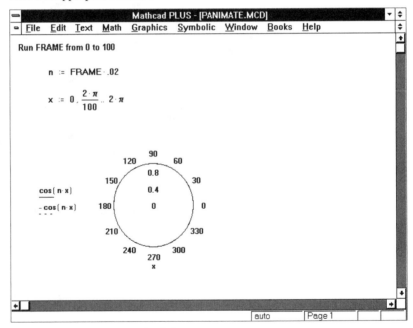

Figure 4: Growing a four-leaf clover.

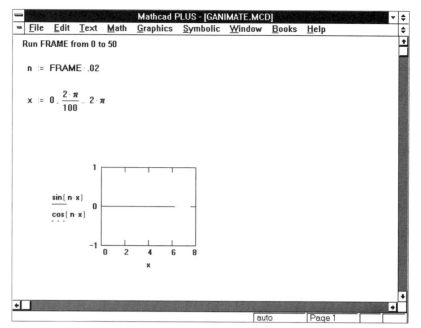

Figure 5: Roller coaster.

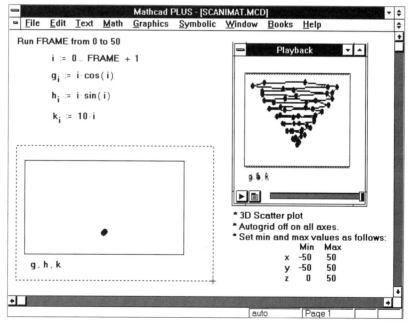

Figure 6: Tornado.

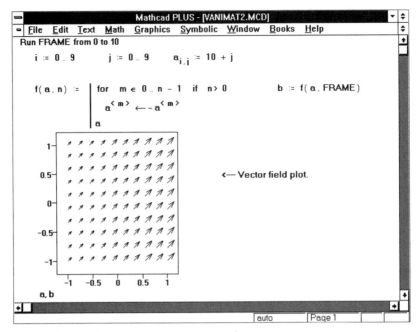

Figure 7: Diffusion of one field across another.

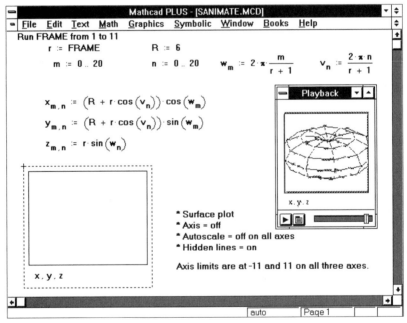

Figure 8: Nested spheroids.

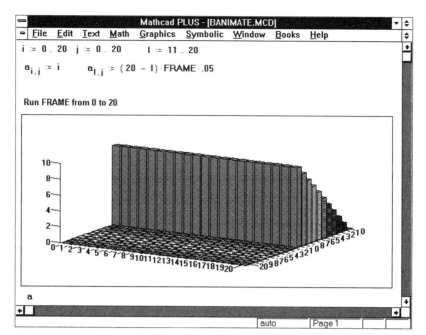

Figure 9: Barn raising. This one may take a few minutes.

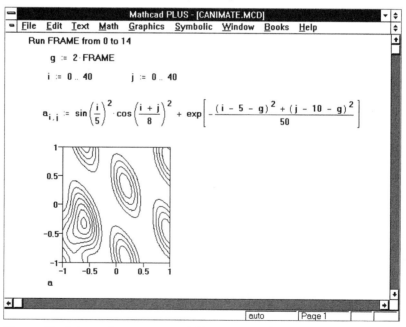

Figure 10: Animated contour map. This one may take a few minutes.

Chapter 27
Importing Graphics

In addition to plots and surface plots, Mathcad lets you put graphics from various sources into your worksheet. These graphics can be imported either by pasting directly from the clipboard, or by referring Mathcad to a file containing the graphics information. After you import a graphic, Mathcad shows the image right in your worksheet.

The following sections make up this chapter:

Importing bitmaps

Importing pictures stored as Windows bitmaps.

Formatting pictures

Changing the positioning and magnification of existing pictures.

Importing bitmaps

Mathcad lets you import graphics stored in the standard Windows bitmap format. Most files with the BMP extension have this format. Many graphics images you can place on the Windows clipboard also have this format.

There are two ways to import graphics:

- Directly, by pasting an image from the clipboard.

- Indirectly, by entering the name of a file containing graphics information.

You can also convert a graphics file to data, import that data into Mathcad as one or more matrices, and use Mathcad to modify it. When finished, you can export the matrix back to your hard disk as a bitmap.

Mathcad's graphics import feature is designed specifically to import graphics created with other software. There are no features for creating and editing graphics in Mathcad. You can however cut a picture from Mathcad, paste it into a graphics editor, make any changes, then paste it back into Mathcad. Since Windows allows multitasking, you can do all this without having to quit Mathcad.

Importing from the clipboard

To place a graphics image from the clipboard into Mathcad, do the following:

- Place the graphics image on the clipboard. This step can be done by any program that permits you to copy a graphics image to the clipboard. Many Windows applications have this feature.

- Click the mouse wherever you want the image.

- Choose **Paste** from the **Edit** menu, or press [Ctrl]V if you prefer. Mathcad creates a graphics region and puts into it the image stored on the clipboard.

When you import directly from the clipboard, the graphics information is stored as part of the Mathcad worksheet. This makes the document take up more disk space. It also means that when you copy the worksheet, the graphics information travels along with it. This is generally the most convenient way to import graphics.

If, on the other hand, many of your worksheets use the same picture, it is a waste of space to store a copy of this same picture with each worksheet. Moreover, if you want to change the picture, you must open each worksheet and paste the new image into it all over again. To avoid this, Mathcad allows you to store the filename of the image rather than the image itself. This means that if you change the image, the change shows up in every worksheet that uses that image. The following section describes how to do this.

Chapter 27 Importing Graphics

Importing from a file

To create a graphics image from a file, you must do the following:

- Choose **Create Picture** from the **Graphics** menu. This creates a graphics region with an empty placeholder.

- In the placeholder, type the name of the file containing the graphics information. Note that a period here just separates a filename from its extension. It doesn't create a literal subscript. Mathcad will hide the name as soon as you click outside the graphics region.

- Press [**F9**]. Mathcad displays the image.

Note that if you change the graphics file on disk after you put it into Mathcad, you won't see the changes unless you click in the image and press [**F9**] again.

The file containing graphics information can be a Windows bitmap file. These are created by many Windows applications and usually have the extension BMP after the filename.

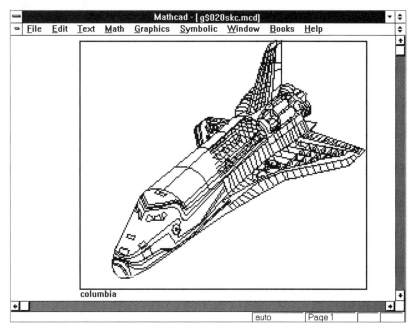

Figure 1: An imported picture.

Importing files from other directories

When you specify a filename in the placeholder, Mathcad looks in the current directory for a file with that name. You can however, import a file from another disk or directory. To do so, you place a *file variable* in the placeholder instead of a file name. A file variable is just like any variable except that instead of assigning it an expression or a number, you assign to it a filename, complete with a path and drive. The process of assigning a specific filename to a file variable is called *filename association.*

The following example shows how to associate the file variable *instrument* with the specific file `c:\orchestr\brass\tuba.bmp`

- Choose **Create Picture** from the **Graphics** menu. Type the file variable, in this case *instrument*, in the placeholder.

- Choose **Associate Filename** from the **File** menu. This brings up the dialog box shown below.

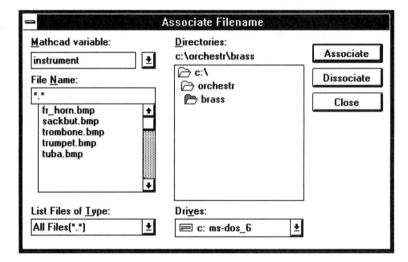

- In the text box under "Mathcad variable," type the file variable which in this case is *instrument.*

- In the text box labeled "File Name," place the pathname to the file which in this case is `c:\orchestr\brass\tuba.bmp`. You can use the scrolling list of filenames to assist you in naming the file.

- Click the "Associate" button.

- Click the "Close" button. Mathcad will now open the file named `c:\orchestr\brass\tuba.bmp` and place its contents into any graphics region that uses the file variable *instrument.*

- Press [**F9**]. Mathcad displays the image.

Once you have made the file association for a variable, it remains in effect until you change it or remove it. File associations affect all pictures and file-access functions in your worksheet that use the specified variable name.

Since Mathcad can have only a finite number of files open at once, you may want to sever the link between a variable when it is no longer needed. This may be necessary if you see a *"too many files"* error message. To do so, Choose **Associate Filename** from the **File** menu and type the name of the variable you want to disassociate from a file on your disk. Then click the "Dissociate" button.

Importing files from OLE servers

If the picture you want to import came from an OLE (Object Linking and Embedding) server, choosing **Paste** from the **Edit** menu automatically *embeds* the picture into your worksheet. This means that when you double-click on the embedded picture, the server application that created the picture opens, and a copy of the picture is placed in its worksheet window for you to edit.

When you make changes to an embedded picture as described above, the changes affect only the copy of the picture stored in the Mathcad worksheet. The file, if any, from which the picture came is unchanged.

You can also use OLE to change the original picture file created and stored by the server application. To do so:

- In the server application, copy the picture to the clipboard.

- Choose **Paste Special** from Mathcad's **Edit** menu.

- Click on the "Paste Link" button in the Paste Special dialog box. If this button is grayed out, the picture file you've copied has not yet been saved. You'll have to choose **Save** from the server application's **File** menu before proceeding.

Instead of just being embedded, the picture you paste into Mathcad is now *linked* to a file. If you double-click on this picture, make changes to it with the server application, and save it, you change not just the picture in the Mathcad worksheet, but the actual file from which the picture came.

To paste a picture as a regular bitmap, choose **Paste Special** from the **Edit** menu, choose "Bitmap" from the Paste Special dialog box, and click on the Paste button. The pasted picture will not be embedded. Double-clicking on it brings up the Picture Format dialog box rather than the server application that created the picture.

Importing a graphics file as data

To import a file as data into Mathcad, use one of these functions:

- READBMP(*file*) to create a matrix containing a grayscale representation of the bitmap image in *file*. Each element in the matrix corresponds to a pixel. The value of a matrix element determines the shade of gray associated with the corresponding pixel. Each element is an integer between 0 (black) and 255 (white).

- READRGB(*file*) to create a matrix in which the color information in *file* is represented by the appropriate values of red, green, and blue. This matrix consists of three submatrices, each with the same number of columns and rows. Three matrix elements, rather than one, correspond to each pixel. Each element is an integer between 0 and 255. The three corresponding elements, when taken together, establish the color of the pixel.

Each of these functions takes the single argument file, the name of the file containing the image. Each function returns a matrix of numbers used to represent the image.

To create the matrix, type either **M:=READBMP(filename)** or **M:=READRGB(filename)**.

To read from a file other than the one that matches the argument of *READBMP* or *READRGB* or to read from a file that is not in your Mathcad directory, use the **Associate Filename** command on the **File** menu. See the section Importing files from other directories," earlier in this chapter.

To divide the matrix for a color image into its three components, you can use the formulae shown in Figure 2.

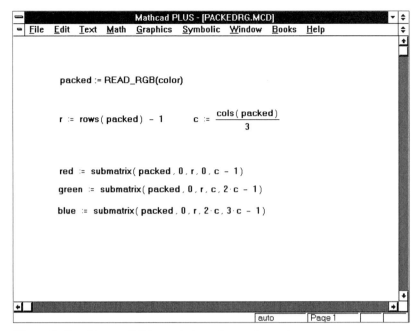

Figure 2: Breaking an RGB matrix into three submatrices.

The processing in Figure 2 converts the color.bmp bitmap file into three submatrices: red, green, and blue.

Once you have read the file into Mathcad, you can use the picture operator to view it. Choose **Create Picture** from the **Graphics** menu. Type the name of the matrix in the placeholder. If necessary use the **Associate Filename** command on the File menu.

To display an image in color, you must provide the three matrices containing the red, green and blue color values of the image. Otherwise, the displayed image will be in grayscale. For example, to display the image in Figure 2, you would choose **Create Picture** from the **Graphics** menu and type `red,green,blue` into the placeholder. If you want to display only the red components of the image that was used for Figure 2, you still must include the green and blue submatrices, but they both should contain only zeros.

Keep in mind that the colors of the image that you ultimately see may be distorted to the extent that you don't display 256 colors on your monitor.

If you have been working with submatrices for a color file, you can recombine them by using by defining an augment3($\mathbf{X}$, $\mathbf{Y}$, $\mathbf{Z}$) function:

```
augment3(X,Y,Z):=augment(X,augment(Y,Z))
```

$\mathbf{X}$, $\mathbf{Y}$, and $\mathbf{Z}$ are the names of the submatrices and must have the same number of rows. The resulting matrix has the same number of rows as X but three times the number of columns.

Once you finish processing a matrix, you may want to save it to disk for later use. To do this, use one of the following functions:

- WRITEBMP(*file*) to create a grayscale BMP file out of the matrix.

- WRITERGB(*file*) to create a colored BMP file out of a matrix in which the image is stored in RGB format.

You can use the augment function to combine submatrices at the time you are saving a file to your disk. For example, the following function saves the submatrices that were created in Figure 2 as one 24-bit color image called "newcolor.bmp":

```
WRITERGB(newcolor):=augment(red, aug-
ment(green,blue))
```

Formatting pictures

Once you've created a graphics region, you can change its size or frame it in a box.

Resizing graphics

To resize a graphics region, do the following:

- Click the mouse just outside the graphics region. This anchors one corner of the selection rectangle.

- Press and hold down the left mouse button. With the button still held, drag the mouse. A selection rectangle framed by dashed lines emerges from the anchor point.

- When the selection rectangle just encloses the graphics region, let go of the left mouse button.

- Move the mouse pointer to the right or bottom edge of the selection rectangle. It will change to a double headed arrow.

- Press and hold down the mouse button. With the mouse button still pressed, move the mouse. The graphics region will be stretched in the direction of motion.

- Once the graphics region is the right size, let go of the mouse button.

When you change the size of the graphics region, the graphics inside may be distorted. You can avoid distortion by setting the size of the graphics region to be the same as that of the original image. To do so:

- Click on the graphics region to select it. This encloses the graphics region in a selection box.

- Choose **Picture Format** from the **Graphics** menu. Alternatively, double-click on the picture itself. This brings up the Picture Format dialog box.

- Click on the box labeled "Use original size."

- Click the "OK" button. Mathcad changes the size of the graphics region to match that of the original image.

Framing graphics

Mathcad allows you to place a border all the way around a graphics region. To do so:

- Click on the graphics region to select it. This encloses the graphics region in a selection box.

- Choose **Picture Format** from the **Graphics** menu. Alternatively, double-click on the picture itself. This brings up the Picture Format dialog box.

- Click on the box labeled "Show border."

- Click the "OK" button. Mathcad draws a border around the graphics region.

Deleting and moving graphics

Graphics regions behave like other Mathcad regions. You can use the **Cut**, **Copy** and **Paste** commands to move or delete a graphics region.

To delete a graphics region:

- Click inside the region to select it. This will place a selection box around the graphics region.

- Press [Ctrl]X, or choose **Cut** from the **Edit** menu.

To move a graphics region:

- Click inside the region to select it. This will place a selection box around the graphics region.

- Press [Ctrl]X, or choose **Cut** from the **Edit** menu.

- Click wherever you want to move the graphics region to.

- Press [Ctrl]V, or choose **Paste** from the **Edit** menu.

Note that you cannot remove just the image from a graphics region. Once you place an image into a graphics region, the only way to remove it is by replacing it with another image. When you select a graphics region, Mathcad selects the entire graphics region, not just the image. Therefore when you press [Ctrl]C or [Ctrl]X, Mathcad places both the image *and* the rest of the region into the clipboard.

Chapter 27 Importing Graphics

Appendices

Appendix A
Reference

This appendix lists functions, operators, menu commands, keys and other reference material. It is made up of the following sections:

Menu commands

Function keys

Greek letters

Operators

Built-in functions by name

Predefined variables

Suffixes for numbers

Arrow and movement keys

Menu commands

Control Menu (application window)

Restore		Turn icon back to application window.
Move		Move application window.
Size		Resize application window.
Minimize		Turn application window into icon.
Maximize		Expand application window to cover desktop.
Close	[Alt][F4]	Exit Mathcad. Return to Program Manager.
Switch To...	[Ctrl][Esc]	Bring up the Program Manager task list.

Control Menu (worksheet window)

Restore		Turn icon back to worksheet window.
Move		Move worksheet window.
Size		Resize worksheet window.
Minimize		Turn worksheet window into icon.
Maximize		Expand worksheet window to fill application window.
Close	[Ctrl][F4]	Turn worksheet window into icon.
Next	[Ctrl][F6]	Make next worksheet active.

File menu

New	[F7]	Open new worksheet.
Open...	[F5]	Open existing worksheet.
Save	[F6]	Save current worksheet.
Save As...		Save current worksheet under new name.
Export Worksheet...		Save worksheet in RTF format.
Insert...		Insert existing worksheet into current one.
Mail...		Mail current worksheet.
Close	[Ctrl][F4]	Close current worksheet.
Open URL...		Open a Mathcad worksheet stored on the Internet.

Get From Notes...		Open Mathcad worksheet stored in a Notes database.
Save To Notes...		Save Mathcad worksheet to an existing Notes database.
Save Configuration...		Save current configuration in a configuration file.
Execute Configuration File...		Execute configuration file.
Associate Filename...		Associate selected variable with data file.
Page Setup...		Set margins, suppress printing beyond right margin.
Print Preview...		Show worksheet as it will appear when printed.
Print...	[Ctrl]O	Print worksheet or selected regions.
Exit	[Alt][F4]	Quit Mathcad; return to Program Manager.

Edit menu

Undo Last Edit	[Alt][BkSp]	Undo most recent edit.
Cut	[Ctrl]X	Delete selection.
Copy	[Ctrl]C	Copy selection.
Clear		Delete selection from the worksheet and leaves clipboard unaffected.
Paste	[Ctrl]V	Insert selection most recently copied or cut.
Paste Special...		Similar to paste, but using Windows' OLE (Object Linking and Embedding) to create a dynamic link to other Windows applications.
Regions$\Rightarrow$		
View Regions		Toggle between boxed and unboxed display of regions.
Select All		Select every region in the worksheet.
Separate	[Ctrl]S	Separate overlapping regions.

Align Regions⇒

    Horizontal — Align selected regions to a horizontal line midway between the highest and the lowest region.

    Vertical — Align selected regions to a vertical line midway between the rightmost and the leftmost region.

Include... — Include variable and function definitions from another worksheet in current worksheet.

Link⇒

    New... — Create a hypertext link to another worksheet.

    Erase — Deactivate any hypertext links associated with the current selection.

Lock Regions⇒

    Set Lock Area — Define extent of a write-protected area on the worksheet.

    Lock Area... — Write protect selected area.

    Unlock Area... — Permit editing in a locked area.

Ins/Del Blank Lines... — Insert or delete one or more blank lines below cursor.

Insert Pagebreak — Insert a hard pagebreak.

Right Margin⇒

    Set — Mark right-hand boundary of printed page.

    Clear — Remove right-hand boundary of printed page.

Headers/Footers... — Specify headers and footers for printouts.

Find...   [Ctrl][F5] — Search for math or text string.

Replace...   [Shift][F5] — Search for and replace math or text string.

Go to Page... — Position the top of a specified page at the top of your window.

Text Menu

Create Text Region	"	Start new text region at crosshair location.
Create Text Paragraph	[Ctrl]T	Start paragraph on line containing crosshair.
Embed Math		Create a math region inside a text region or paragraph.
Change Font...		Choose font, size, color, and style of selected text.
Change Paragraph Format...		Change alignment and left margin for selected paragraph.
Change Defaults⇒		
Font...		Change font of all text except text whose font characteristics have been changed explicitly using the **Change Font** command.
Paragraph format...		Choose alignment and left margin of all paragraphs having the default paragraph format.
Check Spelling...		Search text for misspelled words.

Math menu

Matrices...	[Ctrl]M	Create or change size of matrix.
Built-in Variables...		Set values of built-in variables.
Units ⇒		
Insert Units...	[Ctrl]U	Show a scrolling list of available units.
Change System of Units...		Choose unit system for the default display of results.
Dimensional Format...		Change names of fundamental dimensions *mass*, *length*, *time*, *charge* and *temperature*.
Choose Function...		Show a scrolling list of available built-in functions.
Randomize...		Reset random numbers.
Calculate	[F9]	Update all results on screen.
Calculate Worksheet		Update all results in worksheet.
Toggle Equation		Make Mathcad ignore an equation. If equation is already ignored, makes Mathcad evaluate it.
Highlight Equation		Highlight selected equation.

Automatic Mode		Toggle between automatic mode in which Mathcad updates screen continuously, and manual mode.
Live Symbolics		Turn live symbolics feature on or off. This feature lets the symbolic equal sign be used to evaluate any expression symbolically. When the live symbolic feature is on, this menu item is checked.
Optimize		Turn optimize feature on and off. This feature causes Mathcad to attempt to simplify any expression to the right of ":=" or "=". When the optimize feature is on, this menu item is checked.
Numerical Format...		Change display of numbers.
Font Tag...		Change font of selected name or of all names having the same font tag.
Change to Greek Variable	[Ctrl]G	Change character behind insertion point from roman to Greek and vice versa.

Graphics menu

Create X-Y Plot	@	Create two-dimensional Cartesian plot.
Create Polar Plot	[Ctrl]7	Create a plot for plotting radius against angle.
Create Surface Plot	[Ctrl]2	Create a plot for displaying a surface in three dimensions.
Create Contour Plot	[Ctrl]5	Create a plot for level curves of a surface.
Create 3D Scatter Plot		Create three-dimensional scatter plot.
Create Vector Field Plot		Create a vector field plot for two-dimensional vectors.
Create 3D Bar Chart		Create three-dimensional bar chart.
Create Picture		Create region for graphics import.
X-Y Plot Format...		Change characteristics for all future Cartesian plots in current worksheet.
Polar Plot Format...		Change characteristics for all future polar plots in current worksheet.
3D Plot Format...		Change characteristics for the currently selected three-dimensional plot.
Picture Format...		Change characteristics of graphic import region.

X-Y Plot menu

Format...	Change characteristics of currently selected two-dimensional graph.
Trace...	Read coordinates directly from currently selected two-dimensional graph.
Zoom...	Magnify view of portion of graph.
Title...	Change a title or its position.
Axis Labels...	Control the format of labels for the x and y axes.

Polar Plot menu

Format...	Change characteristics of currently selected two-dimensional polar plot.
Trace...	Read coordinates directly from currently selected two-dimensional polar plot.
Zoom...	Magnify view of portion of polar plot.
Title...	Change a title or its position.

Symbolic menu

Evaluate $\Rightarrow$

Evaluate Symbolically	[Shift][F9]	Carry out symbolic evaluation of an expression.
Complex Evaluation		Carry out symbolic evaluation of a complex expression. The result is expressed in the form $a + b \cdot i$.
Floating Point Evaluation...		Return a floating point number for constants rather than a symbolic expression. A dialog box allows you to choose the floating point precision.
Simplify		Simplify the selected expression, performing arithmetic, canceling common factors and using basic trigonometric and inverse function identities.
Expand Expression		Expand all powers and products of sums in the selected expression.

Factor Expression	Factor the selected expression into a product, if the entire expression can be written as a product. To factor a subexpression of a larger expression, select the subexpression.
Collect on Subexpression	Collect terms containing like powers of the selected subexpression, which may be a single variable or a function together with its argument. The result is a polynomial in the selected expression.
Polynomial Coefficients	Find the coefficients of the expression when written as a polynomial in the selected variable or function.
Differentiate on Variable	Differentiate the entire expression containing the selected variable with respect to that variable. Other variables are treated as constants.
Integrate on Variable	Integrate the entire expression containing the selected variable with respect to that variable.
Solve for Variable	Find the value of the selected variable that makes the expression containing the variable equal to zero. If you select a variable in an equation or inequality, this command solves the equation or inequality for the selected variable.
Substitute for Variable	Substitute the contents of the clipboard for each occurrence of a selected variable in an expression. To use this menu command, first put the expression being substituted in the clipboard by selecting and choosing **Copy** or **Cut**. Then select an occurrence of the variable you are substituting for and choose this menu command.
Expand to Series...	Derive an expansion series for an expression with respect to the variable you have selected. A dialog box allows you to choose the order of the series.
Convert to Partial Fraction	Generate a partial fraction expansion for an expression by factoring the numerator and denominator with respect to the selected variable.
Matrix Operations ⇒	
Transpose Matrix	Return transpose of the selected matrix.
Invert Matrix	Return symbolic inverse of the selected square matrix.

Determinant of Matrix	Return symbolic determinant of the selected square matrix.
Transforms $\Rightarrow$	
Fourier Transform	Evaluate Fourier transform of expression with respect to the selected variable. Result is in terms of ω.
Inverse Fourier Transform	Evaluate the inverse Fourier transform of the expression with respect to the selected variable. Result is in terms of t.
Laplace Transform	Evaluate the Laplace transform of the expression with respect to the selected variable. Result is in terms of s.
Inverse Laplace Transform	Evaluate the inverse Laplace transform of the expression with respect to the selected variable. Result is in terms of t.
z-Transform	Evaluate the z-transform of the expression with respect to the selected variable. Result is in terms of z.
Inverse z-Transform	Evaluate the inverse z-transform of the expression with respect to the selected variable. Result is in terms of n.
Derivation Format...	Choose the format for symbolic results. A dialog box presents the options, which include vertically stacked display of results and comments, horizontal display, and display without derivation comments.
Derive in Place	Command causes symbolic results to be substituted directly for the original expression rather than displayed in derivation format.

Window menu

Cascade		Stack all worksheet windows neatly, with title bars showing.
Tile Horizontal		Arrange all worksheet windows horizontally so that they don't overlap.
Tile Vertical		Arrange all worksheet windows vertically so that they don't overlap.
Arrange Icons		Arrange worksheet icons neatly along lower left edge of application window.
Zoom...		Zoom in for a close-up or out for an overall view.
Refresh	[Ctrl]R	Force screen redraw.
Animation ⇒		
Create...		Create an animation clip.
Playback...		Play an existing animation clip.
Hide Palette		Hide symbol palette. When palette is hidden, this menu item is checked.
Hide Tool Bar		Hide tool bar. When tool bar is hidden, this item is checked.
Hide Font Bar		Hide font bar. When font bar is hidden, this menu item is checked.
Change Colors ⇒		
Background Color...		Change color of window background.
Text Color...		Change color of all characters in text regions.
Equation Color...		Change color of equations and plots.
Highlight Color...		Change color of highlighted equations.
Annotation Color...		Change color of any changes made to an Electronic Book.

Books menu

Open Book...	Show list of available Electronic Books.
History...	List all Books sections looked at since the Book was opened.
Search Book...	Search through all Electronic Book sections.
Annotate Book	When checked, Mathcad will let you save an annotated copy of the currently open Electronic Book.
Annotate Options⇒	
Save Edited Section	Save changes in the currently open section of the Electronic Book.
Save All Edits	Save all changes made since the last time the Electronic Book was opened.
View Original Section	Show the original, unedited version of the currently displayed section.
View Edited Section	Show the annotated version of the currently displayed section.
Restore Original Section	Permanently delete any annotations made to the current section.
Restore Original Book	Permanently delete the annotated copy of the current Electronic Book.
Highlight Edits	When checked, Mathcad displays any changes you've made to an Electronic Book in a different color.
List of Books	List any Electronic Books available on this system.

Help menu

Index...	[F1]	Show index for on-line help.
Keyboard...		Show help on keyboard.
Using Help...		Show instructions for using Help.
QuickSheets...		Open a collection of templates for performing routine Mathcad calculations.
Technical Support...		Show Help on getting Mathcad running properly on your system.
About Mathcad...		Show version number and serial number.

Function keys

Keys	Actions
[F1]	Help.
[Shift][F1]	Context sensitive help.
[F2]	Copy selected region to clipboard.
[F3]	Cut selected region to clipboard.
[F4]	Paste contents of clipboard.
[Ctrl][F4]	Close worksheet.
[Alt][F4]	Exit Mathcad.
[F5]	Open a worksheet.
[Ctrl][F5]	Search for a string.
[Shift][F5]	Replace a string.
[F6]	Save current worksheet.
[Ctrl][F6]	Make next window active.
[F7]	Open a new worksheet.
[F9]	Recalculate everything on the screen. With READ, WRITE or other file I/O function selected, forces Mathcad to read or write to disk.
[Ctrl][F9]	Insert blank line.
[Ctrl][F10]	Delete blank line.

Greek letters

To type a Greek letter into an equation or into text, press the corresponding roman equivalent from the table below, followed by [Ctrl]G. For uppercase Greek letters, use the corresponding uppercase roman equivalent.

Name	Uppercase	Lowercase	Roman equivalent
alpha	A	α	A
beta	B	β	B
chi	X	χ	C
delta	Δ	δ	D
epsilon	E	ε	E
eta	H	η	H
gamma	Γ	γ	G
iota	I	ι	I
kappa	K	κ	K
lambda	Λ	λ	L
mu	M	μ	M
nu	N	ν	N
omega	Ω	ω	W
omicron	O	o	O
phi	Φ	φ	F
pi	Π	π	P
psi	Ψ	ψ	Y
rho	P	ρ	R
sigma	Σ	σ	S
tau	T	τ	T
theta	Θ	θ	Q
upsilon	Y	υ	U
xi	Ξ	ξ	X
zeta	Z	ζ	Z

Note: In equations, the Greek letter π is so commonly used that it has its own keyboard shortcut: [Ctrl]P.

Operators

In this table:

- **A** and **B** represent arrays, either vector or matrix.

- **u** and **v** represent vectors with real or complex elements.

- **M** represents a square matrix.

- z and w represent real or complex numbers.

- x and y represent real numbers.

- m and n represent integers.

- i represents a range variable.

- t represents any variable name.

- f represents a function.

- X and Y represent variables or expressions of any type.

Operation	Appearance	Keystroke	Description
Parentheses	(X)	'	Grouping operator.
Subscript	A_n	[	Returns indicated element of array.
Superscript	$A^{<n>}$	[Ctrl]6	Extracts column n from array **A**. Returns a vector.
Vectorize	$\vec{X}$	[Ctrl]–	Forces operations in expression X to take place element by element. All vectors or matrices in X must be the same size.
Factorial	$n!$	!	Returns $n \cdot (n-1) \cdot (n-2)\ldots$ The integer n cannot be negative.
Complex conjugate	$\overline{X}$	"	Inverts the sign of the imaginary part of X.
Transpose	A^T	[Ctrl]1	Returns a matrix whose rows are the columns of **A** and whose columns are the rows of **A**. **A** can be a vector or a matrix.
Power	z^w	^	Raises z to the power w.
Powers of matrix, matrix inverse		^	n^{th} power of square matrix **M** (using matrix multiplication). n must be a whole number. $\mathbf{M}^{-1}$ represents the inverse of **M**. Other negative powers are powers of the inverse. Returns a matrix.
Negation	$-X$	–	Multiplies X by -1.
Vector sum	$\Sigma \mathbf{v}$	[Ctrl]4	Sums elements of vector **v**; returns a scalar.
Square root	$\sqrt{z}$	\	Returns positive square root for positive z; principal value for negative or complex z.

nth root	$\sqrt[n]{z}$	[Ctrl]\	Returns n^{th} root of z; returns a real valued root whenever possible.
Magnitude	$\lvert z \rvert$	|	Returns $\sqrt{\mathrm{Re}(z)^2+\mathrm{Im}(z)^2}$.
Magnitude of vector	$\lvert \mathbf{v} \rvert$	|	Returns $\sqrt{\mathbf{v} \cdot \mathbf{v}}$ if all elements in $\mathbf{v}$ are real. Returns $\sqrt{\mathbf{v} \cdot \overline{\mathbf{v}}}$ if any element in $\mathbf{v}$ is complex.
Determinant	$\lvert \mathbf{M} \rvert$	|	Returns the determinant of the square matrix $\mathbf{M}$.
Division	$\dfrac{X}{z}$	/	Divides the expression X by the non-zero scalar z. If X is an array, divides each element of the array by z.
Multiplication	$X{\cdot}Y$	*	Returns the product of X and Y if both X and Y are scalars. Multiplies each element of Y by X if Y is an array and X is a scalar. Returns the dot product (inner product) if X and Y are vectors of the same size. Performs matrix multiplication if X and Y are conformable matrices.
Cross product	$\mathbf{u} \times \mathbf{v}$	[Ctrl]8	Returns cross-product (vector product) for the three-element vectors $\mathbf{u}$ and $\mathbf{v}$.
Summation	$\displaystyle\sum_{i\,=\,m}^{n} X$	[Ctrl] [Shift]4	Performs summation of X over $i = m, m+1, \ldots n$. X can be any expression. It need not involve i but it usually does. m and n must be integers.
Product	$\displaystyle\prod_{i\,=\,m}^{n} X$	[Ctrl] [Shift]3	Performs iterated product of X for $i = m, m+1, \ldots n$. X can be any expression. It need not involve i but it usually does. m and n must be integers.
Range sum	$\displaystyle\sum_{i} X$	$	Returns a summation of X over the range variable i. X can be any expression. It need not involve i but it usually does.
Range product	$\displaystyle\prod_{i} X$	#	Returns the iterated product of X over the range variable i. X can be any expression. It need not involve i but it usually does.
Limit	$\displaystyle\lim_{x \to a} f(x)$	[Ctrl]L	Returns the limit of $f(x)$ as x approaches a. Must be evaluated symbolically.
Left-hand limit	$\displaystyle\lim_{x \to a^-} f(x)$	[Ctrl]B	Returns the limit of $f(x)$ as x approaches a from the left. Must be evaluated symbolically.
Right-hand limit	$\displaystyle\lim_{x +> a^+} f(x)$	[Ctrl]A	Returns the limit of $f(x)$ as x approaches a from the right. Must be evaluated symbolically.
Integral	$\displaystyle\int_{a}^{b} f(t)\,dt$	&	Returns the definite integral of $f(t)$ over the interval $[a, b]$. a and b must be real scalars. All variables in the expression $f(t)$, except the variable of integration t, must be defined. The integrand, $f(t)$, cannot return an array.
Indefinite Integral	$\displaystyle\int f(t)\,dt$	[Ctrl]I	Returns the indefinite integral of $f(t)$. Must be evaluated symbolically.

Derivative	$\dfrac{d}{dt}f(t)$	?	Returns the derivative of $f(t)$ evaluated at t. All variables in the expression $f(t)$ must be defined. The variable t must be a scalar value. The function $f(t)$ must return a scalar.
n^{th} Derivative	$\dfrac{d^n}{dt^n}f(t)$	[Ctrl]?	Returns the nth derivative of $f(t)$ evaluated at t. All variables in $f(t)$ must be defined. The variable t must be a scalar value. The function $f(t)$ must return a scalar. n must be 0, 1, 2, 3, 4 or 5 for numerical evaluation or any positive integer for symbolic evaluation.
Addition	$X + Y$	+	Performs scalar addition if X, Y, or both are scalars. Performs element by element addition if X and Y are vectors or matrices of the same size. If X is an array and Y is a scalar, adds Y to each element of X.
Subtraction	$X - Y$	–	Performs scalar subtraction if X, Y, or both are scalars. Performs element by element subtraction if X and Y are vectors or matrices of the same size. If X is an array and Y is a scalar, subtracts Y from each element of X.
Addition with line break	$X \dots$ $+ Y$	[Ctrl][↵]	Works exactly like addition. Line break is purely cosmetic.
Greater than	$x > y$	>	Returns 1 if $x > y$, 0 otherwise. x and y must be real scalars.
Less than	$x < y$	<	Returns 1 if $x < y$, 0 otherwise. x and y must be real scalars.
Greater than or equal	$x \geq y$	[Ctrl]0	Returns 1 if $x \geq y$, 0 otherwise. x and y must be real scalars.
Less than or equal	$x \leq y$	[Ctrl]9	Returns 1 if $x \leq y$, 0 otherwise. x and y must be real scalars.
Not equal to	$z \neq w$	[Ctrl]3	Returns 1 if $z \neq w$, 0 otherwise. z and w must be scalars.
Equal to	$z = w$	[Ctrl]=	Returns 1 if $z = w$, 0 otherwise. z and w must be scalars. Appears on the screen as a bold equals sign.

Built-in functions by name

This section lists Mathcad's built-in functions alphabetically, with a short description of each one. For more information, see Chapter 12, "Built-in Functions." For more information on matrix or vector functions, see Chapter 9. "Vectors and Matrices." For a complete listing of Mathcad's differential equation solvers, see Chapter 16, "Solving Differential Equations."

In this table,

- x and y represent real numbers.

- z represents either a real or a complex number.

- m, n, i, j and k represent integers.

- **v, u** and any names beginning with **v** represent vectors.

- **A** and **B** represent matrices or vectors.

- **M** and **N** represent square matrices.

- **F** represents a vector-valued function.

- *file* is either a filename or a variable associated with a filename.

Any function that expects an angle as an argument expects that angle in radians. Similarly, any function that returns an angle as a result, returns the angle in radians. Complex or multivalued functions always return the principal value.

Function names are case sensitive. You must type them as shown here. Names of built-in functions are not, however, font sensitive.

Function	Returns...
$\mathrm{acos}(z)$	Inverse cosine. Result in radians. Principal value for complex z.
$\mathrm{acosh}(z)$	Inverse hyperbolic cosine. Result in radians. Principal value for complex z.
$\mathrm{angle}(x, y)$	Angle from x-axis to (x, y). x and y real. Result in radians.
APPEND(*file*)	Single value to append to data file *file*.
APPENDPRN(*file*)	Matrix to append to structured data file *file*.
$\mathrm{arg}(z)$	Angle in complex plane to number z.
$\mathrm{asin}(z)$	Inverse sine. Result in radians. Principal value for complex z.
$\mathrm{asinh}(z)$	Inverse hyperbolic sine. Result in radians. Principal value for complex z.
$\mathrm{atan}(z)$	Inverse tangent. Result in radians. Principal value for complex z.
$\mathrm{atanh}(z)$	Inverse hyperbolic tangent. Principal value for complex z.

	augment(**A**, **B**)	A matrix formed by putting the two argument matrices side by side. **A** and **B** must have the same number of rows. Either or both arguments may be vectors.
	ceil(x)	Least integer $\geq x$. x must be real.
	cfft(**A**)	Fast Fourier transform of complex data. Returns an array of same size as its argument.
	CFFT(**A**)	Identical to cfft(**A**), except uses a different normalizing factor and sign convention. Returns an array of same size as its argument.
⊕	cholesky(**M**)	A lower triangular matrix **L** such that $\mathbf{L} \cdot \mathbf{L}^T = \mathbf{M}$. This function assumes **M** is symmetric and uses only the upper triangular part of **M**.
	cnorm(x)	Cumulative normal distribution.
	cols(**A**)	Number of columns in array **A**. Returns a scalar.
⊕	cond1(**M**)	Condition number of the matrix **M** based on the L_1 norm.
⊕	cond2(**M**)	Condition number of the matrix **M** based on the L_2 norm.
⊕	conde(**M**)	Condition number of the matrix **M** based on the Euclidean norm.
⊕	condi(**M**)	Condition number of the matrix **M** based on the infinity norm.
	corr(**A**, **B**)	Correlation (Pearson's r) of two arrays **A** and **B** having the same number of rows and columns. Returns a scalar.
	cos(z)	Cosine. Argument in radians.
	cosh(z)	Hyperbolic cosine.
	cot(z)	Cotangent. Argument in radians.
	coth(z)	Hyperbolic cotangent.
	csc(z)	Cosecant. Argument in radians.
	csch(z)	Hyperbolic cosecant.
	csort(**A**, n)	Sort columns so as to put row n in ascending order.
	cspline(**vx**, **vy**)	Coefficients of cubic spline with cubic ends. **vx** and **vy** are real vectors of same size. Elements of **vx** must be in ascending order.
	cspline(**Mxy**, **Mz**)	Vector of second derivatives for data arrays **Mxy** and **Mz**. This vector becomes the first argument of the *interp* function. The resultant surface is cubic at the edges of the region spanned by **Mxy**.
	cvar(**A**, **B**)	Covariance of elements in **A** and **B**. **A** and **B** must have the same number of rows and columns.
⊕	diag(**v**)	Diagonal matrix containing on its diagonal the elements of **v**.
⊕	dbeta(x,s1,s2)	Probability density for a beta distribution.

	dbinom(k,n,p)	Binomial distribution of a random variable.
⊕	dcauchy(x,l,s)	Probability density for the Cauchy distribution.
	dchisq(x,d)	Probability density for the chi-squared distribution.
⊕	dexp(x,r)	Probability density for the exponential distribution.
	dF($x,d1,d2$)	Probability density for the F distribution.
⊕	dgamma(x,s)	Probability density for the Gamma distribution.
⊕	dgeom(k, p)	$P(X = k)$ when the random variable X has the geometric distribution.
⊕	dlnorm(x, μ, σ)	Probability density for the log normal distribution.
⊕	dlogis(x, l, s)	Probability density for the logistic distribution.
⊕	dnbinom(k, n, p)	$P(X = k)$ when the random variable X has the negative binomial distribution.
	dnorm(x, μ, σ)	Probability density for the normal distribution.
	dpois(k, λ)	$P(X = k)$ when the random variable X has the Poisson distribution.
	dt(x, d)	Probability density for the Student's t distribution.
	dunif(x, a, b)	Probability density for the uniform distribution.
⊕	dweibull(x, s)	Probability density for the Weibull distribution.
	eigenvals(**M**)	A vector of eigenvalues for the matrix **M**.
	eigenvec(**M**, z)	A vector containing the normalized eigenvector corresponding to the eigenvalue z of the square matrix **M**.
⊕	eigenvecs(**M**)	A matrix containing the normalized eigenvectors corresponding to the eigenvalues of the matrix **M**. The nth column of the matrix is the eigenvector corresponding to the nth eigenvalue returned by *eigenvals*.
	erf(z)	Error function.
	exp(z)	Exponential: e^{z}
	find(*var1, var2, . . .*)	Values of *var1, var2, . . .* that solve the system of equations. Returns a scalar if only one argument; otherwise, returns a vector of answers.
	fft(**v**)	Fast Fourier transform of real data. **v** must be a real vector with 2^{n} elements, where n is an integer. Returns a vector of size $2^{n-1} + 1$.
	FFT(**v**)	Identical to fft(**v**), except uses a different normalizing factor and sign convention. **v** must be a real vector with 2^{n} elements, where n is an integer. Returns a vector of size $2^{n-1} + 1$.
	floor(x)	Greatest integer $\leq x$. x must be real.

⊕	genfit(**vx**, **vy**, **vg**, **F**)	A vector containing the parameters that make a function f of x and n parameters $u_0, u_1, \ldots, u_{n-1}$ best approximate the data in **vx** and **vy**. **F** is a function that returns an $n + 1$ element vector containing f and its partial derivatives with respect to its n parameters. **vx** and **vy** must be the same size. **vg** is an n element vector of guess values for the n parameters.
⊕	geninv(**A**)	Matrix **L**, the left inverse of matrix **A**, such that $\mathbf{L} \cdot \mathbf{A} = \mathbf{I}$, where **I** is the identity matrix having the same size as **A**. Matrix **A** is an $m \times n$ real-valued matrix, where $m \geq n$.
⊕	genvals(**M**, **N**)	Vector **v** of computed eigenvalues each of which satisfies the generalized eigenvalue problem $\mathbf{M} \cdot \mathbf{x} = v_i \cdot \mathbf{N} \cdot \mathbf{x}$. Matrices **M** and **N** contain real values. Vector **x** contains the corresponding eigenvectors.
⊕	genvecs(**M**, **N**)	A matrix containing the normalized eigenvectors corresponding to the eigenvalues in **v**, the vector returned by *genvals*. The nth column of this matrix is the eigenvector **x** satisfying the generalized eigenvalue problem $\mathbf{M} \cdot \mathbf{x} = v_n \cdot \mathbf{N} \cdot \mathbf{x}$. Matrices **M** and **N** contain real values.
	hist(**intervals**, **data**)	Histogram. **intervals** is a vector of interval limits, in ascending order. **data** is an array of data. Returns a vector of size one less than the size of **intervals**, showing how many points of **data** fall in each interval.
	I0(x)	Bessel function $I_0(x)$. Argument must be real.
	I1(x)	Bessel function $I_1(x)$. Argument must be real.
	In(m, x)	Bessel function $I_m(x)$. x must be real; $0 \leq m \leq 100$.
	icfft(**A**)	Inverse Fourier transform corresponding to *cfft*. Returns an array of the same size as its argument.
	ICFFT(**A**)	Inverse transform corresponding to *CFFT*. Returns an array of the same size as its argument.
	identity(n)	Identity matrix of size n. n must be a positive integer.
	if(*cond, x, y*)	Conditional: returns x or y depending on value of *cond*. If *cond* is true (non-zero), returns x. If *cond* is false (zero), returns y.
	ifft(**v**)	Inverse Fourier transform corresponding to *fft* Takes a vector of size $1 + 2^{n-1}$, where n is an integer. Returns a real vector of size 2^n.
	IFFT(**v**)	Inverse transform corresponding to *FFT*. Takes a vector of size $1 + 2^{n-1}$, where n is an integer. Returns a real vector of size 2^n.
	Im(z)	Imaginary part of complex number z. Also works on vectors and matrix arguments.

intercept(**vx**, **vy**)		Intercept of regression line. Takes two vector arguments **vx** and **vy** of same size. The elements of **vx** must be in ascending order. Returns a scalar: the y-intercept of the regression line.
interp(**vs**, **vx**, **vy**, x)		Interpolated value from spline coefficients. Takes three vector arguments **vs**, **vx**, and **vy** of same size and a scalar x at which to interpolate; returns a scalar. The elements of **vx** should be in ascending order. **vs** should be a vector computed with *cspline*, *lspline*, or *pspline*.
interp(**vs**, **Mxy**, **Mz**, **v**)		Spline interpolated value of **Mz** at the x and y coordinates specified in **v**.
⊕ iwave(**v**)		Inverse wavelet transform corresponding to *wave*. Takes a 2^n element vector of real data, where n is an integer.
J0(x)		Bessel function $J_0(x)$. Argument must be real.
J1(x)		Bessel function $J_1(x)$. Argument must be real.
Jn(m, x)		Bessel function $J_m(x)$. x must be real; $0 \leq m \leq 100$.
K0(x)		Bessel function $K_0(x)$. Argument must be positive.
K1(x)		Bessel function $K_1(x)$. Argument must be positive.
Kn(m, x)		Bessel function $K_m(x)$. x must be positive; $0 \leq m \leq 100$.
⊕ ksmooth(**vx**,**vy**, b)		An n-element vector created by using a Gaussian kernel to return weighted averages of **vy**. **vy** and **vx** are n-element vectors of real numbers. The bandwidth b controls the smoothing window and should be set to a few times the spacing between your x data points.
last(**v**)		Index of last element in vector **v**. Returns a scalar.
length(**v**)		Number of elements in vector **v**. Returns a scalar.
linfit(**vx**, **vy**, **F**)		A vector containing the coefficients used to create a linear combination of the functions in **F** which best approximates the data in **vx** and **vy**. **F** is a function that returns a vector.
linterp(**vx**, **vy**, x)		Linearly interpolated value. Takes two vector arguments **vx** and **vy** of same size and a scalar x at which to interpolate; returns a scalar. The elements of **vx** should be in ascending order.
ln(z)		Natural logarithm of z (to base e). Returns principal value (imaginary part between π and $-\pi$) for complex z.
⊕ loess(**vx**, **vy**, *span*)		Vector required by the *interp* function to find the set of second order polynomials that best fit particular neighborhoods of data points specified in arrays **vx** and **vy**. **vx** is an m element vector containing x coordinates. **vy** is an m element vector containing the y coordinates corresponding to the m points specified in **vx**. The argument *span* (*span* > 0) specifies how large a neighborhood *loess* will consider in performing this local regression.

⊕	loess(**Mxy**, **vz**, *span*)	Vector required by the *interp* function to find the set of second order polynomials that best fit particular neighborhoods of data points specified in arrays **Mxy** and **vz**. **Mxy** is an $m\times 2$ matrix containing x-y coordinates. **vz** is an m element vector containing the z coordinates corresponding to the m points specified in **Mxy**. The argument *span* (*span* > 0) specifies how large a neighborhood *loess* will consider in performing this local regression.
	log(*z*)	Common logarithm of z (to base 10).
⊕	lsolve(**M**, **v**)	Solution vector **x** such that $M \cdot x = v$.
	lspline(**vx**, **vy**)	Coefficients of cubic spline with linear ends. **vx** and **vy** are real vectors of same size. Elements of **vx** must be in ascending order.
	lspline(**Mxy**, **Mz**)	Vector of second derivatives for data arrays **Mxy** and **Mz**. This vector becomes the first argument of the *interp* function. The resultant surface is linear at the boundaries of the region spanned by **Mxy**.
⊕	lu(**M**)	One matrix containing the three square matrices **P**, **L**, and **U**, all having the same size as **M** and joined together side by side, in that order. These three matrices satisfy the equation $P \cdot M = L \cdot U$. **L** and **U** are lower and upper triangular respectively.
	matrix(*m*, *n*, *f*)	Creates a matrix in which the ij^{th} element contains $f(i, j)$ where $i = 0, 1,...m$ and $j = 0, 1,...n$.
	max(**A**)	Largest element in **A**. Returns a scalar. If **A** is complex, returns $\max(\text{Re}(A)) + i \cdot \max(\text{Im}(A))$.
	mean(**A**)	Mean of elements of an array **A**. Returns a scalar.
	median(**A**)	Median of elements in array **A**. Returns a scalar.
	medsmooth(**vy**,*n*)	An m-element vector created by smoothing **vy** with running medians. **vy** is an m-element vector of real numbers. The smoothing window has size n.
	min(**A**)	Smallest element in **A**. Returns a scalar. If **A** is complex, returns $\min(\text{Re}(A)) + i \cdot \min(\text{Im}(A))$.
	minerr(*var1*, *var2*, . . .)	Values of *var1*, *var2*, . . . coming closest to solving the system of equations. Returns a scalar if only one argument; otherwise, returns a vector of answers.
	mod(*x*, *modulus*)	Remainder on dividing x by *modulus*. Arguments must be real. Result has same sign as x.
⊕	norm1(**M**)	The L_1 norm of the matrix **M**.
⊕	norm2(**M**)	The L_2 norm of the matrix **M**.
⊕	norme(**M**)	The Euclidean norm of the matrix **M**.
⊕	normi(**M**)	The infinity norm of the matrix **M**.
⊕	pbeta(*x*, s_1, s_2)	Cumulative standard normal distribution function.

	pbinom(k, n, p)	Cumulative binomial distribution for k successes in n trials.
$\oplus$	pcauchy(x, l, s)	Cumulative Cauchy distribution with scale parameters l and s.
	pchisq(x, d)	Cumulative chi-squared distribution in which $d > 0$ is the degrees of freedom and $x > 0$.
$\oplus$	pexp(x, r)	Cumulative exponential distribution in which $r > 0$ is the rate and $x > 0$.
	pF(x, d_1, d_2)	Cumulative F distribution in which $d_1, d_2 > 0$ are the degrees of freedom. $x > 0$.
$\oplus$	pgamma(x, s)	Cumulative Gamma distribution in which $s > 0$ is the shape parameter. $x > 0$.
$\oplus$	pgeom(k, p)	Cumulative geometric distribution. p is the probability of success. $k \geq 0$ and $0 < p \leq 1$.
$\oplus$	plnorm(x, μ, σ)	Cumulative log normal distribution in which μ is the log of the mean, $\sigma > 0$ is the log of the standard deviation, and $x > 0$.
$\oplus$	plogis(x, l, s)	Cumulative logistic distribution. l is the location parameter. $s > 0$ is the scale parameter.
$\oplus$	pnbinom(k, n, p)	Cumulative negative binomial distribution in which $n > 0$ and $0 < p \leq 1$.
	pnorm(x, μ, σ))	Cumulative normal distribution with mean μ and standard deviation σ.
	polyroots(**v**)	Roots of the nth degree polynomial whose coeffients are in **v**, a vector of length $n + 1$.
	ppois(k, λ)	Cumulative Poisson distribution. $\lambda > 0$.
$\oplus$	predict(**v**, m, n)	A vector of n predicted values based on m consecutive elements in **v**, a vector whose values represent samples taken at equal intervals.
	pspline(**vx**, **vy**)	Coefficients of cubic spline with parabolic ends. **vx** and **vy** are real vectors of same size. Elements of **vx** must be in ascending order.
	pspline(**Mxy**, **Mz**)	Vector of second derivatives for data arrays **Mxy** and **Mz**. This vector becomes the first argument of the *interp* function. The resultant surface is parabolic at the boundaries of the region spanned by **Mxy**.
	pt(x, d)	Cumulative Student's t distribution. d is the degrees of freedom. $x > 0$ and $d > 0$.
	punif(x, a, b)	Cumulative uniform distribution. b and a are the endpoints of the interval. $a < b$.
$\oplus$	pweibull(x, s)	Cumulative Weibull distribution. $s > 0$.
$\oplus$	qbeta(p, s_1, s_2)	Inverse beta distribution with shape parameters s_1 and s_2. $0 \leq p \leq 1$ and $s_1, s_2 > 0$.

	qbinom(p, n, q)	Number of successes in n trials of the Bernoulli process such that the probability of that number of successes is p. q is the probability of success on a single trial. $0 \le q \le 1$ and $0 \le p \le 1$.
⊕	qcauchy(p, l, s)	Inverse Cauchy distribution with scale parameters l and s. $s > 0$ and $0 < p < 1$.
	qchisq(p, d)	Inverse chi-squared distribution in which $d > 0$ is the degrees of freedom. $0 \le p < 1$.
⊕	qexp(p, r)	Inverse exponential distribution in which $r > 0$ is the rate. $0 \le p < 1$.
	qF(p, d_1, d_2)	Inverse F distribution in which $d_1, d_2 > 0$ are the degrees of freedom. $0 \le p < 1$.
⊕	qgamma(p, s)	Inverse Gamma distribution in which $s > 0$ is the shape parameter. $0 \le p < 1$.
⊕	qgeom(p, q)	Inverse geometric distribution. q is the probability of success on a single trial. $0 < p < 1$ and $0 \le q < 1$.
⊕	qlnorm(p, μ, σ)	Inverse log normal distribution in which μ is the log of the mean, $\sigma > 0$ is the log of the standard deviation. $0 \le p < 1$.
⊕	qlogis(p, l, s)	Inverse logistic distribution. l is the location parameter. $s > 0$ is the scale parameter. $0 < p < 1$.
⊕	qnbinom(p, n, q)	Inverse negative binomial distribution with size n and probability of failure q. $0 \le q \le 1$ and $0 \le p \le 1$.
	qnorm(p, μ, σ)	Inverse normal distribution with mean μ and standard deviation σ. $0 < p < 1$ and $\sigma > 0$.
	qpois(p, λ)	Inverse Poisson distribution. $\lambda > 0$ and $0 \le p \le 1$.
⊕	qr(**A**)	A matrix whose first n columns contain the square, orthonormal matrix **Q**, and whose remaining columns contain the upper triangular matrix, **R**. Matrices **Q** and **R** satisfy the equation $\mathbf{A} = \mathbf{Q} \cdot \mathbf{R}$, where **A** is a real-valued array.
	qt(p, d)	Inverse Student's t distribution. d is the degrees of freedom. $d > 0$ and $0 < p < 1$.
	qunif(p, a, b)	Inverse uniform distribution. b and a are the endpoints of the interval. $a < b$ and $0 \le p \le 1$.
⊕	qweibull(p, s)	Inverse Weibull distribution. $s > 0$ and $0 < p < 1$.
⊕	rank(**A**)	The rank of real-valued matrix **A**.
⊕	rbeta(m, s_1, s_2)	Vector of m random numbers having the beta distribution. $s_1, s_2 > 0$ are the shape parameters.
	rbinom(m, n, p)	Vector of m random numbers having the binomial distribution. $0 \le p \le 1$. n is an integer satisfying $n > 0$.
⊕	rcauchy(m, l, s)	Vector of m random numbers having the Cauchy distribution. l and $s > 0$ are scale parameters.
	rchisq(m, d)	Vector of m random numbers having the schi squared distribution. $d > 0$ is the degrees of freedom.

	Re(z)	Real part of complex number z.
	READ(*file*)	Single value read from data file *file.*
	READBMP(*file*)	Array containing a grayscale representation of the bitmap image in *file.*
	READPRN(*file*)	Matrix read from structured data file *file.*
	READRGB(*file*)	Array in which the color information in *file* is represented by the appropriate values of red, green, and blue. This array is formed by combining the three arrays giving the red, green, and blue components of the image into a single array with three times as many columns as the image.
	regress(**vx**, **vy**, n)	Vector required by the *interp* function to find the nth order polynomial that best fits data arrays **vx** and **vy**. **vx** is an m element vector containing x coordinates. **vy** is an m element vector containing the y coordinates corresponding to the m points specified in **vx**.
	regress(**Mxy**,**vz**, n)	Vector required by the *interp* function to find the nth order polynomial that best fits data arrays **Mxy** and **vz**. **Mxy** is an $m{\times}2$ matrix containing x-y coordinates. **vz** is an m element vector containing the z coordinates corresponding to the m points specified in **Mxy**.
	reverse(**v**)	Reverse order of elements in **v**.
⊕	rexp(m, r)	Vector of m random numbers having the exponential distribution. $r > 0$ is the rate.
	rF(m, d_1, d_2)	Vector of m random numbers having the F distribution. $d_1, d_2 > 0$ are the degrees of freedom.
⊕	rgamma(m, s)	Vector of m random numbers having the gamma distribution. $s > 0$ is the shape parameter.
⊕	rgeom(m, p)	Vector of m random numbers having the geometric distribution. $0 < p \leq 1$.
⊕	rlnorm(m, μ, σ)	Vector of m random numbers having the log normal distribution in which μ is the log of the mean and $\sigma > 0$ is the log of the standard deviation.
⊕	rlogis(m, l, s)	Vector of m random numbers having the logistic distribution in which l is the location parameter and $s > 0$ is the scale parameter.
⊕	rnbinom(m, n, p)	Vector of m random numbers having the negative binomial distribution. $0 < p \leq 1$. n is an integer satisfying $n > 0$.
	rnd(x)	Random number between 0 and x. x real.

	rnorm(m, μ, σ)	Vector of m random numbers having the normal distribution. σ > 0.
	root(*expr, var*)	Value of *var* where *expr* is zero.
	rows(**A**)	Number of rows in array **A**. Returns a scalar.
	rpois(m, λ)	Vector of m random numbers having the Poisson distribution. λ > 0.
⊕	rref(**A**)	A matrix representing the row-reduced echelon form of **A**.
	rsort(**A**, n)	Sort rows so as to put column n in ascending order.
	rt(m, d)	Vector of m random numbers having the Student's t distribution. $d > 0$.
	runif(m, a, b)	Vector of m random numbers having the uniform distribution in which b and a are the endpoints of the interval and $a < b$.
⊕	rweibull(m, s)	Vector of m random numbers having the Weibull distribution in which $s > 0$ is the shape parameter.
	sec(z)	Secant. Argument in radians.
	sech(z)	Hyperbolic secant.
	sin(z)	Sine. Argument in radians.
	sinh(z)	Hyperbolic sine.
	slope(**vx**, **vy**)	Slope of regression line. Takes two vector arguments **vx** and **vy** of the same size. The elements of **vx** must be in ascending order.
	sort(**v**)	Sort elements in vector **v**.
	stack(**A**, **B**)	Array formed by placing **A** above **B**. The arrays **A** and **B** must have the same number of columns.
	stdev(**A**)	Standard deviation of elements of **A**. Uses n in the denominator. Returns a scalar.
	submatrix(**A**, ir, jr, ic, jc)	Submatrix of **A** consisting of all elements common to rows ir through jr and columns ic through jc. To maintain order of rows and/or columns, make sure $ir \geq jr$ and $ic \geq jc$, otherwise order of rows and/or columns will be reversed.
⊕	supsmooth(**vx**,**vy**)	An n-element vector created by the piecewise use of a symmetric k-nearest neighbor linear least square fitting procedure in which k is adaptively chosen. **vy** and **vx** are n-element vectors of real numbers. The elements of **vx** must be in increasing order.
⊕	svd(**A**)	One matrix containing two stacked matrices **U** and **V**, where **U** is the upper $m \times n$ submatrix and **V** is the lower $n \times n$ submatrix. Matrices **U** and **V** satisfy the equation $\mathbf{A} = \mathbf{U} \cdot \mathrm{diag}(\mathbf{s}) \cdot \mathbf{V}^T$, where **s** is a vector containing the first n elements returned by svds(**A**). **A** is an $m \times n$ array of real values, where $m \geq n$.

⊕	svds(**A**)	A vector containing the singular values of the $m \times n$ real-valued array **A**, where $m \geq n$.
	tan(z)	Tangent. Argument in radians.
	tanh(z)	Hyperbolic tangent.
	tr(**M**)	Trace of square matrix **M**: sum of diagonal elements.
	until(x, y)	Returns y until x is negative.
	var(**A**)	Variance of elements of **A**. Uses n in the denominator. Returns a scalar.
⊕	wave(**v**)	Discrete wavelet transform of real data using Daubechies four-coefficient wavelet filter. Vector **v** must contain 2^n real values, where n is an integer.
	WRITE(*file*)	Single value written to a data file *file*.
	WRITEBMP(*file*)	Grayscale BMP file out of a matrix.
	WRITEPRN(*file*)	Structured data file out of a matrix.
	WRITERGB(*file*)	Colored BMP bitmap file out of an array formed by juxtaposing the three arrays giving the red, green, and blue values of a bitmap image.
	Y0(x)	Bessel function $Y_0(x)$. Argument must be positive.
	Y1(x)	Bessel function $Y_1(x)$. Argument must be positive.
	Yn(m, x)	Bessel function $Y_m(x)$. x must be positive; $0 \leq m \leq 100$.
	$\delta(x, y)$	Kronecker delta function. Returns 1 if $x = y$; otherwise, returns 0. (To type δ, press **d[Ctrl]G**)
	$\varepsilon(i, j, k)$	Completely antisymmetric tensor of rank three. i, j, and k must be integers between 0 and 2 (or between ORIGIN and ORIGIN+2, if ORIGIN≠0). Result is 0 if any two are the same, 1 if the three arguments are an even permutation of (0 1 2), and −1 if the three arguments are an odd permutation of (0 1 2). (To type ε, press **e[Ctrl]G**)
	$\Gamma(z)$	Euler's gamma function. (To type Γ, press **G[Ctrl]G**)
	$\Phi(x)$	Heaviside step function. Returns 1 if $x \geq 0$; otherwise, returns 0. (To type Φ, press **F[Ctrl]G**)

Predefined variables

Mathcad's predefined variables are listed here, together with their default starting values.

Constant=Value	Meaning
$\pi = 3.14159...$	Pi. Mathcad uses the value of π to 15 digits. To type π, press [**Ctrl**]**p**.
$e = 2.71828...$	The base of natural logarithms. Mathcad uses the value of e to 15 digits.
$\infty = 10^{307}$	Infinity. This symbol represents values larger than the largest real number representable in Mathcad (about 10^{307}). Do not use this variable in place of actual infinities in numerical formulas. To type ∞, press [**Ctrl**]**z**.
$\% = 0.01$	Percent. Use in expressions like **10*%** (appears as $10 \cdot \%$) or as a scaling unit at the end of an equation with an equals sign.
$\mathbf{TOL} = 10^{-3}$	Tolerance. The tolerance Mathcad uses in numerical approximation algorithms (integrals, equation solving, etc.). For more information, see the section on the specific operation in question.
$\mathbf{ORIGIN} = 0$	Array origin. Specifies the index of the first element in arrays.
$\mathbf{PRNCOLWIDTH} = 8$	Column width used in writing files with WRITEPRN function.
$\mathbf{PRNPRECISION} = 4$	Number of significant digits used when writing files with the WRITEPRN function.
$\mathbf{FRAME} = 0$	Used as a counter for creating animation clips.

Suffixes for numbers

The table below shows how Mathcad interprets numbers. (A number is any string beginning with a digit.)

Suffix	Examples	Meaning
i j	4i, 1i $3 + 1.5j \cdot 10^{-2}$	Imaginary
H h	0aH 8BCh	Hexadecimal
O o	757O 100o	Octal
L l	1L −2.54l	Standard length unit
M m	1M 2.2m	Standard mass unit
T t	1T 3600t	Standard time unit
Q q	1Q −100q	Standard charge unit
K k	1K −273k	Standard absolute temperature unit

Arrow and movement keys

Keys	Actions
[↑]	Move crosshair up. In equation, make selection box bigger. In text, move insertion point up to previous line.
[↓]	Move crosshair down. In equation, make selection box smaller. In text, move insertion point down to next line.
[←]	Move crosshair left. In equation, enclose left operand in selection box. In text, move insertion point one character left.
[→]	Move crosshair right. In equation, enclose right operand in selection box. In text, move insertion point one character right.
[Shift][↑]	In equation, move crosshair outside and above equation. In text, highlight from insertion point up to previous line.
[Shift][↓]	In equation, move crosshair outside and below equation. In text, highlight from insertion point down to next line.
[Shift][←]	In equation, move crosshair outside and to the left of equation. In text, highlight towards the left of the insertion point, character by character.
[Shift][→]	In equation, move crosshair outside and to the right of equation. In text, highlight towards the right of the insertion point, character by character.
[Ctrl][↑]	In text, move insertion point to the beginning of a line.
[Ctrl][↓]	In text, move insertion point to the beginning of next line.
[Ctrl][←]	In text, move insertion point left to the beginning of a word.
[Ctrl][→]	In text, move insertion point to the beginning of next word.
[Ctrl][Shift][↑]	In text, highlight from insertion point up to the beginning of a line.
[Ctrl]Shift][↓]	In text, highlight from insertion point to end of the current line.
[Ctrl]Shift][←]	Highlight left from insertion point to the beginning of a word.
[Ctrl]Shift][→]	Highlight from insertion point to beginning of the next word.

Keys	Actions
[Space]	In denominator, exponent, radical, or subscript, selects the whole fraction, power, radical, or subscripted variable.
[Tab]	In text: inserts a five-character space. In array or plot: move to next placeholder.
[Shift][Tab]	In array or plot: move to previous placeholder.
[PgUp]	Move up 5 lines.
[PgDn]	Move down 5 lines.
[Ctrl][PgUp]	Move 80% up the window.
[Ctrl][PgDn]	Move 80% down the window.
[Shift][PgUp]	Move up to previous pagebreak.
[Shift][PgDn]	Move down to next pagebreak.
[Home]	In equation, move to beginning previous region. In text, move to beginning of current line.
[End]	In equation, move to next region. In text, move to end of current line.
[Ctrl][Home]	Scroll to beginning of worksheet. In text, move insertion point to beginning of text region or paragraph.
[Ctrl][End]	Scroll to end of worksheet. In text, move insertion point to end of text region or paragraph.
[↵]	In text: start new line. In equation or plot: move crosshair below region, even with left edge of region.
[Shift][↵]	In text, move crosshair outside and below region.

Appendix A Reference

Appendix B
Error Messages

This appendix is an alphabetical list of Mathcad's equation error messages. These error messages appear when you try to enter, process, or calculate an equation and Mathcad detects an error. For a description of the error messages given by the symbolic processor, see Chapter 17, "Symbolic Calculation."

If Mathcad finds an error while trying to evaluate a user-defined function, it marks the error on the function name, not on the function definition. Check the definition to determine what caused the error.

array size mismatch

You tried to perform a vector or matrix operation on arrays whose sizes don't match. Many operations require vectors that are the same size, for example, the dot product and the *linterp* and *corr* functions. Vector addition and subtraction requires vectors or matrices that are the same size. Matrix multiplication requires that the number of columns in the first matrix match the number of rows in the second matrix.

cannot be defined

You put something other than a legally definable expression on the left side of the definition symbol (: =). Mathcad accepts any of the following on the left side of a definition:

- A variable name: x.

- A variable name with a subscript: x_i.

- A variable name with a superscript: $\mathbf{x}^{<1>}$.

- An explicit vector or matrix generated by typing [**Ctrl**]**M**. The vector or matrix can hold variable names or subscripted variable names only.

- A function name with arguments: $f(x, y)$.

Any other expression is illegal. If you want to compute a result instead of defining a variable, use an equals sign (=) instead of a colon.

cannot take subscript

You used a subscript on something other than a vector or matrix.

cannot take superscript

You used a superscript on something other than a matrix.

definition stack overflow

You used too many nested function definitions.

did not find solution

In a solve block, Mathcad was unable to find a solution to the constraints. To see the results of the solve block anyway, use *Minerr* instead of *Find*. For more information see Chapter 15, "Solving Equations."

dimension to nonreal power

You raised an expression with units to a complex or imaginary power. If an expression is defined with units, you can raise it only to a real scalar power; otherwise, Mathcad cannot determine units for the result.

domain error

You evaluated a function at an illegal argument value. For example, you see this error if you try to compute ln(0).

duplicate

You tried to define the same variable twice in the same definition. You see this error if you create a vector on the left side of a definition and use the same name twice in that vector.

equation too large

You entered an equation too complicated for Mathcad to evaluate. Break the equation down into two or more subequations.

error in constant

Mathcad has interpreted the indicated expression as an invalid constant. Mathcad tries to interpret anything beginning with a digit as a constant. If you enter a digit immediately followed by a few letters, Mathcad will interpret it as an invalid constant. For a complete list of valid forms for constants, see "Suffixes for numbers" in Appendix A.

error in list

The indicated function definition contains an invalid list of arguments. A valid function definition begins like this:

$$f(x, y, z \ldots) = \ldots$$

The argument list between parentheses must be a name or a list of names separated by commas. Any other expression is illegal.

You also see this error message if you create an invalid list in another context, for example, in the list of y-axis expressions for a plot.

error in solve block

You see this error if you evaluate a user function that is defined in terms of a solve block, and there is an error in the solve block. To fix the error, fix the problem in the solve block. (If you evaluate the solve block directly, instead of defining a function with it, you will see a more specific error message.)

file error

Mathcad encountered an error trying to read values from a data file using READ or READPRN. See Chapter 18, "Data Files," for a description of valid formats for data files.

file not found

Mathcad was unable to find the data file for READ, READPRN or for import into a graphics region. See Chapter 18, "Data Files," and Chapter 27, "Importing Graphics."

illegal array operation

You applied a function or an operation that requires a scalar to a vector or matrix. For example, you see this message if you try to take the sine or square root of a matrix. If you want to apply an operator or a function to each element in turn, use the vectorize operator as described in Chapter 9, "Vectors and Matrices."

illegal context

You used an operator or a function in a context that Mathcad does not allow. For example, you see this error message if:

- You entered a semicolon somewhere other than in a legal range definition. (The semicolon appears as two dots called an *ellipsis*.) You can use a semicolon only in the definition of a range for a range variable.

- You used a WRITE or APPEND function anywhere other than on the left side of a definition. These functions cannot appear in expressions or on the right side of a definition.

- You used an existing function name as a variable name or an existing variable name as a function name.

- You used a constraint with ≠ in a solve block.

illegal factor

You entered an illegal expression in the units placeholder at the end of an equation that returns a numerical result. The placeholder at the end of such an equation requires real, non-zero, scalar values.

illegal function name

You used an expression that Mathcad interprets as a function, but the function name is invalid. You see this error, for example, if you use a number as a function name: **6(x)**. You may see this error if you omit an operator like *****, causing Mathcad to interpret the parentheses in your equation as defining a function instead of as a way to group operations.

illegal ORIGIN

You defined ORIGIN with a non-integer value or a value of magnitude greater than 16,000,000. This error marks the first use of a subscript after the illegal definition of ORIGIN.

illegal range

You defined a range variable with a range Mathcad could not interpret. When you define a range, you must use one of the following forms:

```
Rvar := n1 .. n2
Rvar := n1, n2 .. n3
```

These are typed by pressing **Rvar:n1;n2** and **Rvar:n1,n2;n3** respectively.

You can use at most one comma and one semicolon in the definition of a range for a range variable. If you use the second form, the value of $n2$ must lie between the values of $n1$ and $n3$, but not equal $n1$.

illegal tolerance

This error marks an expression that uses TOL — an integral, or instance of *Root*, *Find*, or *Minerr* — for which TOL > 1 or TOL < 0. To fix the error, define TOL with a value between 0 and 1 above the indicated expression.

incompatible units

that adds, subtracts, or performs another operation that is illegal for two expressions having different dimensions. You see this error if you:

- try to add or subtract two expressions having different dimensions, for example $3 \cdot cm + 5 \cdot 6 \cdot hr$.

- create a vector, matrix, or table in which not all elements have the same dimensions.

- create a plot in which two expressions having different dimensions share the same axis.

indeterminate dimension

You raised an expression with units to a power involving a range variable or vector. Mathcad cannot determine the dimensions of the result; they would vary depending on the exponent. If an expression is defined with units, you can raise it only to a fixed real power.

index out of bounds

This message marks a subscript or superscript that refers to a non-existent array value. You see this message if you use a subscript or superscript less than 0 (or less than ORIGIN, if ORIGIN≠0), or if you use a subscript or superscript to refer to an array value beyond those defined earlier in the document.

input list too long

You entered too many elements in a list separated by commas. This can occur if you try to plot more expressions than Mathcad's capacity or if you try to create a table with more than fifty elements.

interrupted

You interrupted Mathcad by pressing [**Esc**] while it was calculating. To recalculate the marked equation, click in the equation and press [**F9**].

invalid order

You attempted to evaluate an nth order derivative at an inappropriate order. The order, n, must be an integer between 0 and 5 inclusive.

misplaced comma

You used a comma in an illegal place. You can use a comma in any of the following ways:

- to separate function arguments

- to separate the first two elements of a range in the definition of a range variable

- to separate arguments on the same axis in a plot.

- to separate elements in an input table

- to separate subscripts for a matrix variable

Any other use of commas in Mathcad expressions is illegal.

missing operand

An operand is missing from an expression. For example, you see this message if you enter a plus sign without entering two expressions to add and you then press =. Mathcad shows a placeholder (a small rectangle) in place of the missing operand.

missing operator

An operator is missing from an equation or expression.

must be 3-vector

You used a cross product on expressions that are not three-element vectors. The cross product works only on three-element vectors.

must be a multidimensional array

You must use a matrix having more than one row or more than one column.

must be array

You performed an operation on a scalar that should be performed only on an array. For example, you'd see this error if you tried to take the transpose of a number since transpose has no meaning in this context.

must be dimensionless

The indicated expression uses units but appears in a place where units are not permitted. Units are not permitted in the arguments for certain functions (for example, *cos* and *ln*) or in exponents. For example, the expressions $\cos(1L)$ and 2^{1M} are invalid.

must be increasing

You used a vector whose elements are not in increasing order as the argument to a function that requires a strictly increasing argument. The first argument of *lspline*, *pspline*, *cspline*, *interp*, *linterp*, and *hist* must be a vector whose elements are strictly increasing. (Note that Mathcad includes v_0 as a vector element. If you do not explicitly define it, Mathcad sets $v_0 = 0$ if ORIGIN is zero.)

must be integer

You used a non-integer expression where an integer is required, for example, as an argument to the *identity* function or as a subscript or superscript. (Although you can define range variables with fractional values — for example, $x := 1, 1.1 .. 10$ — you cannot use such ranges as subscripts.)

must be nonzero

You tried to evaluate a built-in function at zero even though the function is undefined at zero.

must be positive

This error message marks a plot in which the limits or values for a logarithmic axis are zero or negative. Mathcad can plot only positive values on a logarithmic axis.

must be range

You used something other than a range variable in a place that requires a range variable, for example, as the index for a summation. The index for a summation appears below the summation symbol. The index must be a variable that is defined earlier as a range variable.

must be real

You used an imaginary- or complex-valued expression where Mathcad requires a real-valued expression. For example, Mathcad requires real-valued subscripts and real-valued arguments for some built-in functions.

must be scalar

You used a vector or matrix expression where a scalar is required, for example, as the argument to the *identity* function.

must be square

This error marks a non-square matrix in an operation that requires a square matrix, such as determinants, inverse, or raising to a power.

must be vector

This error marks a matrix or scalar in an operation that requires a vector, for example, with the Σ operator.

nested solve block

You used the word *Given* twice in a row with no intervening *Find* or *Minerr*. Mathcad does not allow nested solve blocks, although you can define functions with solve blocks and use those function in other solve blocks. See Chapter 15, "Solving Equations."

no matching Given

This error marks a *Find* or *Minerr* function with no matching *Given*. Each solve block that ends with *Find* or *Minerr* must begin with a region containing only the name *Given*.

non-scalar value

You used a vector or ranged expression where a scalar is required. For example, you see this message if i is a range variable and you try to enter an equation like $x := i$. You cannot define one range variable in terms of another. To define x in terms of the range variable i, enter an equation like x_i. This error often arises in plots when you put a vector name **x** instead of $x_i := i$ on a placeholder.

not a name

You used a number or other combination of symbols where Mathcad requires a name, for example, as the second argument of the *root* function. Examples of things that aren't names are $f(x)$ (a function), 3 (a number), x^2 (an expression).

not converging

Mathcad was unable to compute an answer for an integral, derivative, *root*, *Find*, or *Minerr* function within the required tolerance. See the descriptions of these operators and functions for more information.

only one array allowed

You entered more than one array in the placeholder of a contour plot. Mathcad will only accept one array at a time because contour plots can only represent a single surface at a time.

overflow

You evaluated an expression that exceeds the largest number that Mathcad can represent (about 10^{307}). This can happen not only if the result itself is large but also if at any time in the course of getting the result, Mathcad has to calculate a large number.

range not allowed

You used a range variable inside a solve block. To solve a system of equations for several values of a parameter, see the section "Using the solver effectively" on page 349.

result has name too long

You tried to evaluate a symbolic expression that was so long that it couldn't be displayed.

significance lost

This error message indicates that you tried to evaluate a function for a value beyond the accurate range for the function. For example, you see this message if you try to evaluate $\sin(10^{100})$. Since the value of $\sin(10^{100})$ depends on the ones digit of 10^{100}, any value that Mathcad could return would have no significant digits. Instead of returning a value of dubious accuracy, Mathcad shows this error message.

singularity

You evaluated a function or performed an operation at an illegal value. For example, you see this error if you divide by zero or if you try to invert a singular (determinant = 0) matrix.

stack overflow

You evaluated an expression that overflows Mathcad's internal stack. This can happen when an expression is too complex or when you define a function in terms of itself.

subscript too large

You tried to use a subscript that exceeds Mathcad's limit.

---

symbolic operator only

You have tried to evaluate an expression numerically when it must be evaluated symbolically. Certain operators must be evaluated symbolically as described in Chapter 17, "Symbolic Calculation."

too few arguments

The indicated expression contains a function with fewer than the required number of arguments. For built-in functions, the number of arguments is fixed; see Chapter 12, "Built-in Functions." For user functions, the number of arguments depends on the definition in your document.

too few constraints

This error marks a *Find* or *Given* with fewer constraints than variables to be solved. Add dummy constraints or decrease the number of variables to be solved. See Chapter 15, "Solving Equations," for a more complete description.

too few elements

This error message marks a Fourier transform, cubic spline, or linear interpolation function applied to a vector with too few elements. Splines and linear interpolation require vectors with at least two elements. Fourier transform functions and their inverses require at least four elements.

too few subscripts

You used one subscript on a matrix. You must use two subscripts separated by a comma to specify a matrix element.

too large to display

You tried to display a vector or matrix bigger than Mathcad can display.

too many arguments

The indicated expression contains a function with more than the required number of arguments. For built-in functions, the number of arguments is fixed; see Chapter 12, "Built-in Functions." For user functions, the number of arguments depends on the definition in your document.

too many constraints

You included more than fifty constraints in a solve block.

too many files

You have opened too many files using *WRITEPRN*, *READPRN* and similar file access functions discussed in Chapter 18. No more than thirty separate files can be opened at one time. Choose **Associate Filename** from the **File** menu, type the name of one of your file variables (you'll find these between the parentheses on any file access function like *READPRN* or *WRITEPRN*), and click "Dissociate."

too many points

You tried to plot more points than Mathcad can handle in one plot.

too many subscripts

You used two or more subscripts on a vector, or three or more subscripts in a matrix.

undefined

The variable or function highlighted in reverse video is undefined. To define it, enter the variable name, followed by a colon (:) and an expression or number for its definition. This error often means you have typed an equals sign (=) instead of a colon to define a variable. To define a variable, you must use a colon. If you use an equals sign, Mathcad assumes you want to *calculate* the value of the variable.

You also see this message if you use a variable incorrectly in a global definition. If you use a variable on the right side of a global definition, the variable must be globally defined *above* the definition in which it is used. If you use a locally defined variable or a variable whose global definition is *below* the place where it is used, Mathcad marks the variable as undefined.

An *undefined* error is often an indication that another equation further up in the document is in error. If a definition is in error, then any other equations further down in the document that depend on that definition will be displayed in reverse video.

unmatched parenthesis

You entered or calculated an equation that contains a left parenthesis without the matching right parenthesis. Edit the equation by removing the left parenthesis or adding a matching right parenthesis.

wrong size vector

This error marks a Fourier transform function whose argument has the wrong number of elements. *fft* requires vectors with 2^n elements, where n is a whole number greater than 1. *ifft* requires an argument vector with $1 + 2^n$ elements, where n is a whole number greater than 0. Mathcad includes v_0 as an element of the argument vector unless you change ORIGIN.

Appendix C
Unit Tables

Mathcad comes with three built-in systems of units. You select a system of units by choosing **Units** from the **Math** menu as discussed in Chapter 8.

Once you make a selection, several dozen variable names are automatically reserved for unit definitions unique to whatever system of units you chose. This appendix lists all the unit definitions associated with each of the three available unit systems.

If you choose a system of units, you should try not to use the predefined variables listed in this appendix as anything but units.

MKS units

Base units

$$m = 1L \qquad kg = 1M \qquad sec = 1T$$

$$coul = 1Q \qquad K = 1K$$

Angular measure

$$rad = 1$$

$$deg = \frac{\pi}{180} \cdot rad$$

Length

$$cm = .01 \cdot m \qquad km = 1000 \cdot m \qquad mm = .001 \cdot m$$

$$ft = .3048 \cdot m \qquad in = 2.54 \cdot cm \qquad yd = 3 \cdot ft$$

$$mi = 5280 \cdot ft$$

Mass

$$gm = 10^{-3} \cdot kg \qquad tonne = 1000 \cdot kg \qquad lb = 453.59237 \cdot gm$$

$$mg = 10^{-3} \cdot gm \qquad ton = 2000 \cdot lb \qquad slug = 32.174 \cdot lb$$

$$oz = \frac{lb}{16}$$

Time

$$min = 60 \cdot sec \qquad hr = 3600 \cdot sec \qquad day = 24 \cdot hr$$

$$yr = 365.2422 \cdot day$$

Area, Volume

$$hectare = 10^4 \cdot m^2 \qquad acre = 4840 \cdot yd^2 \qquad liter = (.1 \cdot m)^3$$

$$mL = 10^{-3} \cdot liter \qquad fl\_oz = 29.57353 \cdot cm^3 \qquad gal = 128 \cdot fl\_oz$$

Velocity, Acceleration

$$mph = \frac{mi}{hr} \qquad kph = \frac{km}{hr} \qquad g = 9.80665 \cdot \frac{m}{sec^2}$$

Force, Energy, Power

$$newton = kg \cdot \frac{m}{sec^2} \qquad dyne = 10^{-5} \cdot newton \qquad lbf = g \cdot lb$$

$$kgf = g \cdot kg \qquad joule = newton \cdot m \qquad erg = 10^{-7} \cdot joule$$

$$cal = 4.1868 \cdot joule$$

$$\text{kcal} = 1000 \cdot \text{cal}$$

$$\text{BTU} = 1.05506 \cdot 10^3 \cdot \text{joule}$$

$$\text{watt} = \frac{\text{joule}}{\text{sec}}$$

$$\text{hp} = 550 \cdot \frac{\text{ft} \cdot \text{lbf}}{\text{sec}}$$

$$\text{kW} = 1000 \cdot \text{watt}$$

Pressure, Viscosity

$$\text{Pa} = \frac{\text{newton}}{\text{m}^2}$$

$$\text{psi} = \frac{\text{lbf}}{\text{in}^2}$$

$$\text{atm} = 1.01325 \cdot 10^5 \cdot \text{Pa}$$

$$\text{torr} = 1.33322 \cdot 10^2 \cdot \text{Pa}$$

$$\text{in\_Hg} = 3.38638 \cdot 10^3 \cdot \text{Pa}$$

$$\text{stokes} = 10^{-4} \cdot \frac{\text{m}^2}{\text{sec}}$$

$$\text{poise} = .1 \cdot \text{Pa} \cdot \text{sec}$$

Electrical

$$\text{volt} = \frac{\text{watt}}{\text{amp}}$$

$$\text{mV} = 10^{-3} \cdot \text{volt}$$

$$\text{KV} = 10^3 \cdot \text{volt}$$

$$\text{ohm} = \frac{\text{volt}}{\text{amp}}$$

$$\text{mho} = \frac{1}{\text{ohm}}$$

$$\text{siemens} = \frac{1}{\text{ohm}}$$

$$\Omega = \text{ohm}$$

$$\text{K}\Omega = 10^3 \cdot \text{ohm}$$

$$\text{M}\Omega = 10^6 \cdot \text{ohm}$$

$$\text{henry} = \frac{\text{weber}}{\text{amp}}$$

$$\text{mH} = 10^{-3} \cdot \text{henry}$$

$$\mu\text{H} = 10^{-6} \cdot \text{henry}$$

$$\text{amp} = \frac{\text{coul}}{\text{sec}}$$

$$\mu\text{A} = 10^{-6} \cdot \text{amp}$$

$$\text{mA} = 10^{-3} \cdot \text{amp}$$

$$\text{KA} = 10^3 \cdot \text{amp}$$

$$\text{farad} = \frac{\text{coul}}{\text{volt}}$$

$$\text{pF} = 10^{-12} \cdot \text{farad}$$

$$\text{nF} = 10^{-9} \cdot \text{farad}$$

$$\mu\text{F} = 10^{-6} \cdot \text{farad}$$

$$\text{weber} = \text{volt} \cdot \text{sec}$$

$$\text{oersted} = \frac{1000}{4 \cdot \pi} \cdot \frac{\text{amp}}{\text{m}}$$

$$\text{tesla} = \frac{\text{weber}}{\text{m}^2}$$

Frequency

$$\text{Hz} = \frac{1}{\text{sec}}$$

$$\text{KHz} = 10^3 \cdot \text{Hz}$$

$$\text{MHz} = 10^6 \cdot \text{Hz}$$

$$\text{GHz} = 10^9 \cdot \text{Hz}$$

Temperature

$$\text{R} = 0.556 \cdot \text{K}$$

CGS units

Base units

$$\text{cm} = 1\text{L} \qquad\qquad \text{gm} = 1\text{M} \qquad\qquad \text{sec} = 1\text{T}$$

$$\text{coul} = 1\text{Q} \qquad\qquad \text{K} = 1\text{K}$$

Angular measure

$$\text{rad} = 1 \qquad\qquad \deg = \frac{\pi}{180} \cdot \text{rad}$$

Length

$$\text{m} = 100 \cdot \text{cm} \qquad\qquad \text{km} = 1000 \cdot \text{m} \qquad\qquad \text{mm} = .1 \cdot \text{cm}$$

$$\text{ft} = 30.48 \cdot \text{cm} \qquad\qquad \text{in} = 2.54 \cdot \text{cm} \qquad\qquad \text{yd} = 3 \cdot \text{ft}$$

$$\text{mi} = 5280 \cdot \text{ft}$$

Mass

$$\text{kg} = 1000 \cdot \text{gm} \qquad\qquad \text{tonne} = 1000 \cdot \text{kg} \qquad\qquad \text{lb} = 453.59237 \cdot \text{gm}$$

$$\text{mg} = 10^{-3} \cdot \text{gm} \qquad\qquad \text{ton} = 2000 \cdot \text{lb} \qquad\qquad \text{slug} = 32.174 \cdot \text{lb}$$

$$\text{oz} = \frac{\text{lb}}{16}$$

Time

$$\text{min} = 60 \cdot \text{sec} \qquad\qquad \text{hr} = 3600 \cdot \text{sec} \qquad\qquad \text{day} = 24 \cdot \text{hr}$$

$$\text{yr} = 365.2422 \cdot \text{day}$$

Area, Volume

$$\text{hectare} = 10^4 \cdot \text{m}^2 \qquad\qquad \text{acre} = 4840 \cdot \text{yd}^2 \qquad\qquad \text{liter} = 1000 \cdot \text{cm}^3$$

$$\text{mL} = \text{cm}^3 \qquad\qquad \text{fl\_oz} = 29.57353 \cdot \text{cm}^3 \qquad\qquad \text{gal} = 128 \cdot \text{fl\_oz}$$

Velocity, Acceleration

$$\text{mph} = \frac{\text{mi}}{\text{hr}} \qquad\qquad \text{kph} = \frac{\text{km}}{\text{hr}} \qquad\qquad \text{g} = 980.665 \cdot \frac{\text{cm}}{\text{sec}^2}$$

$$\text{c} = 2.997925 \cdot 10^{10} \cdot \frac{\text{cm}}{\text{sec}} \qquad\qquad \text{c\_} = \text{c} \cdot \frac{\text{sec}}{\text{m}}$$

Force, Energy, Power

$$\text{dyne} = \text{gm} \cdot \frac{\text{cm}}{\text{sec}^2} \qquad\qquad \text{newton} = 10^5 \cdot \text{dyne} \qquad\qquad \text{lbf} = \text{g} \cdot \text{lb}$$

$$kgf = g \cdot kg$$

$$erg = dyne \cdot cm$$

$$joule = 10^7 \cdot erg$$

$$cal = 4.1868 \cdot 10^7 \cdot erg$$

$$BTU = 1.05506 \cdot 10^{10} \cdot erg$$

$$kcal = 1000 \cdot cal$$

$$watt = \frac{joule}{sec}$$

$$kW = 1000 \cdot watt$$

$$hp = 550 \cdot \frac{ft \cdot lbf}{sec}$$

Pressure, Viscosity

$$Pa = 10 \cdot \frac{dyne}{cm^2}$$

$$psi = \frac{lbf}{in^2}$$

$$atm = 1.01325 \cdot 10^5 \cdot Pa$$

$$in\_Hg = 3.38638 \cdot 10^3 \cdot Pa$$

$$torr = 1.33322 \cdot 10^2 \cdot Pa$$

$$stokes = \frac{cm^2}{sec}$$

$$poise = .1 \cdot Pa \cdot sec$$

Electrical

These are CGS-esu units, based only on mass, length, and time. The "stat" units are defined in terms of dyne, cm, and sec.

$$statamp = dyne^{.5} \cdot cm \cdot sec^{-1}$$

$$statcoul = dyne^{.5} \cdot cm$$

$$statvolt = dyne^{.5}$$

$$statohm = sec \cdot cm^{-1}$$

$$statsiemens = cm \cdot sec^{-1}$$

$$statfarad = cm$$

$$statweber = dyne^{.5} \cdot cm$$

$$stathenry = sec^2 \cdot cm^{-1}$$

$$stattesla = dyne^{.5} \cdot sec \cdot cm^{-2}$$

Frequency

$$Hz = \frac{1}{sec}$$

$$KHz = 10^3 \cdot Hz$$

$$MHz = 10^6 \cdot Hz$$

$$GHz = 10^9 \cdot Hz$$

Temperature

$$R = 0.556 \cdot K$$

Conversions to SI Units

$$amp = \frac{c\_}{10} \cdot statamp$$

$$volt = \frac{watt}{amp}$$

$$ohm = \frac{volt}{amp}$$

$$coul = amp \cdot sec$$

$$farad = \frac{coul}{volt}$$

$$henry = volt \cdot \frac{sec}{amp}$$

U.S. customary units

Base units

$$ft = 1L \qquad lb = 1M \qquad sec = 1T$$

$$coul = 1Q \qquad K = 1K$$

Angular measure

$$rad = 1 \qquad deg = \frac{\pi}{180} \cdot rad$$

Length

$$in = \frac{ft}{12} \qquad m = \frac{ft}{.3048} \qquad yd = 3 \cdot ft$$

$$cm = .01 \cdot m \qquad mi = 5280 \cdot ft \qquad km = 1000 \cdot m$$

$$mm = .001 \cdot m$$

Mass

$$slug = 32.174 \cdot lb \qquad oz = \frac{lb}{16} \qquad ton = 2000 \cdot lb$$

$$kg = \frac{lb}{.45359237} \qquad tonne = 1000 \cdot kg \qquad gm = 10^{-3} \cdot kg$$

$$mg = 10^{-3} \cdot gm$$

Time

$$min = 60 \cdot sec \qquad hr = 3600 \cdot sec \qquad day = 24 \cdot hr$$

$$yr = 365.2422 \cdot day$$

Area, Volume

$$acre = 4840 \cdot yd^2 \qquad hectare = 10^4 \cdot m^2 \qquad fl\_oz = 29.57353 \cdot cm^3$$

$$liter = (.1 \cdot m)^3 \qquad mL = 10^{-3} \cdot liter \qquad gal = 128 \cdot fl\_oz$$

Velocity, Acceleration

$$mph = \frac{mi}{hr} \qquad kph = \frac{km}{hr} \qquad g = 32.174 \cdot \frac{ft}{sec^2}$$

Force, Energy, Power

$$lbf = g \cdot lb \qquad newton = kg \cdot \frac{m}{sec^2} \qquad dyne = 10^{-5} \cdot newton$$

$$kgf = g \cdot kg \qquad joule = newton \cdot m \qquad erg = 10^{-7} \cdot joule$$

$$\text{cal} = 4.1868 \cdot \text{joule}$$

$$\text{watt} = \frac{\text{joule}}{\text{sec}}$$

$$\text{kcal} = 1000 \cdot \text{cal}$$

$$\text{hp} = 550 \cdot \frac{\text{ft} \cdot \text{lbf}}{\text{sec}}$$

$$\text{BTU} = 1.05506 \cdot 10^3 \cdot \text{joule}$$

$$\text{kW} = 1000 \cdot \text{watt}$$

Pressure, Viscosity

$$\text{psi} = \frac{\text{lbf}}{\text{in}^2}$$

$$\text{torr} = 1.33322 \cdot 10^2 \cdot \text{Pa}$$

$$\text{poise} = .1 \cdot \text{Pa} \cdot \text{sec}$$

$$\text{Pa} = \frac{\text{newton}}{\text{m}^2}$$

$$\text{in\_Hg} = 3.38638 \cdot 10^3 \cdot \text{Pa}$$

$$\text{atm} = 1.01325 \cdot 10^5 \cdot \text{Pa}$$

$$\text{stokes} = \frac{\text{cm}^2}{\text{sec}}$$

Electrical

$$\text{volt} = \frac{\text{watt}}{\text{amp}}$$

$$\text{ohm} = \frac{\text{volt}}{\text{amp}}$$

$$\Omega = \text{ohm}$$

$$\text{henry} = \frac{\text{weber}}{\text{amp}}$$

$$\text{amp} = \frac{\text{coul}}{\text{sec}}$$

$$\text{KA} = 10^3 \cdot \text{amp}$$

$$\text{nF} = 10^{-9} \cdot \text{farad}$$

$$\text{oersted} = \frac{1000}{4 \cdot \pi} \cdot \frac{\text{amp}}{\text{m}}$$

$$\text{mV} = 10^{-3} \cdot \text{volt}$$

$$\text{mho} = \frac{1}{\text{ohm}}$$

$$\text{K}\Omega = 10^3 \cdot \text{ohm}$$

$$\text{mH} = 10^{-3} \cdot \text{henry}$$

$$\mu\text{A} = 10^{-6} \cdot \text{amp}$$

$$\text{farad} = \frac{\text{coul}}{\text{volt}}$$

$$\mu\text{F} = 10^{-6} \cdot \text{farad}$$

$$\text{tesla} = \frac{\text{weber}}{\text{m}^2}$$

$$\text{KV} = 10^3 \cdot \text{volt}$$

$$\text{siemens} = \frac{1}{\text{ohm}}$$

$$\text{M}\Omega = 10^6 \cdot \text{ohm}$$

$$\mu\text{H} = 10^{-6} \cdot \text{henry}$$

$$\text{mA} = 10^{-3} \cdot \text{amp}$$

$$\text{pF} = 10^{-12} \cdot \text{farad}$$

$$\text{weber} = \text{volt} \cdot \text{sec}$$

$$\text{gauss} = 10^{-4} \cdot \text{tesla}$$

Frequency

$$\text{Hz} = \frac{1}{\text{sec}}$$

$$\text{GHz} = 10^9 \cdot \text{Hz}$$

$$\text{KHz} = 10^3 \cdot \text{Hz}$$

$$\text{MHz} = 10^6 \cdot \text{Hz}$$

Temperature

$$\text{R} = 0.556 \cdot \text{K}$$

Alphabetical list of units

Unless otherwise specified, all units are available in MKS, CGS, and US systems.

Unit	Measures...	Available in...
acre	area	
amp	current	
atm	pressure	
BTU	energy	
c	velocity	CGS
c_	dimensionless	CGS
cal	energy	
cm	length	
coul	charge	
day	time	
deg	angle	
dyne	force	
erg	energy	
farad	capacitance	
fl_oz	volume	
ft	length	
g	acceleration	
gal	volume	
gauss	magnetic flux density	MKS, US
GHz	frequency	
gm	mass	
hectare	area	
henry	inductance	
hp	power	
hr	time	
Hz	frequency	
in	length	
in_Hg	pressure	
joule	energy	
KA	current	
kcal	energy	
K	temperature	
kg	mass	
kgf	force	

Unit	Measures...	Available in...
KHz	frequency	
km	length	
kph	velocity	
KV	potential	
kW	power	
lb	mass	
lbf	force	
liter	volume	
μA	current	
μF	capacitance	
μH	inductance	
m	length	
MΩ	resistance	
mA	current	
mH	inductance	
mho	conductance	
MHz	frequency	
mi	length	
min	time	
mg	mass	
mL	volume	
mm	length	
mph	velocity	
mV	potential	
newton	force	
nF	capacitance	
oersted	magnetic field strength	MKS, US
ohm	resistance	
oz	mass	
Pa	pressure	
pF	capacitance	
poise	viscosity (dynamic)	
psi	pressure	
R	temperature	
rad	angle	
sec	time	
siemens	conductance	MKS, US
slug	mass	

Unit	Measures...	Available in...
statamp	current	CGS
statcoul	charge	CGS
statfarad	capacitance	CGS
stathenry	inductance	CGS
statohm	resistance	CGS
statsiemens	conductance	CGS
stattesla	magnetic flux density	CGS
statvolt	potential	CGS
statweber	magnetic flux	CGS
stokes	viscosity (kinematic)	
tesla	magnetic flux density	MKS, US
ton	mass	
tonne	mass	
torr	pressure	
volt	potential	
Ω	resistance	
watt	power	
weber	magnetic flux	MKS, US
yd	length	
yr	time	

Appendix D
Numerical Methods

This appendix describes the details of Mathcad's numerical algorithms.

The following sections make up this appendix:

A note about numerical methods

The importance of understanding numerical methods.

Zero as a factor or a numerator

Efficiency issues with zero as a factor or a numerator.

Integrals

Mathcad's Romberg integration algorithm.

Derivatives

How Mathcad computes numerical derivatives.

The root function

Finding roots with the secant method.

Solve blocks

Using the Levenberg-Marquardt algorithm to solve simultaneous equations and inequalities.

Matrix operations

Methods used for matrix inversion and determinants.

Sorting

Mathcad's sorting algorithms.

A note on numerical methods

This appendix describes the numerical methods Mathcad uses for some types of calculations, including derivatives, integrals, the *root* function, solve blocks, and matrix operations.

On a computer, these calculations are inherently limited in accuracy. Since Mathcad is a general-purpose calculation program, it uses methods that work in a wide variety of different contexts. However, as with any numerical algorithms, it is always possible to find specific examples for which Mathcad's methods return inaccurate or misleading results.

You can verify the accuracy of your results and avoid numerical problems by following these principles:

■ When you use a Mathcad function or operation that involves a numerical approximation (integrals, derivatives, the *root* function, solve blocks, matrix inversion, or determinants), be sure your results are reasonable. For simple calculations, just use common sense. For more complicated calculations, include redundancy checks in your documents to estimate whether results are approximately correct.

■ Read the section in the *User's Guide* on the operator or function in question. The sections that describe how to use these features also mention the types of problems that are likely to yield anomalous answers or no answer at all. In cases where you suspect Mathcad's methods may fail, restate the problem in a more stable form or use Mathcad's other features (summation, iteration, and so on) to approximate the answer.

■ Set the built-in variable TOL to achieve the desired accuracy and speed for numerically computed answers. TOL can take on only values between 0 and 1. Set TOL to a number closer to zero to attain a higher degree of accuracy. Set TOL to a number closer to 1 to calculate more quickly, but less accurately. See the descriptions that follow for information on how Mathcad uses TOL in its estimates.

■ Become familiar with the numerical methods described here and their limitations. You can use these descriptions to get a better understanding of the conditions under which numerical methods will fail or return inaccurate answers.

Zero factor or numerator

For efficiency reasons, Mathcad always assumes that for any expression x:

$$0 \cdot x = 0$$

and

$$0 / x = 0$$

Presented with a calculation of this type, Mathcad will not even evaluate x. This has the following consequences:

- Mathcad will instantly compute a result of zero for these expressions, even if x requires a time-consuming calculation like an integral or a summation.

- If computing x would result in an error, Mathcad will return zero without detecting the error. In some cases this is desirable; in others, it isn't.

- Mathcad evaluates 0/0 as zero, not as an error.

Integrals

Mathcad computes definite integrals numerically using a Romberg algorithm. The Romberg method accelerates the convergence of a sequence of simple trapezoidal or midpoint approximations to the integral by extrapolating the sequence of estimates and the corresponding subinterval widths.

This section describes how Mathcad computes the integral of $f(x)$ from a to b. In this description, $estimate_0$, $estimate_1$, and so on represent Mathcad's internal approximations to the answer. Only the last estimate, the one that passes Mathcad's tolerance test, is available to the user.

To compute the integral of $f(x)$ from a to b, Mathcad follows these steps:

- Calculate an estimate for the integral using the trapezoidal rule. The first trapezoidal estimate is:

$$estimate_0 = \frac{f(a) + f(b)}{2} (b - a)$$

The second trapezoidal estimate doubles the number of subintervals, using two subintervals each of width $b - a/2$. To begin the algorithm, compute the first three estimates, subdividing the interval into one, two, and four subintervals, respectively.

- Fit a polynomial to the sequence of trapezoidal estimates computed so far and the corresponding subinterval widths. Extrapolate this polynomial to width zero to produce a Romberg estimate for the integral.

- Compare the two most recent Romberg estimates according to the following test (where *reltol* is the larger of TOL and TOL·$\left| estimate_n \right|$:

$$\left| estimate_n - estimate_{n-1} \right| < reltol$$

- If the two most recent estimates agree according to this test, check also whether $estimate_{n-1}$ and $estimate_{n-2}$ also agreed. If they did, then return the most recent Romberg estimate as the value of the integral. If not, double the number of subintervals and return to the first step.

Mathcad sets a limit on the number of times it will iterate this procedure. If the routine reaches this limit without converging, or if the integrand is singular at one or both of the endpoints of the interval of integration, then Mathcad switches to an *open-ended* Romberg method.

In the open-ended method, the preliminary estimates are obtained by using the *midpoints* of subintervals, avoiding the necessity to evaluate the function at the endpoints *a* and *b*. (See *Handheld Calculator Evaluates Integrals*, by William Kahan, Ph.D., in *Hewlett-Packard Journal*, August 1980, for a full description.) The sample points are concentrated near the ends of the interval of integration, where integrands that are singular or that have an infinite derivative are likely to to be changing most rapidly. The number of subintervals is tripled at each step.

For its open-ended Romberg method, Mathcad follows these steps:

- Calculate an open-ended estimate for the integral by summing terms computed by multiplying the function value at the midpoint of a subinterval by the width of that subinterval. Begin with one interval: the estimate is:

$$estimate_0 = f\left(\frac{a+b}{2}\right)(b-a)$$

  The next estimate uses three points, the next nine points, and so on. Begin by making the first three estimates.

- At each step, extrapolate the sequence of midpoint estimates to produce a Romberg estimate.

- Compare the two most recent estimates according to the following test (where *reltol* is the larger of TOL and TOL·$\left| estimate_n \right|$:

$$\left| estimate_n - estimate_{n-1} \right| < reltol$$

- If the two most recent estimates agree according to this test, return the most recent open-ended estimate as the value of the integral. If not, triple the number of subintervals and return to the first step.

Again Mathcad sets a limit to the number of steps. If it reaches this limit without returning an answer, the integral is marked with the error "*not converging*."

Mathcad can evaluate many integrals for which the integrand is singular at one or both of the endpoints of the interval of integration. Evaluation of these integrals will often be slower than for integrands that are well-behaved. For small values of TOL, the integration may not converge even though the integral has a finite value.

Mathcad generally will not be able to integrate functions that have singularities in the *interior* of the interval of integration. Functions such as step and sawtooth functions that have a large numbers of finite discontinuities may also lead to nonconverging integrals. If you know where the singularities or discontinuities in the integrand are, you can often obtain a correct numerical evaluation by splitting the integral into a sum of integrals with these points as limits. A plot of the integrand may help to indicate the trouble spots.

Derivatives

Mathcad's derivative operator uses a variation of Ridder's method to compute derivatives of orders between 0 and 5 inclusive. Although Mathcad's derivative operator won't compute derivatives of order greater than 5, you can nest derivative operators within each other to compute higher order derivatives.

The modified Ridder's method begins with the determination of an initial stepsize h and the construction of a triangular array of estimates. This proceeds as follows:

- Mathcad computes the first estimate in the table using an $n + 1$-point divided difference approximation.

$$e_{0,0} = \left(\frac{n}{2 \cdot h}\right)^n \sum_{k=0}^{n} (-1)^{n-k} \binom{n}{k} f\left(x - h + k \cdot \frac{2 \cdot h}{n}\right)$$

- The remaining estimates in the first row of the table are computed using the divided difference formula but with a decreasing step-size:

$$e_{0,i} = \left(\frac{n}{2 \cdot \frac{h}{(1.4^i)}}\right)^n \sum_{k=0}^{n} (-1)^{n-k} \binom{n}{k} f\left(x - \frac{h}{(1.4^i)} + k \cdot \frac{2 \cdot \frac{h}{(1.4^i)}}{n}\right)$$

- The remaining elements in this table of estimates are computed using weighted averages of earlier elements:

$$e_{i,j} = \frac{1.4^{2i}}{1.4^{2i} - 1} \cdot e_{i-1,j} + \frac{-1}{1.4^{2i} - 1} \cdot e_{i-1,j-1}$$

- The error for a particular estimate of the derivative's value is given by:

$$err_{i,j} = \max\left(\left|e_{i,j} - e_{i-1,j}\right|, \left|e_{i,j} - e_{i-1,j-1}\right|\right)$$

- Let *errmin* be the smallest of the $err_{i,j}$ and let *der* be the estimate of the derivative's value corresponding to *errmin*. Then if:

$$errmin < \max(E, E \cdot der),$$

where E is a small number depending on the order. Mathcad returns *der* as the value of the derivative. Otherwise, Mathcad marks the derivative with the message *"not converging."*

Note that any numerical differentiation algorithm can lead to computational problems associated with round-off and truncation. This is particularly true of function values lying near a discontinuity or singularity in the function. With Ridder's algorithm, you can expect the first derivative to be accurate to within 7 or 8 significant digits, provided that the value at which you evaluate the derivative is not too close to a singularity of the function. The accuracy of this algorithm tends to decrease by one significant digit for each increase in the order of the derivative.

The root function

Mathcad's *root* function solves for zeros using the secant method.

This section describes how Mathcad computes root($f(x)$, x). In this description, $estimate_0$, $estimate_1$, and so on represent Mathcad's internal approximations to the answer. Only the last estimate, the one that passes Mathcad's tolerance test, is available to the user.

To compute a root of $f(x)$ using the initial guess x, Mathcad follows these steps:

- If $\left|f(x)\right| <$ TOL, then x is already a root, so return x as the value of the *root* function.

- Set $n = 1$. If $x \neq 0$, set $h =$ TOL $\cdot x$, otherwise, set $h =$ TOL. Make the following initial definitions:

$$estimate_0 = x$$

$$estimate_1 = x + h$$

- Increase n by one. Then compute the straight line connecting the points $(estimate_{n-2}, f(estimate_{n-2}))$ and $(estimate_{n-1}, f(estimate_{n-1}))$. Set x_n to the point where this straight line crosses the zero axis.

- If $\left|f(estimate_n)\right| <$TOL, return $estimate_n$ as the value of the *root* function. Otherwise, go back to step 3.

There is a limit on the number of calculations that Mathcad will perform in search of an answer for the *root* function. If it exceeds this limit without returning an answer, the *root* function is marked with the error "*not converging.*"

Solve blocks

Mathcad's solve areas use the iterative Levenberg-Marquardt method to solve for several constraints simultaneously. Mathcad's method is taken from the public-domain MINPACK algorithms developed and published by the Argonne National Laboratory in Argonne, Illinois. For more information, see the *User's Guide to Minpack I,* by Jorge J. More, Burton S. Garbow, and Kenneth E. Hillstrom, Argonne National Laboratory publication ANL-80-74, 1980.

The error vector

The MINPACK algorithm attempts to find the zeros of, or at worst minimize the sum of squares of, the value of a vector of functions relative to the values of certain variables. The vector of functions Mathcad uses is an *error vector* whose elements represent the errors in the constraints. The errors are defined as follows:

- For equality constraints (constraints using "="):

$$error = left\_side - right\_side$$

- For inequality constraints defined with <, >, ≤, or ≥:

$$error = 0$$

if inequality is true, otherwise

$$error = left\_side - right\_side$$

Mathcad treats the Levenberg-Marquardt algorithm as an algorithm on real variables. When you solve for a complex variable, Mathcad treats the real and imaginary parts as separate variables in the algorithm. When you solve an equality constraint, Mathcad creates two real constraints for the algorithm, one for the real part and one for the imaginary part.

Steps in the Levenberg-Marquardt method

The Levenberg-Marquardt method is a quasi-Newton method (a variation on the gradient method). At each step, Mathcad estimates the first partial derivatives of the errors with respect to the variables to be solved to create a *Jacobian matrix.* Ordinarily, Mathcad can determine the next estimate to make by computing the Gauss-Newton step *s* for each variable. In matrix notation, Mathcad solves the matrix equation:

$$\mathbf{J} \cdot \mathbf{s} = -\mathbf{f}(\mathbf{x})$$

In this equation, $\mathbf{J}$ is the Jacobian matrix, $\mathbf{s}$ is the step to take, and $\mathbf{x}$ is the vector of current estimates for unknown variables. For the first step, $\mathbf{x}$ is the vector of guesses; at each subsequent step, the new $\mathbf{x}$ is the old $\mathbf{x}$ plus $\mathbf{s}$, the vector of steps. Notice that computing this step involves inverting the Jacobian matrix $\mathbf{J}$.

Computing this step is not always possible. Computing the step fails when the Jacobian matrix cannot be inverted or when there are more constraints than variables to be solved. In these cases, Mathcad adds the additional condition that the following quantity be reduced to a minimum:

$$\sum_j D_j{}^2 \cdot s_j{}^2$$

Here $\mathbf{D}$ is a vector of weight factors computed from the norms of the columns of the Jacobian matrix. In these cases, s is computed to satisfy this minimization criteria as well as solving the Newton equation with the Jacobian.

The Levenberg-Marquardt method does not work when there are fewer constraints than variables. In these cases, Mathcad returns the error "*too few constraints.*"

Termination criteria

The Levenberg-Marquardt method ends when it reaches one of the following termination criteria:

- When it is no longer possible to reduce the norm of the error vector significantly. In this context, "significantly" means by more than the larger of TOL and TOL · |*error_vector*|. This criterion stops the solver when the errors cannot be reduced further.

- When s becomes relatively close to zero. In this method, "relatively close" means a norm smaller than the larger of TOL and TOL · |$\mathbf{v}$|. This criterion stops the solver when there is no preferred direction to move the guesses.

When it reaches one of these termination conditions, Mathcad checks the magnitude of the error vector and returns an answer:

- If the magnitude of the error vector is less than or equal to TOL, Mathcad returns the variable values as a solution.

- If the solve block ends in *Find* and the magnitude of the error vector is greater than TOL, Mathcad marks the *Find* with the error "*did not find solution.*" If the solve block ends in *Minerr*, Mathcad returns the solution anyway, even though the error vector is not close to zero.

There is a limit on the number of calculations that Mathcad will perform in search of an answer for a solve block. If it exceeds this limit without returning an answer, the *Find* or *Minerr* is marked with the error "*not converging.*"

In all cases, when the solver stops, Mathcad sets the value of the variable ERR to the magnitude of the error vector.

Mathcad's modifications to the Levenberg-Marquardt method

To make the Levenberg-Marquardt method more effective on actual problems, Mathcad includes the following modifications to the basic method:

- The first time the solver stops at a point that is not a solution, Mathcad adds a small random amount to all the variables and tries again. This helps avoid getting stuck in local minima and other points from which there is no preferred direction. Mathcad does this only once per solve, the first time the solver stops on a point that is not a solution.

- If you include inequality constraints in a solve block, Mathcad solves the subsystem consisting of only the inequalities first before adding in the equality constraints and attempting a full solution. This is equivalent to moving the guesses into an area where the inequalities are all satisfied before starting the solver.

Matrix operations

This section describes Mathcad's algorithms for computing determinants and inverses for square matrices.

To compute the determinant or inverse of a square matrix $\mathbf{M}$, Mathcad decomposes it into a lower-triangular matrix $\mathbf{L}$ and an upper-triangular matrix $\mathbf{U}$, such that:

$$\mathbf{M} = \mathbf{L} \cdot \mathbf{U}$$

This is called the *LU decomposition* of the matrix.

The LU decomposition makes the solution of a system of equations $\mathbf{M} \cdot \mathbf{x} = \mathbf{y}$ into a matter of simple substitutions with the elements of $\mathbf{L}$, $\mathbf{U}$, and $\mathbf{y}$.

Performing the decomposition

Mathcad performs the LU decomposition using Crout's method with partial pivoting. This method is not described here. See *Numerical Recipes in C* by William H. Press, Brian P. Flannery, Saul A. Teukolosky and William T. Vetterling (Cambridge University Press, 1986), pp. 31 to 39, for a complete description.

Computing the inverse and the determinant

To compute the inverse, Mathcad solves the equations $\mathbf{M} \cdot \mathbf{v}_j = \mathbf{e}_j$, where $\mathbf{e}$ is a vector with a one in element j and a zero in all other elements. The solution vectors $\mathbf{v}$ for each j form the columns of the inverse matrix.

The determinant of the original matrix is simply the product of the diagonal elements of $\mathbf{U}$, the upper-triangular matrix in the LU decomposition.

Sorting

Mathcad's *sort* function sorts a vector into ascending order on the real parts of the elements. If the array is purely imaginary, *sort* sorts on the imaginary parts.

The functions *csort* and *rsort* sort a matrix on a given column or row. The *csort* function puts the elements of the given column in order by rearranging the rows of the matrix. Thus, rows stay together in the column sort. The *rsort* function similarly puts the elements of the given row in order by rearranging the columns of the matrix.

Mathcad's sorting routine uses a heapsort algorithm. See *Numerical Recipes in C*, by William H. Press, Brian P. Flannery, Saul A. Teukolsky, and William T. Vetterling (Cambridge University Press, 1988) for a description of heapsort algorithms.

The heapsort procedure is not a stable sort. This means that if you sort a matrix on a column that contains *equal* elements, the rows containing these elements will be adjacent in the sorted array, but will appear in an arbitrary order.

Appendix D Numerical Methods

Appendix E
Dynamic Data Exchange

This appendix provides some details on Mathcad's DDE (Dynamic Data Exchange) interface. DDE enables you to use another Windows application to exchange data with Mathcad. This interface enables you to make use of many of Mathcad's features from within another Windows application.

DDE provides a mechanism for using Mathcad from within another Windows application. The application from which you call Mathcad is called the "client." Mathcad, in this context, becomes the "server."

To communicate with Mathcad through DDE, the client must have a text-based macro facility. The details of this macro facility will depend on the particular client you intend to use and are therefore best left to the documentation associated with that client. For the most part though, these details amount to just different words for the same ideas. Once you have the ideas, it becomes a matter of looking up the right way to say them with your client's macro language.

Using DDE, you can use Mathcad to perform calculations and paste the results of the calculation back into the client application. You do this by running a macro from within the client application.

You may want to use DDE if, for example, the calculation you wish to perform is difficult or impossible to do in the client application. Many of Mathcad's functions and operators do not exist on other applications. By using DDE, you can, in effect, graft many of Mathcad's advanced mathematical features into any application capable of functioning as a DDE client.

The following example shows you how to use Mathcad's gamma function to calculate $\Gamma(4)$ and place the result in a spreadsheet. In this example, Excel 4.0 is used as a DDE client application. The steps, broadly outlined, are as follows:

- Open the Mathcad document shown in Figure 1. The Mathcad application must be running before a DDE link can be established.

- Create an Excel macro by choosing **New** from Excel's **File** menu. Choose *Macro Sheet* when prompted by the dialog box.

- Type in the macro shown in Figure 2.

- Type the value you want to assign to the Mathcad variable *a* in cell *A1*.

- Click the first cell of the macro (*B6* in the example) and choose **Run** from Excel's **Macro** menu. The result of the calculation appears in the selected cell.

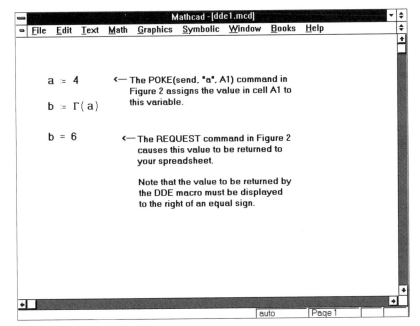

Figure 1: Mathcad document for evaluating the Gamma function.

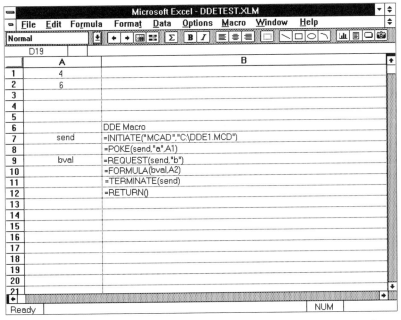

Figure 2: An Excel macro used to call the Mathcad document in Figure 1.

Although the macro shown in Figure 2 is written with commands unique to Excel, any macro language usable for DDE will have substantially equivalent commands. An examination of this macro is therefore useful for understanding the principles of DDE.

The steps in this macro are as follows:

DDE Macro
    The first line is simply the macro's title.

send=INITIATE("MCAD","C:\DDE1.MCD")
    The second line opens a conversation with Mathcad and instructs it to open the document **dde1.mcd** in the root directory of the **C:** drive.

=POKE(send,"a",A1)
    The third line tells Excel to take whatever is in cell *A1*, in this case 4, and assign it to the variable *a* in the Mathcad document that was just opened.

bval=REQUEST(send,"b")
    The fourth line instructs Excel to assign the value of the Mathcad variable *b* from Figure 1 to an Excel variable called *bval*.

=FORMULA(bval, A2)
    The fifth line instructs Excel to place the value of *bval* in cell *A2*.

=TERMINATE(send)
=RETURN()
    The last two lines terminate the DDE connection and the Excel macro.

Before running this macro, you must "bind" the variables *send* and *bval* in cells *A7* and *A9* to their corresponding formulas in cells *B7* and *B9*. To do so, choose **Define Names** from Excel's **Formula** menu. In the Define Name dialog box, select the variable name and indicate the cell containing the corresponding formula. Then click on the "Command" button.

To run this macro, select the first cell of the macro (*B6* in Figure 2) and choose **Run** from the **Macro** menu. Mathcad evaluates the gamma function with whatever is in cell *A1* as an argument. The result then appears in cell *A2* as indicated by the command **FORMULA(bval,A2)**.

Each DDE macro, no matter how complicated, can be broken down into three steps:

■ Creating a link between Mathcad and the DDE client (in this case, Excel).

■ Assigning values to variables in the Mathcad documents.

■ Recovering results from the Mathcad documents.

Any macro language suitable for DDE should be able to perform these three functions. In Excel, these functions are performed by the *INITIATE*, *POKE* and *REQUEST* commands respectively. Your particular client application may use different command names. Consult the documentation associated with you client application for details.

Passing data to Mathcad

A common use of DDE is to pass something from a client application into Mathcad. In Figure 2, you saw how to pass a number. You can, however, use DDE to pass expressions and arrays of numbers into existing Mathcad expressions. This section describes how to perform these tasks.

Passing an expression into Mathcad

The example in Figure 2 showed how to pass a number into a Mathcad document using the *POKE* command. The last argument in the statement **POKE(send,"a",A1)** told the client to take whatever is in cell *A1* and assign it to the right-hand side of whatever equation has *a* on the left-hand side. In Figure 2, the contents of cell *A1* happened to be a number. The contents could just as easily have been an expression as shown in Figure 3. This expression is then passed into the right-hand side as shown in Figure 4. The result of the calculation appears in the cell *A2* as specified by the *FORMULA* command.

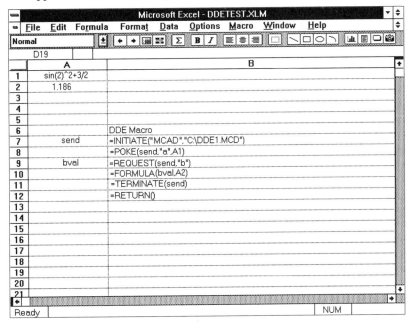

Figure 3: Passing an expression into a Mathcad document.

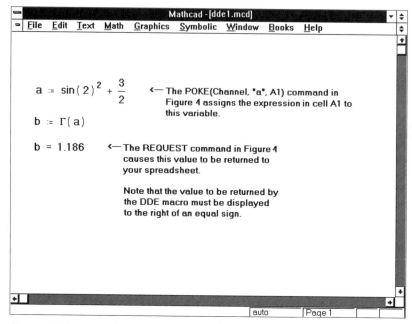

Figure 4: Note that the expression passed by the client now replaces the right-hand side of the assignment for "a."

Note that the expression you pass should be typed the way you would type it into Mathcad itself. For example, you would use ^ to precede an exponent and / to precede a denominator. Because of this, you may find that as the expression becomes more complicated, it becomes progressively more difficult to type it in.

Passing an array into Mathcad

The last argument in the statement **POKE(send,"a",A1)** told the client to take whatever is in cell *A1* and assign it to the right-hand side of whatever equation has *a* on the left-hand side. This last argument need not be a single cell however. You can refer to a range of cells and have the client pass the contents of those cells into Mathcad. This results in the creation of a matrix or a vector in the right-hand side of the assignment statement.

Figure 5 shows how you pass the contents of a range of cells into Mathcad. Note that the last argument of *POKE* is now a range of cells rather than a single cell. This results in the matrix shown in Figure 6.

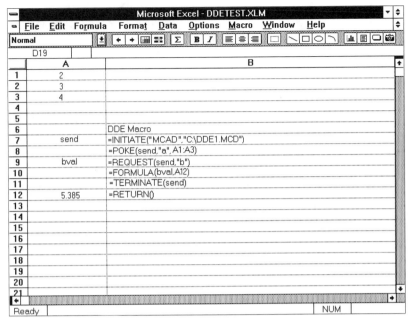

Figure 5: Passing an array of values into a Mathcad document.

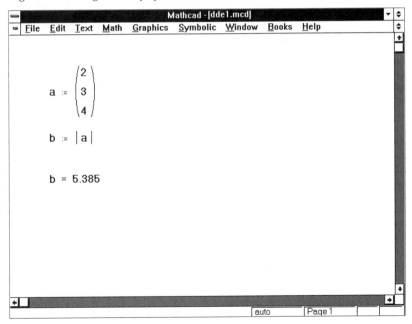

Figure 6: A matrix created by passing an array of numbers from the client application.

The example in Figures 1 and 2 showed how to recover a single number from a Mathcad expression. Using DDE, you can recover arrays of numbers as well as single numbers as shown in that example. The only limitations on recovering a number are that the number be real and that it be dimensionless.

This is analogous to passing an array except that instead of using a range of cells in the *POKE* command you specify it in the *REQUEST* command. Figure 7 shows a Mathcad document in which the result to be passed into the client is an array rather than a single number.

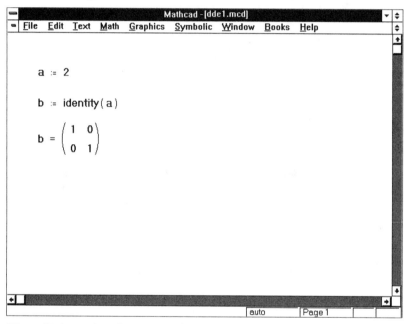

Figure 7: A matrix to be recovered by the client application.

Figure 8 shows the procedure for recovering the array. Note that:

- The second argument of the *REQUEST* command is now a range of cells rather than a single cell.

- You must place an exclamation point before the range to make Excel return the array to your worksheet rather than to your macro sheet.

- You must run this macro from the worksheet, not the macro sheet.

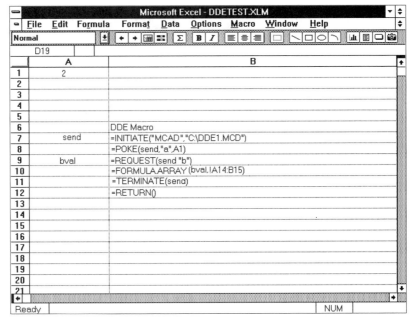

Figure 8: Using the REQUEST command to recover a matrix. Note that you must use [Ctrl][Shift][↵] after filling in cell B10.

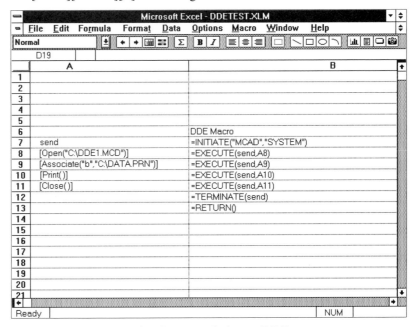

Figure 9: Executing Mathcad commands from a DDE macro.

Executing Mathcad commands

Certain Mathcad commands are accessible from the client application. These permit you to perform programming-like tasks using Mathcad as a computation engine and your client application as a front-end programming interface.

The example in Figure 9 on the previous page shows a DDE macro which opens a Mathcad document called **dde1.mcd**, associates a data file with a file variable, prints the result, and closes the document.

By using a mechanism like that shown in Figure 9, you can use Mathcad to perform the same operation on hundreds of data files, printing out the results as it proceeds unattended.

Mathcad will understand the following commands coming from a DDE client:

Command	Function
`[Open("file")]`	Opens an existing document.
`[Print()]`	Prints whatever document is currently open.
`[Save()]`	Saves the current document under the same name.
`[Saveas("file")]`	Saves the current document under a different name.
`[Manual()]`	Toggles document into manual calculation mode.
`[Automatic()]`	Toggles document into automatic calculation mode.
`[Calculatedoc()]`	Updates all results in the document
`[Close()]`	Closes current document.
`[Associate("var", "file")]`	Associates a file on the disk with a variable in the document.

Appendix F
Creating a User DLL

Extend Mathcad's power by writing your own customized functions. Your functions will have the same advanced features as Mathcad PLUS built-in functions, such as customized error messages, interruption, and exception handling in case of overflow and divide by zero. Your functions will appear in the Choose Function dialog box like all built-in functions. The functions will operate on complex scalars and complex arrays. They will return complex scalars, complex arrays, and error messages.

This appendix describes how to create 32-bit DLLs for Mathcad PLUS. The following sections make up this appendix:

Creating dynamically linked libraries

An overview of how to write your function and fill out the **FUNCTIONINFO** structure.

A sample DLL

A simple example of a user-created DLL with extensive comments. This sample can be used as a template for your own DLL.

Examining a sample DLL

A detailed examination of a simple example DLL, explaining the **COMPLEXARRAY** and **COMPLEXSCALAR** structures, error handling and function registration.

Handling arrays

Using the **COMPLEXARRAY** structure to handle arrays.

Allocating memory

Allocating and freeing memory.

Exception handling

How Mathcad traps the floating point exceptions.

Structure and function definitions

A reference guide to the structures and functions used.

Creating dynamically linked libraries

To create customized functions, you will first need to create source code in C or C++, then compile the source code with a 32-bit compiler. Next, you will link the object files together with the MathSoft-provided `mcaduser.lib` library to create a DLL. Finally, you will place your DLL into the `userefi` subdirectory.

Writing your DLL source code

Provided below is an overview of the steps involved in creating a DLL. Refer to the rest of this appendix for specific details on how to do each step.

Writing a DLL entry point routine

When you start Mathcad PLUS, it looks in the `userefi` directory for library files with a `.dll` extension. Mathcad attempts to load all such files. During this loading process, your DLL must supply Mathcad with information about your library, including the names of the functions in the library, the types of arguments the functions take, the types of values they return, and the text of possible error messages. To supply this information, your DLL must have an entry point routine. A DLL entry point routine is called by the operating system when the DLL is loaded. Because the way to specify the DLL entry point routine is linker specific, refer to the `readme.mcd` file in the `userefi` directory for linking instructions.

Registering your function

For each function in your library, there must be a `FUNCTIONINFO` structure. The `FUNCTIONINFO` structure contains the information that Mathcad uses to register a user function. `FUNCTIONINFO` structure is an argument of `CreateUserFunction`. A call to `CreateUserFunction` inside the DLL entry point routine registers your function with Mathcad.

Writing your function

You must, of course, write a C or C++ function which implements your Mathcad user function. The parameters of your C/C++ function are pointers to the return value and to the arguments. The C/C++ function returns 0 if successful, otherwise it returns an error code. The address of the C/C++ function is passed to Mathcad inside a `FUNCTIONINFO` structure. In this way, Mathcad knows to execute your code when the function is called from a Mathcad document. Refer to the description of `MyCFunction` in the reference section at the end of this appendix.

Error Handling

C/C++ functions which return error messages require an error message table in the DLL code. A call to `CreateUserErrorMessageTable` inside the DLL entry point routine informs Mathcad of the meaning of error codes returned by the C/C++ functions from the DLL.

Compiling and linking your DLL

To create your DLL you will need a 32-bit compiler such as Microsoft Visual C++ (32-bit version), Borland C++ version 4.5, or Watcom C++32 version 10.0. Instructions on compiling and linking your DLL are given in a `readme.mcd` file located in the `userefi` directory. For more specific instructions on how to link and compile your source code, refer to the user guide provided with your compiler.

A Sample DLL

To get you started writing DLLs for Mathcad we include a number of code samples. The example below is the file `multiply.c` located in the `userefi\microsoft\sources\simple` subdirectory.

The file contains a function which returns the result of multiplying an array by a scalar. This code implements the Mathcad user function *multiply*(*a*, **M**), which returns the result of an array **M** multiplied by a scalar *a*. The source code is explained in detail in later sections.

Sample code

```
#include "mcadincl.h"
#define   INTERRUPTED                        1
#define   INSUFFICIENT_MEMORY                2
#define   MUST_BE_REAL                       3
#define   NUMBER_OF_ERRORS                   3

// red box error messages
// if your function never returns an error, you do not need to create this table
char * myErrorMessageTable[NUMBER_OF_ERRORS] =
{
    "interrupted",
    "insufficient memory",
    "must be real"
};

// this code executes the multiplication
// see the information on MyCFunction to find out more
LRESULT  MultiplyRealArrayByRealScalar(
    COMPLEXARRAY * const Product,
    const COMPLEXSCALAR * const Scalar,
    const COMPLEXARRAY * const Array )

{
    unsigned int row, col;
```

```
// check that the scalar argument is real
if ( scalar->imag != 0.0 )

    // if not, display "must be real" under scalar argument
    return MAKELRESULT( MUST_BE_REAL, 1 );

// check that the array argument is real
if ( Array->hImag != NULL )

    // if not, display "must be real" under array argument
    return MAKELRESULT( MUST_BE_REAL, 2 );

// allocate memory for the product
if( !MathcadArrayAllocate( Product, Array-rows,
Array-cols,

    // allocate memory for the real part
    TRUE ,

    // do not allocate memory for the imaginary part
    FALSE ))

    // if allocation is not successful, return with the appropriate error code
    return  INSUFFICIENT_MEMORY;

// if all is well so far, perform the multiplication
for (  col = 0; col < Product-> cols; col++ )
{
    // check that a user has not tried to interrupt the calculation
    if ( isUserInterrupted() )
    {
        // if user has interrupted, free the allocated memory
        MathcadArrayFree( Product );

        // and return with an appropriate error code
        return INTERRUPTED;
    }
    for ( row = 0; row < Product-> rows; row++ )
        Product->hReal[col][row] =
            Scalar-> real*Array-> hReal[col][row];
}
// normal return
return 0;
}
```

```
// fill out a FunctionInfo structure with
// the information needed for registering the function with Mathcad
FUNCTIONINFO multiply =
{
// name by which Mathcad will recognize the function
"multiply",

// description of "multiply" parameters for the Insert Function dialog box
"a,M",

// description of the function for the Insert Function dialog box
"returns the product of real scalar a and real array M",

// pointer to the executable code
// i.e. code that should be executed when a user types in "multiply(a,M)="
(LPCFUNCTION)MultiplyRealArrayByRealScalar;

// multiply(a, M) returns a complex array
COMPLEX_ARRAY,

// multiply(a,M) takes on two arguments
2,

// the first is a complex scalar, the second a complex array
{ COMPLEX_SCALAR, COMPLEX_ARRAY}
};

// all Mathcad DLLs must have a DLL entry point code
// the_CRT_INIT function is needed if you are using Microsoft's 32-bit compiler
BOOL WINAPI _CRT_INIT(HINSTANCE hinstDLL, DWORD dwReason,
LPVOID lpReserved);
BOOL WINAPI  DllEntryPoint (HINSTANCE hDLL, DWORD dwReason,
LPVOID lpReserved)
{
    switch (dwReason)
    {
        case DLL_PROCESS_ATTACH:
            // DLL is attaching to the address space of the current process.
            // the next two lines are Microsoft-specific
            if (!_CRT_INIT(hDLL, dwReason, lpReserved))
                return FALSE;

            // register the error message table
            // if your function never returns an error,
            // you don't need to register an error message table
            if ( CreateUserErrorMessageTable( hDLL,
```

```
                     NUMBER_OF_ERRORS   , myErrorMessageTable ) )
                     // and if the errors register OK, register the user function
                     CreateUserFunction( hDLL, &multiply );

              break;
          case DLL_THREAD_ATTACH:
          case DLL_THREAD_DETACH:
          case DLL_PROCESS_DETACH:

              // the next two lines are Microsoft-specific
              if (!_CRT_INIT(hDLL, dwReason, lpReserved))
                  return FALSE;
              break;
      }
      return TRUE;
}
#undef INTERRUPTED
#undef INSUFFICIENT_MEMORY
#undef MUST_BE_REAL
#undef NUMBER_OF_ERRORS
```

Compiling and linking the sample DLL

If you are using a Microsoft 32-bit compiler you can compile this file with the following command

```
cl -c -I..\..\include -DWIN32 multiply.c
```

This creates an object file `MULTIPLY.OBJ`. You can use the following command to link `MULTIPLY.OBJ` with the appropriate library and place `MULTIPLY.DLL` in the `userefi` directory.

```
link -out:..\..\..\multiply.dll -dll
-entry:"DllEntryPoint" multiply.obj
..\..\lib\mcaduser.lib
```

Check to make sure the `MULTIPLY.DLL` file is in the `userefi` subdirectory. Start Mathcad and verify that *multiply* appears in the Choose Function dialog box. You are now ready to use *multiply* in Mathcad.

This section will examine the source code of the simple example in the previous section. Refer to the code in the sample DLL.

MyCFunction

The heart of the program is `MyCFunction`, called `MultiplyRealArrayByRealScalar` function. It performs the actual multiplication. When the user types `multiply(a,M)=`, Mathcad executes the `MultiplyRealArrayByRealScalar` routine. The value of *a* is passed to the `MultiplyRealArrayByRealScalar` function in the `Scalar` argument. The value of **M** is passed in the `Array` argument. A pointer to the return value `Product` is the first argument of the `MultiplyRealArrayByRealScalar` function.

COMPLEXSCALAR structure

The scalar value *a* is passed to the `MultiplyRealArrayByRealScalar` function in a `COMPLEXSCALAR` structure. The structure has two members, *real* and *imag*. The real part of *a* is stored in `Scalar-> real`, the imaginary part in `Scalar-> imag`.

COMPLEXARRAY structure

The array value **M** is passed to the `MultiplyRealArrayByRealScalar` function in a `COMPLEXARRAY` structure. The `COMPLEXARRAY` structure has four members, *rows, cols, hReal,* and *hImag.* The number of rows in **M** is found in `Array-> rows`, the number of columns is found in `Array-> cols`. The real part of the element $M_{row,col}$ is found in `Array-> hReal[col][row]` and the imaginary part in `Array-> hImag[col][row]`. If no element of **M** has an imaginary part, `Array-> hImag` is equal to NULL. If all elements of **M** are purely imaginary, `Array-> hReal` is equal to NULL.

The result of the multiplication of **M** by *a* is stored by the program in the `COMPLEXARRAY` structure pointed to by the argument `Product`. Note the memory for the multiplication result is allocated inside the `MultiplyRealArrayByRealScalar` function with a call to the `MathcadArrayAllocate` function.

Error Messages

If the multiplication was successful, `MultiplyRealArrayByRealScalar` stores the result in the `COMPLEXARRAY` structure pointed to by the argument `Product` and returns 0. In the case of an error, its return value has two components. One is the error code and the other is the location in which to display the error message.

Look at the error message table from the top of the file:

```
char * myErrorMessageTable[NUMBER_OF_ERRORS] =
{
```

```
        "interrupted",
        "insufficient memory",
        "must be real"
};
```

The function `MultiplyRealArrayByRealScalar` returns `MAKELRE-SULT(3,1)` to display string number 3, "must be real," under the first argument of `multiply(a,M)`. If `MathcadArrayAllocate` is unable to allocate memory, `MultiplyRealArrayByRealScalar` returns 2 to display string number 2, "insufficient memory," under the function name.

As shown in the sample DLL code, the following steps are involved in producing an error message:

- creation of an array of error message strings.

- registering the error message strings with Mathcad via a call to `CreateUserErrorMessageTable`. This call is made within the DLL entry point routine.

- returning an appropriate error code from the user function.

DLL entry point function

The DLL entry point is called by the operating system when the DLL is loaded. Mathcad requires that you register your user functions and your error message table while the DLL is being loaded. Note how this is done in the following code lines.

```
BOOL WINAPI  DllEntryPoint (HINSTANCE hDLL, DWORD dwReason,
LPVOID lpReserved)
{
    switch (dwReason)
    {
        case DLL_PROCESS_ATTACH:

            if ( CreateUserErrorMessageTable( hDLL,
                NUMBER_OF_ERRORS  , myErrorMessageTable ) )
                // if the errors register OK, register user function
                CreateUserFunction( hDLL, &multiply );

            break;
        case DLL_THREAD_ATTACH:
        case DLL_THREAD_DETACH:
        case DLL_PROCESS_DETACH:
            break;
    }
    return TRUE;

}
```

`CreateUserErrorMessageTable` registers the error messages. `CreateUserFunction` registers the function. You can register only one error message table per DLL, but you can register more than one function per DLL.

FUNCTIONINFO structure

The FUNCTIONINFO structure, *multiply*, is used for registering the DLL function with Mathcad. It contains information about the name by which Mathcad recognizes the function, the description of the function parameters, its arguments, its return value, and the pointer to the code which executes the function.

```
FUNCTIONINFO multiply =
{
"multiply",
"a,M",
"returns the product of real scalar a and real array M",
(LPCFUNCTION)MultiplyRealArrayByRealScalar;
COMPLEX_ARRAY,
2,
{COMPLEX_SCALAR, COMPLEX_ARRAY}
};
```

Precision

Data is passed between Mathcad and MyCFunction in double precision. Use the appropriate conversion inside MyCFunction for different data types.

mcadincl.h

MathSoft provides the mcadincl.h include file. This file contains the prototypes for the following functions: CreateUserFunction, CreateUserErrorMessageTable, MathcadAllocate, MathcadFree, MathcadArrayAllocate, MyCFunction, MathcadArrayFree, isUserInterrupted. mcadincl.h also includes the type definitions for the structures COMPLEXSCALAR, COMPLEXARRAY, and FUNCTIONINFO.

Handling arrays

If your function takes an array as its argument or returns an array, refer to the COMPLEXARRAY structure description in the reference section, "Structure and function definitions." Note that the arrays are two-dimensional and the structure contains information about the size of the arrays and the pointers to the real and imaginary parts of the array. Refer to the next section "Allocating Memory" for how to allocate memory inside COMPLEXARRAY structures.

Allocating memory

The first argument of `MyCFunction` is a pointer to a return value. If it points to a `COMPLEXARRAY` structure, you will need to allocate memory for the members of this structure using `MathcadArrayAllocate`. If `MyCFunction` is returning an error, free the memory allocated for the return value using `MathcadArray-Free`. In the case of an error-free return, do not free the memory allocated for the return value.

Use the `MathcadAllocate` and `MathcadFree` functions to allocate and free memory inside `MyCFunction`.

Exception handling

Mathcad traps the following floating point exceptions; overflow, divide by zero, and invalid operation. In the case of these exceptions, Mathcad will display a floating point error message under the function. Mathcad will also free all the memory allocated inside `MyCFunction` with `MathcadArrayAllocate` and `MathcadAllocate`.

Structure and function definitions

This section describes in more detail the structures and functions used in creating your own dynamically linked library.

The COMPLEXSCALAR Structure

```
typedef struct tagCOMPLEXSCALAR {
    double real;
    double imag;
} COMPLEXSCALAR;
```

The `COMPLEXSCALAR` structure is used to pass scalar data between Mathcad and a user DLL. The real part of a scalar is stored in the *real* member of a `COMPLEXSCALAR`, and the imaginary in the *imag* member.

Member	Description
real	Contains the real part of a scalar.
imag	Contains the imaginary part of a scalar.

The COMPLEXARRAY Structure

```
typedef struct tagCOMPLEXARRAY  {
    unsigned int rows;
    unsigned int cols;
    double **hReal;
    double **hImag;
} COMPLEXARRAY;
```

The COMPLEXARRAY structure is used to pass array data between Mathcad and a user DLL. It contains the information about the size of the array and whether any of the elements in the array has an imaginary or a real component.

Member	Description
rows	Number of rows in the array.
cols	Number of columns in the array.
hReal	Points to the real part of a complex array *hReal[i][j]* contains the element in the *i*th column and the *j*th row of the array. *hReal* is equal to NULL if the array has no real component.
hImag	Points to the imaginary part of a complex array *hImag[i][j]*, contains the element in the *i*th column and the *j*th row of the array. *hImag* equals NULL if the array has no imaginary component.

Comments

hReal and *hImag* members of the argument array are indexed as two-dimensional array of the range $[0..cols-1][0..rows-1]$.

The FUNCTIONINFO Structure

```
typedef struct  tagFUNCTIONINFO{
    char * lpstrName;
    char * lpstrParameters;
    char * lpstrDescription;
    LPCFUNCTION lpfnMyCFunction;
    long unsigned int returnType;
    unsigned int nArgs;
    long unsigned int argType[MAX_ARGS];
} FUNCTIONINFO;
```

The FUNCTIONINFO structure contains the information that Mathcad uses to register a user function. Refer below for each member and its description.

Member	Description
lpstrName	Points to a NULL-terminated string that specifies the name of the user function.
lpstrParameters	Points to a NULL-terminated string that specifies the parameters of the user function. The string is used by the Choose Function dialog box.
lpstrDescription	Points to a NULL-terminated string that specifies the function description for the Choose Function dialog box.

lpfnMyCFunction	Pointer to the code that executes the user function.
returnType	Specifies the type of value returned by the function. The values are **COMPLEX_ARRAY** or **COMPLEX_SCALAR**.
nArgs	Specifies the number of arguments expected by the function. Must be between 1 and **MAX_ARGS**.
argType	Specifies an array of long unsigned integers containing input parameter types.

CreateUserFunction

```
const void * CreateUserFunction(hDLL, functionInfo)
HINSTANCE hDLL;
FUNCTIONINFO * functionInfo ;
```

`CreateUserFunction` is called when the DLL is attaching to the address space of the current process in order to register the user function with Mathcad.

Parameter	Description
hDLL	Handle of the DLL supplied by the DLL entry point routine.
functionInfo	Points to the **FUNCTIONINFO** structure that contains information about the function. The **FUNCTIONINFO** structure has the following form:

```
typedef struct  tagFUNCTIONINFO{
    char *  lpstrName;
    char *  lpstrParameters;
    char *  lpstrDescription;
    LPCFUNCTION  lpfnMyCFunction;
    long unsigned int returnType;
    unsigned int nArgs;
    long unsigned int argType[MAX_ARGS];
} FUNCTIONINFO;
```

Return value

The return value is a non-NULL handle if the registration is successful. Otherwise, it is NULL.

CreateUserErrorMessageTable

```
BOOL CreateUserErrorMessageTable(hDLL,n,ErrorMessageTable)
HINSTANCE hDLL;
unsigned int n;
char * ErrorMessageTable [ ];
```

`CreateUserErrorMessageTable` is called when the DLL is attaching to the address space of the current process in order to registers the user error message table with Mathcad.

Parameter	Description
hDLL	Handle of the DLL supplied by the DLL entry point routine.
n	Number of error messages in the table.
ErrorMessageTable	An array of *n* strings with the text of the error messages.

Return value

The return value is TRUE if the registration is successful. Otherwise, it is FALSE.

MathcadAllocate

```
char * MathcadAllocate(size)
unsigned int size;
```

Should be used to allocated memory inside the `MyCFunction`. Allocates a memory block of a given size (in bytes) of memory.

Parameter	Description
size	Size (in bytes) of memory block to allocate. Should be non-zero.

Return value

Returns a pointer to the storage space. To get a pointer to a type other than char, use a type cast on the return value. Returns NULL if the allocation failed or if size is equal to 0.

MathcadFree

```
void MathcadFree(address)
char * address;
```

Should be used to free memory allocated with `MathcadAllocate`. The argument address points to the memory previously allocated with `MathcadAllocate`. A NULL pointer argument is ignored.

Parameter	Description
address	Address of the memory block that is to be freed.

Return value

The function does not return a value.

MathcadArrayAllocate

```
BOOL MathcadArrayAllocate(array, rows, cols, allocateReal,
allocateImaginary)
COMPLEXARRAY* const array;
unsigned int rows;
unsigned int cols;
BOOL allocateReal;
BOOL allocateImaginary;
```

Allocates memory for a **COMPLEXARRAY** of *cols* columns and *rows* rows. Sets the *hReal*, *hImag*, *rows* and *cols* members of the argument array.

Parameter	Description
array	Points to the **COMPLEXARRAY** structure that is to be filled with the information about an array. The **COMPLEXARRAY** structure has the following form: ```typedef struct tagCOMPLEXARRAY {\n unsigned int rows;\n unsigned int cols;\n double **hReal;\n double **hImag;\n} COMPLEXARRAY;```
rows	Row dimension of the array that is being allocated. After a successful allocation, the *rows* member of the argument array is set to the value of *rows*.
cols	Column dimension of the array that is being allocated. After a successful allocation, the *cols* member of the argument array is set to the value of *cols*.
allocateReal	Boolean flag indicating whether a memory block should be allocated to store the real part of the array. If *allocateReal* is FALSE the function does not allocate storage for the real part of array and sets the *hReal* member to NULL.
allocateImag	Boolean flag indicating whether a memory block should be allocated to store the imaginary part of the array. If *allocateImag* is FALSE the function does not allocate storage for the imaginary part of array and sets the *hImag* member to NULL.

Return value

Returns TRUE if the allocation is successful, FALSE otherwise.

Comments

hReal and *hImag* members of the argument array are allocated as 2-dimensional array of the range [0..*cols*–1][0..*rows*–1].

MyCFunction

```
LRESULT MyCFunction(returnValue, argument1,...)
void * const returnValue;
const void * const argument1;
...
```

MyCFunction is the actual code which executes the user function. Mathcad arguments and a pointer to a return value are passed to this function. It puts the result of the calculation in the return value.

Parameter	Description
returnValue	Points to a COMPLEXARRAY or a COMPLEXSCALAR structure where the function result is to be stored. If you are implementing a Mathcad user function which returns a scalar, *returnValue* is a pointer to a COMPLEXSCALAR structure. If you are implementing a Mathcad user function that returns an array, *returnValue* points to a COMPLEXARRAY structure.
argument1	Points to a read-only COMPLEXARRAY or a COMPLEXSCALAR structure where the first function argument is stored. If you are implementing a Mathcad user function that has a scalar as its first argument, *argument1* is a pointer to a COMPLEXSCALAR structure. If you are implementing a Mathcad user function that has an array as its first argument, *argument1* points to a COMPLEXARRAY structure.
...	If you are implementing a Mathcad user function that has more than one argument, your MyCFunction will have additional arguments. The additional arguments will be pointers to the read-only COMPLEXARRAY or a COMPLEXSCALAR structures where the data for the corresponding Mathcad user function argument is stored.

Return value

MyCFunction should return 0 to indicate an error-free return. To indicate an error MyCFunction should return an error code in the low word of the returned LRESULT, and in the high word the number of the argument under which the error box should be placed. If the high word is zero the error message box is placed under the function itself. See the section on error handling to find out more about error codes.

Comments

MyCFunction is a place-holder for the library-supplied function name. You can name the function that executes your Mathcad user function anything you would like, but you must register the address of your executable code with Mathcad by setting the lpfnMyCFunction member of the FUNCTIONINFO structure.

MathcadArrayFree

```
void MathcadArrayFree(array)
COMPLEXARRAY * const array;
```

Frees memory that was allocated by the **MathcadArrayAllocate** function to the the *hReal* and *hImag* members of the argument array.

Parameter	Description
array	Points to the **COMPLEXARRAY** structure that is to be filled with the information about an array.
	The **COMPLEXARRAY** structure has the following form:

```
typedef struct tagCOMPLEXARRAY  {
unsigned int rows;
unsigned int cols;
double **hReal;
double **hImag;
} COMPLEXARRAY;
```

Return value

The function does not return a value.

isUserInterrupted

```
BOOL isUserInterrupted(void)
```

The **isUserInterrupted** function is used to check whether a user has pressed the **[Esc]** key. Include this function if you want to be able to interrupt your function like other Mathcad functions.

Parameter

The function does not take on any parameters.

Return value

Returns TRUE if the **[Esc]** key has been pressed, FALSE otherwise.

Index

Index

G

H

I

inserting in front of expression 60
MKS units 177
mod function 273
mode
    See auto calc mode, manual calc mode
moving
    crosshair 52, 608
    graphs 442
    insertion point 55, 608
    pictures 575
    regions 68
    scrollbar 75
    selection box 52
    to bottom of worksheet 75
    to top of worksheet 75
    windows 76
multigrid function 374
multiple integrals 256
multiple roots, finding with solve blocks 344
multiple summations 244, 246
multiplication 241
multivalued functions 167, 269
multivariate cubic spline interpolation 301

N

names
    font sensitive 133
    variable and function names 158
    vectors and scalars use same names 186
natural log 270
negating an expression 60, 241
negative binomial distribution 291
nested arrays 212
New Personal Dictionary command 119
noisy data 313
non-linear
    differential equations 360
    regression 310
    systems of equations 339
non-scalar value (error message) 219
norm
    functions 201
    of matrix 201
    of vector 198, 241
norm1 and *norm2* functions 201

normal distribution 290, 291
norme and *normi* functions 201
not converging (error)
    integrals 254
    root function 335
notation used in manual 13
Notes database 83
Notes template 84
nth order derivative 251
nth root 167, 241
numbering pages 95
numbers 163
    complex 164, 165
    dimensional values 164
    displayed as zero 125
    exponential notation for 125, 164
    format for computed results 124
    formatting 25, 124
    hexadecimal 164
    imaginary 164, 165
    octal 164
    radix (base) for results 124
numeric format
    See result format
numerical methods 632
    differentiation 248, 251
    for derivatives 635
    for matrix inversion and determinants 639
    for *root* function 636
    for solve blocks 637
    integrals 633
    integration 252
    sorting vectors and matrices 640

O

octal numbers 124, 164
OLE
    graphics import 571
    text import 114
Open Book command 40
Open Personal Dictionary command 119
Open URL command 78
opening a worksheet 78
operators
    boolean 280

top-to-bottom evaluation 142
trace (*tr*) function 201
Trace command (Polar Plot) 488
Trace command (X-Y Plot) 465
traces
    graphs 447
    polar plots 473
Traces page
    polar plots 479, 482
    X-Y plots 455
trailing zeros 125
transcendental functions 267
transforms
    Fourier (numerical) 273
    Fourier (symbolic) 407
    Laplace 408
    symbolic 407
    wavelet 277
    z 409
Transpose Matrix command 405
transpose of matrix 198, 215, 240, 405
trigonometric functions 267, 268
    with degrees and radians 175
troubleshoooting 9
truncation 272, 273
    See floor function
two point boundary value problems 370
typing over text 101

U

undefined variables 143, 145
uniform distribution 291
unit impulse function 282
unit step function 282
units 169
    base units 177
    CGS system 177
    changing dimension names 179
    common sources of error 171
    converting calculated results 174
    defining 177
    defining your own 172
    dimensional consistency 171
    dimensional values 164
    errors in dimensions 171

    in calculated values 173
    in equations 170
    in tables 223
    metric 177
    placeholder 173, 174
    US Customary 177
Unlock Area command 89
until function 279, 281
update
    file access functions 428
    results in window 149
    window manually 150
    worksheet 151
    worksheet window 151
URL (for Internet address) 79
US Customary units 177
user functions 139
    array arguments 211
    defined in terms of root 337
    defined in terms of solve blocks 349
    errors in 155
    evaluating variables in 141
    valid names 158

V

values
    See numbers
variables
    complex 165
    defining 18, 138
    defining several at once 210
    font tag 130
    global definitions of 144
    in reverse video 145, 153
    matrices 182
    names 158
    predefined 162
    range variables 23, 218
    substituting for 394
    variable names 158
    vectors 182
variance (*var*) function 286
vector field plots 549
    creating 550, 551
    formatting 553

W